Just a Matter of Time

*A grassroots look at Canada's cattle industry
struggling through the aftermath of mad cow disease.*

Karen Emilson

NORDHEIM BOOKS

Published by Nordheim Books, Box 223, Vogar, Manitoba R0C 3C0

September 2005

Printed and bound in Canada by
Hignell Printing, Winnipeg Manitoba

Text design and typesetting by Andrea Tétrault/Karen Emilson

CANADIAN CATALOGUING IN PUBLICATION DATA

Emilson, Karen, 1963—
Just a Matter of Time: A grassroots look at Canada's cattle industry struggling through the aftermath of Mad Cow Disease

Includes bibliographic references

ISBN 0-9681242-2-4

1. Cattle Industry—Canada—Case studies.

for my father-in-law, Siggi Emilson

INTRODUCTION

In September 2004, I set out on a journey into cattle country to talk with grassroots producers about how they have been affected by the closed border. Most of the people I interviewed are determined to weather this crisis. Some are not so sure and asked that their stories not be printed. A few have decided to leave the industry or were forced out of business by circumstances or creditors no longer willing to take a risk on their operation. What I came away with is a series of interviews that focus on the people who are steadfast in their belief of the industry's future.

The result is an honest talk with cattle men and women about their operations and their lives. Traditionally, ranch people are private, stoic and not often willing to discuss their worries—especially regarding finances and their ability to provide. The people in these pages are industry leaders—everyday cattle producers who have helped put a face on this crisis and in doing so, will help others understand.

During my travels and afterward when I sat down to begin piecing this all together, I was searching for an image to compare to the industry and the story I planned to tell. As hard as I looked, I couldn't find it.

Then one evening this past spring, it was there right in front of me in Dorothy Halldorson's sewing room. I realized the image had followed me across the prairies. It covered Mel and Betty McCrea's couch and was on the bed where I slept at the Jahnkes.

It made me think of earlier days when homesteaders came west, bringing with them a cow and whatever necessities they could afford. The woman of the house would milk the cow in the morning and evening, work all day, then piece together scraps of cloth into a quilt at night. Both the cow and the quilt were economic necessities. The days of milking a cow are long past and quilting has become a hobby, but the regard for each still exists today.

I believe that the cattle industry is much like a quilt. The top layer is an exquisite compilation of people and landscapes, all shapes and sizes, bound together by a common theme into a continuum with no beginning or end. Some of the pieces are more colourful than the others. Many are a spectacular canola yellow or barn red, others are made in the quieter tones of alfalfa blue or a shade of lilac unique to the prairie sky. There are the grounding, practical shades of half-grown barley green, ploughed field brown and lake blue.

Flip over a quilt and you'll usually find one solid colour, often times a single piece of fabric stretching from end to end. Much like the land, this is the foundation on which everything our industry is built. It may not be the prettiest piece, but the quilt can't exist without it.

Between the two layers lies the batting. It is the reason for pulling together the pieces in the first place. The centre provides the warmth, comfort and knowledge that the top and bottom layers have been brought together for a reason, that there is an enduring purpose to it all.

When you look at a quilt your eyes will be drawn to the colour and patterns and sometimes you won't necessarily see that the edges are bound together by one continuous strip of fabric. During the economic crisis brought about by BSE, there was a lot of support that wrapped itself around cattlemen, and that is what kept the edges of the industry from fraying.

And finally, holding everything place are the tiny stitches. The cattle that roam across the land, binding the people who care for them to the earth. Like a quilter's stitch, they are a result of patience, care and sacrifice. And like the cattleman, the quilter knows that finishing the job properly will mean a lot of time and plenty of hard work. The end result is a legacy that should last for generations.

PART ONE

SHOCK, DENIAL

CHAPTER ONE

In ancient times the main measure of wealth and
status was the number of livestock a person owned.
Cattle were much more important than land as the
ancient Germanic peoples were essentially nomadic.

– Horik Svensson, *The Runes*

The first thing a rancher does when he gets up in the morning is check the temperature. If the sun is up, he'll look into the sky. Then he listens to the radio forecast. There is nothing that fills his thoughts more than if it will rain or how cold it was last night. The weather is his constant companion. Not only must he go out to work in it every day, but his livelihood begs mercy from it.

In May 2003, ranchers in Alberta, Saskatchewan, and the northwest United States were nearing the end of a multi-year drought. Both British Columbia and Manitoba had seen more moisture in those years, but conditions were still considered dry. When rain does come to the prairies, heavy clouds are known to roll in and release an inch of moisture on one farm while completely overlooking the nearest neighbour.

Because of the drought, cow numbers in both countries were down. There was little forage to eat, so some herds were sold off or boarded at ranches in other parts of the country. Anticipating the growing need to replace the cows butchered because of the drought, astute cattlemen who did have feed were holding back heifers and breeding them in record numbers. Hopes were that these animals would sell for a high price in the fall.

By the end of May, most prairie crops were sown and a few well-timed showers were nudging the fields and pastures green. Optimism was high

Trevor, Betty and Mel McCrea

that this was going to be a good year.

December 9, 2004

The highway between Consort, Alberta, and Macklin, Saskatchewan, is scenic beyond expectation. The Cypress Hills swell up on the southern landscape like a nest of giant goose eggs, surprising travellers who believe that Saskatchewan is flat.

As I turn onto Highway #13 east, the sun lands on the car mirrors, its burnt orange reflection stinging my eyes. Ahead, the frozen blacktop glistens. It's cold enough outside that flurries coming from the southwest dance across the highway instead of lying down. A few inches of snow blanket the lonesome hills.

Weather-ruined barns and broken-down turn-of-the-century homes poke up like gravestones in fields along the highway. The overgrown laneways lead to open doors that force us to wonder about the lives that once existed here. I used to think that these ruins should be torn down, but not anymore. They serve as gentle reminders that life is constantly changing. Nothing out here is guaranteed except that weather will continue to vex the farmer and cattleman as long as he's on the land.

It will be dark soon and I'm running late.

Weeks on the road have taught me that you can't tell a community's size by glancing at its name on a map. Many towns now are nothing but pastures and grain fields, with only a post office or cairn showing where the school once sat. If I'm lucky, Macklin has a gas station.

It has been 18 months since BSE was discovered in Canada and the United States' border slammed shut to live cattle imports. In the back seat, along with my suitcase and snack cooler, are ink-filled notebooks that hold the stories of more than fifty families affected by the crisis.

My thoughts meander for a moment as feelings of longing rise up.

I'll be home tomorrow night.

It's a seven-hour drive from Saskatoon to our ranch nestled along the eastern shore of Lake Manitoba. I've lived in Manitoba for more than 20 years now. My husband, Mark, has been a rancher most of his life. We raised our son, Laurie, into a man on one of the calmest, cleanest places on earth.

The average husband would balk at his wife being away for weeks at a time, but not Mark. Maybe that's because I'm not as easy to live with as I like to think—or maybe it's because he sees the light in my eyes when I am researching and writing about something I love. It's the same shine I see in him when he's with the cattle.

I coast on nothing but fumes toward a nest of lights in a valley that's Macklin. I've run low on gas twice this trip, and blame the back roads of Saskatchewan each time. I find my way through town, fill up the tank, then turn north on the road that will take me to Baldwinton.

Tonight's interview is one of the most important of the entire trip. Knowing this has wound my stomach like a rope. The McCreas have been interviewed so many times this past year, I'm worried they'll have nothing left to say. Having the first homegrown case of BSE in Canada traced back to their farm will have affected them in ways other cattle producers can only imagine.

BSE is the acronym for "Bovine Spongiform Encephalopathy," commonly known as "Mad Cow Disease." It is a perplexing cattle disorder that has taken scientists years to understand. When it was first discovered in Britain in 1986, its origins were a mystery, and similarities to the human disease Creutzfeldt-Jakob Disease (CJD) were troubling. By 1989, Britain banned human consumption of cattle offal because of growing consumer concern that CJD might result from ingesting beef. The British cattle industry began spiralling downward as beef consumption decreased and 23 non-European Union countries, including Canada and the United States, banned the import of British beef. That country's billion-dollar industry was devastated.

Directions to the McCrea farm take me down an unmarked road toward a cluster of lights in an otherwise black expanse that stretches starless into the night. The moon hangs overhead like a clipped toenail and I wonder how its newness will affect the coming week's weather.

A yard light illuminates the roof of a modest white bungalow sitting at the crest of a semi-circular drive. A silhouette glides away from the picture window as I park the car. Gathering my notebook and camera in my arms, I step into the crisp air. All is silent except for the hum of electrical lines overhead. The stillness is soon shattered by the crunching of snow under my boots as I hurry toward the front door. It opens and Betty McCrea beckons me inside.

Though my glasses are fogged, I immediately recognize the modest surroundings of farm people. Honest. Hardworking. Practical. They've spent their entire lives giving everything back to the land and their cattle.

"I was starting to worry," Betty says, taking my coat. She is a soft yet sturdy woman who has the look of someone who can put in a full day outside in the fields or working cattle whenever needed.

I apologize for being late. She waves it off, motioning for me to follow her and the smell of roasted beef through the living room into the kitchen. Nothing here shouts extravagance—not the furnishings or sparse decorating. Not even the older, upright piano that sits along the far wall, sheet music spread out ready to play.

She says the men have already eaten as she pulls out a chair for me at the end of the table. She's kept supper heated and my heart warms to her thoughtfulness.

At first I don't see her husband, Mel, who is sitting in silence at the opposite end of the table. His thick arms are folded firm across his chest. He appraises me, heavy jowls looking somewhat hardened by the intrusion of BSE into his life. On the wall behind him are two paintings—one of Black Angus cattle and the other of a Labrador dog. They look to be commissioned by the same person, a local artist who captures treasured images for a fee.

My glasses clear in time to meet their son, Trevor, who emerges freshly showered from the other end of the house. Trevor nods politely as he slides in behind the table.

The McCreas are long past the need for chitchat and immediately take me back to the Victoria Day long weekend in May 2003. Tissue samples from the brain of a six-year-old, non-ambulatory (downer) cow from Alberta had tested suspicious for BSE and been sent to the BSE World Reference Laboratory in Weybridge, England, for further testing. A positive result was reported back to Canadian officials halfway through the weekend. On Tuesday, May 20, the announcement came that Canada had its first indigenous case of BSE.

It was Mel who answered the phone early the following morning.

"I could tell by the look on his face that something was wrong," Betty says, pushing bowls of food toward me, encouraging me to fill my plate. "By 10 a.m. the CFIA was here to quarantine the farm."

CFIA is the acronym for Canadian Food Inspection Agency, the government department responsible for the delivery of all federal food, animal and plant health inspection programs. The CFIA needed to determine if the infected cow discovered in Alberta was born to the McCrea herd.

The family's immediate reaction was disbelief. The sight of federal inspectors and the media descending upon their home was like a scene from a movie.

Initially, the ranch was quarantined so livestock could not leave or be brought into the yard. Quarantines give the impression of contagion, but in the case of BSE, it is done to account for all animals that may have been exposed to the same feed source.

Days later, the CFIA staff returned and began going through breeding records.

Betty explained that the investigators went all the way back to 1995 and that she had to produce receipts for each year. With 110 cows, the McCrea herd was considered modest in size. Seventy of the cows were purebred animals registered with the Canadian Angus Association, so tracking their progeny's movement from the farm would be easy. Most of the female calves were either kept by the McCreas to replace older "cull" cows or sold as breeding stock. Around a dozen bull calves were raised and sold as herd bulls. Any remaining calves would have been sold at around eight months of age to a feedlot.

The 40 commercial cows' calves would be more difficult to trace because mixed breed animals are not registered at birth. Some of the female (heifer) calves would have gone to a feedlot with the male (steer) calves, but others could have been bought as breeding females and become part of a herd anywhere in Canada or the United States. While the McCreas would know the sire and which calf was born to which cow, they had no way of knowing the animal's fate after it left their farm.

Mel suggested to the CFIA that there were DNA records at the Canadian Angus Association office in Calgary for all the bulls that had been used, but the agency officials didn't seem interested in exploring this route until much later, after receiving pressure from the media.

It took a little more than two days for inspectors to go through breeding and sale records to trace forward all animals that left the farm since 1996. They compared the files with traceback information provided by Marwyn Peaster, the Alberta rancher who bought the seemingly healthy cow in the fall of 2002, shipping it to a packing plant in January 2003. Before that, the cow had lived on a Saskatchewan ranch for four years and gave birth to the same number of calves. And before that, she lived on an Alberta ranch.

As the CFIA combed through the McCrea records, the family was steadfast in the belief that the infected cow couldn't have come from their herd. Like most cow-calf producers who raise beef animals, the McCrea cows eat very little purchased feed. They graze all summer on pasture, then during the winter months are fed silage made from homegrown barley and triticale. This is mixed with processed barley in a feed wagon then fed to the cattle. Since there were no other sick animals on the place, it seemed impossible to believe that the infected cow came from their herd.

Scientists believe that BSE is transmitted when cattle ingest feed containing the brain or spinal cord of an infected animal. In 1997, regulations were changed by the CFIA to stop the feeding of rendered material from cattle back to cattle. In theory, animals born after the feed ban should have no chance of contracting BSE. The McCreas were convinced that somebody must have made a mistake.

But it was a receipt for 400 pounds of calf starter pellets, bought and fed to 92 calves in 1997, that caught the inspector's attention. The family was stunned. They gave it to their baby calves for a short period of time, from March 20 to May 20. A handful looks as harmless as rabbit food.

"I bought it for the first time that year," Trevor says, shaking his head. "I thought we'd try it, to give the calves a boost. I thought we were doing a good thing."

I ask if he examined the label on the bag and he told me that feed companies do not list ingredients, only nutrient percentages. He didn't think to ask the source of the "16 percent protein" listed. Besides, he felt protected by the feed ban quietly imposed that year.

With no live test for BSE, the McCreas could do nothing but wait to hear the fate of their herd. They knew Canada's stringent policy regarding containment and eradication of disease and feared the worst. The answer came just days later—from a newspaper reporter in the yard who'd heard through the newswire that the McCrea herd would be depopulated. It was confirmed by the CFIA hours later.

"I've been in cattle my whole life," Mel says quietly, "so I understood what needed to be done. I was sure the rest of the cattle were clean, but for the sake of the industry, we had to let them go."

I'd heard that Mel had been angry and devastated that the depopulation orders came way too fast. He seems to sense I know this and apologizes for lashing out at the officials and media. I tell him there's no need. It's a reaction cattle people understand.

The CFIA said they would return May 29 with trucks and staff to take all the cattle. The animals would need to be rounded up and corralled, then special ear tags would be inserted indicating they were destined for slaughter. Afterwards, the carcasses would be tested for BSE.

There is an unspoken law among cattlemen that strangers don't interfere with or "work" another man's animals. Producers take great pride in taking responsibility for their livestock, so a few friends and relatives helped Trevor process the animals on May 29. While the CFIA staff stood on the sidelines, the cows, calves and bulls were moved through the chute and up the loading ramp. Mel and Betty were too distressed to watch for long.

"It was time for the cows to go to pasture so they were happy to get on the truck," Betty says.

We sit in silence, Mel and Trevor staring at the table with a wrung out look, reliving the hurt as if it happened yesterday. They weren't consoled to know that depopulation orders were also sent to the three farms where the BSE-infected cow had lived and to the feedlot feeding her most recent calf. In all, 2,900 cattle were destroyed. No others tested positive.

I ask if they thought this was overkill.

They all shrug, then Trevor replies, "Those are the rules."

Betty opens her journal and begins reading her notes out loud. She had the foresight to record the names of everyone she spoke to during those crushing weeks.

She says that with each new development in the BSE story, the phone will ring and it is another call from the media asking for their thoughts. She thumbs to the last entry and adds my name. Then she removes the lid from a shoebox and begins searching through a thick stack of letters. One woman from New Zealand wrote to offer her sympathies. Apparently, their story was in newspapers worldwide.

"People from all over sent us cards," Mel says, "but the government doesn't give a goddamn."

It would be months after the herd was destroyed before the CFIA would agree to conduct DNA testing, after much media pressure to do so. The tests did confirm that a dam in their herd was the infected cow's mother and that a prized bull used during the late 1990s, Anchor R Matlock Mindbar 13C, was the sire.

More than a year later, Mel still finds it hard to believe that the herd he developed through careful selection, over more than 40 years, is gone. This has left him with little to hand down to Trevor who had planned to take over the purebred business.

And while they are grateful for the compensation paid by the government for their animals (pre-BSE market value), the McCreas now find themselves battling Revenue Canada. Because they received a lump sum in one year, they are being taxed at windfall rates and stand to pay one third of it as income tax. Revenue Canada makes no allowances for their situation, even though this is clearly money the McCreas have been counting on to fund their retirement years.

"At that tax rate I'll lose my pension for the year, too," Mel says.

Their only option to beat back the taxman is to invest all the money back into cattle. They bought some heifers, but have the same worries as

other producers about the industry's future; as well, the prospect of rebuilding a purebred herd under the shroud of BSE is daunting.

"Would people buy heifers and bulls from us again?" Trevor asks. "We
just don't know."

I'd heard that the CFIA could be difficult to deal with, so I ask the
family what they think.

Betty says they were treated "fine" at the time, but were offended
recently by news articles that suggest they were somehow to blame for the
herd being depopulated. In the beginning, the CFIA praised them publicly
for keeping good records, but this past spring, Brian Evans, chief veterinary
officer with the agency, implied in a story in the *Western Producer* newspaper that if the McCreas and other producers kept better records, fewer animals would be destroyed during disease outbreak.

This surprises me. The government has always had a long-standing
zero tolerance policy regarding disease control. Herd mates of infected animals are always destroyed, and they have convinced producers this is essential—with no exceptions—to protect the integrity of the national herd. To
now focus back on the producer is unfair. If the CFIA has re-evaluated its
protocols regarding BSE and since changed its policy, then it should simply say so.

The McCreas stop short of casting blame at anyone. They refuse to
point a finger at the company that sold them the feed that was likely tainted. They don't want to cause trouble for anyone, saying that everyone
involved was simply doing their job.

What they do say, though, is how surprising it is that no one from the
government or industry has asked their advice about how the situation
could have been better handled. There must be some insight to gain from
hearing the perspective from their side of the fence.

I sense that these people are still grieving. The fact that the U.S. border is still closed to live Canadian cattle makes their sacrifice seem pointless. Depopulation regulations have relaxed since 2003 and entire herds are
no longer being destroyed. The absolutes they once lived under are shifting daily, and like many others in the industry, the McCreas are crippled by
uncertainty and not ready to commit again to an industry that has left them
bruised and hurting.

The hours have slipped by and I realize it is time for me to go. They
walk me to the door and that's when I notice five aerial farm photos hanging framed on the entrance wall. The earliest dates back to 1965, a photo
showing a small, shingled house, chicken coop and little old barn. Mel

explains he grew up not too far from here and that he bought this place in 1960. Shortly afterwards, in 1962, he and Betty were married.

His thick finger moves to the most recent photo taken in the summer of 2003. Lush fields stretch out in all directions. Modern fencing surrounds a large barn. A half dozen grain bins stand in a neat row along a windbreak of trees. Mel squints as he points at two people standing in the alleyway. The aerial photographer happened by when Trevor was being interviewed by a reporter.

"It would have been a better picture if the cows were still here," Mel sighs, shaking off the sad thought as we both stare for a moment at the empty corrals.

Producers have quipped that the McCreas were one of the few families that got off easy since the border closed. At least they were paid pre-BSE values for their cattle. The look in their eyes, however, tells me an altogether different story—that the business of cows is about more than the money.

Mel extends his hand toward me in friendship and I return the gesture. A cattleman's handshake. As firm as a contract and reliable as the rising sun.

There will be no farm tour following this interview. We exchange goodbyes and long after I'm on my way, I can still feel his hand in mine. It is almost as if everything Mel McCrea has felt these past eighteen months is pulsating up my arm.

CHAPTER TWO

As the Germanic tribes gave up their nomadic existence and
settled the land, cattle played an increasingly important role as
workhorses. The cow is a female symbol representing nourishment
and continuity, and in ancient times would have been essential
for survival in the long dark months of winter.
— Horik Svensson, *The Runes*

The McCreas are in my thoughts the following morning as I pull out of North Battleford and squint into the rising sun.

Fate couldn't have picked a more undeserving family to strike. Most of the producers I've met love their lifestyle and care for their animals, but pure-bred breeders are a different pedigree altogether. For the rest of us, to lose our herd is a shame; for them it's a tragedy. You could say they are the artisans of the cattle world.

Hours of dedication are spent building upon a herd's genetics in a quest to combine the traits that make a perfect breeding animal: strong maternal instincts, good disposition, an abundance of milk, straight solid back and legs, good muscling and light birth weight—a healthy balance of characteristics that produce robust progeny.

Diligence by purebred breeders is the reason that Canada's herd is among the best in the world. And like great works of art, superior cattle are enjoyed by many, but truly appreciated by only the trained eye of a few. Experts in the industry agree that the McCrea cattle were exceptional. Not to say those animals were the best money could buy, but because their breeding program was uniquely their own, those animals couldn't be replaced.

Dr. Chris Clark

Dr. Chris Clark has agreed to meet with me at the Saskatoon Veterinary College at noon. He is an Assistant Professor in the Department of Large Animal Clinical Sciences and considered a BSE expert.

There are so many theories about BSE and the human form, variant CJD, that I'm not sure what to believe. One thing I do know for sure— Creutzfeldt-Jakob is a dreadful disease for which there is no known treatment or cure. During the onset of illness, victims experience pain in the arms and legs, followed by personality change, dementia and difficulty walking. Motor skills continue to deteriorate and eventually the person with CJD will descend into a coma and die. The process takes months and sometimes even years.

Apparently CJD does occur spontaneously in humans at a rate of one-in-a-million. Until 1993, it usually affected elderly people, but then a dairy farmer in the UK whose herd had cases of BSE died of CJD. Four slaughterhouse workers also died, and two years later, the first teenager known to be infected with CJD was discovered. In 1996, scientists who'd examined 10 current cases of the disease confirmed a link between BSE and CJD, calling the disease vCJD.

I have with me a *Winnipeg Free Press* article by Tara Brautigam who interviewed Dr. Neil Cashman, a professor of medicine at the University of Toronto's centre for research in neuro-degenerative diseases.

Dr. Cashman and his research team, which includes colleagues from the United States and the United Kingdom, have identified an antibody specific to an abnormal protein called the prion—a feat scientists have been trying to accomplish for 15 years.[1] They hope to create a cattle vaccine that could lead to a counterpart for humans to prevent vCJD. It could take five to ten years after the vaccine is developed before it would be approved for human use.

Regarding the risk to humans in Canada right now, Dr. Cashman said in an earlier article, "Of course there are risks, but to my mind they are infinitesimal."[2]

I pick up the ringing cell phone in time to get needed directions to the vet college from my husband, Mark. As I merge off Circle Drive in Saskatoon onto Preston Avenue, we update each other on the last 24 hours. I tell him I'll be home by early evening.

The vet clinic is easy to locate. The air inside is heavy with the smell of surgical soap and iodine. The veterinary assistant at the reception desk pages the professor. He arrives in the waiting room minutes later. Stork thin, Chris Clark is shockingly tall and much younger than I expect. So young, in fact, I can't help but tell him so.

He laughs, saying that he's used to it, as he motions for me to follow to his office. Most people tell him they expect a stodgy, old professor with greying hair and thick-rimmed glasses. I run up the stairs behind him as he takes two at a time. Chris apologizes in advance for the mess we'll find as he pushes open the door.

I tell him I once worked for a law firm where files were piled everywhere.

"Good, then you'll feel right at home," he says, moving a stack of books off an extra chair. He hesitates, searching the floor for a bare spot.

We chat for a few minutes before Chris takes a phone call, then holds up an index finger as he answers a knock at the door. He apologizes that a few things need to be done before he and his wife leave for a two-week holiday in Britain. His eyes sparkle at the mention of being home for Christmas.

Chris grew up in rural England near Sussex, and spent his summers working on farms. He earned his vet degree during the BSE outbreak, working at a clinic in Cumbria between 1997 and 1998. He came to Canada to complete a one-year internship, then went back to England after his internship, then returned to Saskatoon to finish his residency. In 2002 he was offered and accepted a position at the college, making him, at the age of 31, one of the youngest faculty members. He loves Canada and especially likes working here. Most of his day is spent teaching and doing clinical service work. He does some research trials—mostly on infectious diseases and the use of antibiotics in animals—but nothing specific to BSE.

I ask how we got BSE in Canada.

Chris explains that once the severity of the situation in Britain was understood, live cattle imports to Canada were banned. The CFIA then traced all cattle already imported from the UK and began monitoring them. There were 182 in total; most of those animals were on ranches in Alberta. When one developed BSE here in 1993, all remaining UK imports were destroyed. It was determined that 68 animals had already died or been slaughtered, and it is believed that at least one of those animals must have been infected and, after its death, rendered into cattle feed. Subsequent studies have shown that ten of these animals came from farms in Britain that had at least one case of BSE.

"One thing we know is that it takes a very small amount of infected material to transmit the disease," he says, explaining that there are no traces of it in the system until at least thirty months, around the time clinical signs begin to appear.

We discuss the McCrea cattle and why only one of 97 calves contracted the disease after eating suspect feed. Chris explains that in Great
Britain, it never was what is considered an epidemic on the farms where it
was discovered. Ninety-five percent of the farms that had BSE had less than
thirteen instances over nearly a twenty-year period. Most had only three or
four cases.

It is curious that some cattle would contract the disease and others do
not. Nobody seemed to understand why, leaving the door open to other
theories, including copper deficiencies,[3] a virus, or use of pituitary hormones.[4] For now, Chris is sticking with the widely accepted, science-based
theory.

But, feeding cows to cows, I ask?

He explains that practice isn't being done any longer. When the 1997
feed ban was implemented, rendered material from cows could only be fed
to chickens and pigs, and vice versa. I grimace, remembering a television
image of a churning vat of blood-red goop. I don't like the idea of herbi-
vores eating meat, so he's going to have a difficult time convincing me this
practice is acceptable. It's as if Chris reads minds.

"Rendering plants are, in fact, some of the first recyclers and the
process is, in many ways, a great thing," he explains. "Materials are heated
to temperatures that kill most disease, removes the water, and stabilizes the
material so it stops rotting. Renderers are able to add value by turning otherwise useless material into products like gelatin, tallow, dog food and addi-
tive to livestock feed. With forty-five percent of the animal not consumed
by humans, the big question is what to do with the waste if it's not rendered."

Searching the bookshelf he pulls out a white book, dusts it off, then
hands it to me. A quick glance through *The Original Recyclers* tells me that
this is a 150-year-old, billion-dollar industry.

He explains that the BSE agent or "prion" is restricted to certain tis-
sues, including the intestines, brain and spinal cord. These specified risk
materials (SRMs) are removed at slaughter, and therefore do not enter the
human food chain. Chris says that he is in favour of excluding all these
identified materials from the rendering process because prions are resistant
to the heat levels in rendering and even sterilization, so instruments used
on patients with CJD can only be used once. Indeed the only way to dispose of prion material is by incineration.

Not wanting to minimize the effect vCJD has had on people with the
disease, Chris still believes it is important for people to understand the disease and keep the risk in perspective. Of the nearly 60 million people living

in Britain during the height of the BSE crisis, many of them would have unknowingly eaten infected material in a variety of cheap, value-added products. In the 1970s, cattle by-product was even used as a stabilizer in baby food, and yet, to date there have been only 160 cases of the disease reported worldwide.

I ask Chris to relate his biggest pet peeve regarding BSE.

He throws back his head and laughs, then stares at the ceiling tiles for a few moments.

"Glad you asked," he chuckles, rolling his chair around to face the computer. He begins searching for something on the hard drive.

"You've seen that image of the dairy cow staggering about," he says over his shoulder. "I'm going to show you the whole clip."

I instantly know the image. It is an alarming, five-second shot of a dairy cow with BSE.

Chris explains that the footage was shot for educational purposes and was somehow obtained by the British media. He launches the video on the computer screen, starting the clip at the beginning.

What bothers him most about the clip is that the portion shown on television is not typical of BSE, but of a cow going down on slippery pavement.

I watch as a herd of dairy cattle walk peacefully through a field, presumably on their way back to the barn for milking. The BSE cow is among them, but at first I can't spot her. Chris points out the subtle difference in the way she walks. Following her herd mates, the cow walks normally for a few steps, then her back legs quicken as if she's hurrying across hot coals. It's those moments of unusual gait that characterize BSE.

We watch as the camera follows the cow as she heads toward the barn. Then as she is singled out from the herd, she becomes nervous, climbing a set of stairs and navigating her way back down, all the while seeming as healthy as the others. She stumbles a bit as she tries to get away from the farmer who is pressing closer. She panics once cornered and points her nose to the ground. All cattle do this when they are trying to line up their vision. She tries to deke her way around him and that's when she slips and goes down.

Chris shuts off the video while saying that another image that bothers him is the footage of burning cattle taken during a foot-and-mouth epidemic. He worries that showing it now sends an inaccurate message to the public that piles of cattle are being burned, or should be destroyed, because of BSE.

His second pet peeve concerns the idea growing within the industry that Canada should begin testing all cattle for BSE. He opposes the idea, saying this is a knee-jerk reaction not based in science—it is well accepted that cattle under 30 months of age do not have BSE. Most animals slaughtered are around the age of 18 months so he calls testing them an expensive waste of time.

Because the instance of the disease is so low, the cost-benefit of testing older animals is also questionable. He believes that the current surveillance program that tests "the four Ds" (dead, dying, down and diseased) is sufficient, especially since annual quotas were ramped up after the first BSE case was discovered.

Chris believes that if at the end of the 2005 surveillance program we haven't found at least one more infected animal, it will be harder to explain than if we do, because it is accepted that if a country has one case it likely has more. If they aren't found, it indicates that the surveillance is not adequate and there will be increased concerns that the meat of infected animals might make it into the food chain.

Chris believes that Canada has the reputation of being very open and honest about BSE, and that consumers worldwide trust us. With the removal of SRMs at slaughter, consumers have nothing to fear and we have nothing to hide. Based on science, the borders should open.

Chris glances at his watch. His flight leaves in a few hours.

The sky has the dull look of a dirty white T-shirt. The wind has picked up and carries with it a dampness that foretells a coming snow-storm. Once out of Saskatoon, I set the cruise control for as fast as I dare.

I think about all the "conspiracy theories" I've heard since BSE was discovered, many of which have since been debunked. It was during those first few months while producers were in denial that the theory emerged that the BSE cow was from the United States, not Canada. Everyone said it was possible since Marwyn Peaster, the producer who shipped the BSE-infected cow to the packing plant, was originally from the United States. He might have brought some cattle with him to Canada. DNA testing proved this theory inaccurate; the cow was indeed born on the McCrea farm.

Peaster was the subject of unfair ridicule outside his own community. Anger intensified. Each day that went by cost the industry another $11 million. In reality, Peaster felt horrible that this had happened and was simply the unfortunate victim of dreadful bad luck.

The ramifications since have been far reaching and Canadian cattle producers aren't the only ones who are suffering. Closed borders and an inability to access processing facilities brought all ruminant livestock producers to their knees. Bison, goat, sheep, elk, deer, llama and alpaca producers cannot access their normal markets because live animals are banned from leaving the country. Because the cattle backlog has spilled over into the smaller abbatoirs, producers of the more exotic species are having a difficult time getting their livestock processed.

Even cattlemen in the U.S. are hurting. Dairy producers have lost the ability to buy replacement heifers from Canada and there are 115 ranchers in Alaska who historically import about 600 head of cattle—replacement heifers and bulls—from Canadian purebred breeders every year.

It is hard to believe that one sick cow could threaten so many livelihoods.

The storm rides my bumper all the way to the Manitoba border. By the time I turn off the highway and follow the winding last few miles home, I wonder how many times I've travelled this road.

Part of what defines "home" is the feeling you get when it comes into sight after being away for a while. It looks comfortably familiar, but fresh at the same time.

Exhausted, I drop the armload of things that shouldn't freeze onto the floor in the porch as Mark and our grown son, Laurie, meet me at the entrance. Our little dog does a double take, then jumps against my legs until I pick him up. We gather into a group hug. Unloading the car can wait until tomorrow.

I tell them they are all looking a little thin as we break from the huddle and climb the stairs to the kitchen.

Mark says it is a good thing I came home today instead of tomorrow. The storm that followed me here is only going to get worse and hang around for a few days.

I think back to all the bad weather I encountered. It was quite the trip.

"Did you see everyone you wanted?" Mark asks as we sit down to a glass of homemade Saskatoon wine.

I tell him that only two people turned me down.

The wine and memories of the people I met warm my insides as we talk about the past few weeks. I leave him sitting for a moment, then return carrying a package of bumper stickers.

"Robert Vander Heyden sent you these," I say. Mark chuckles as he glances at the sticker taped to the outside of the brown package.

So many wonderful people. All with a story to tell. And the best way for me to relay it all is to go back to the beginning of the journey.

Chapter Three

*Some historians believe that cattle were first brought to the
Americas by Norwegian Vikings in the early 1000s. In 1493,
Christopher Columbus brought long-horned cattle from Spain to
Santo Domingo. Descendants of these cattle later were taken
into Mexico and eventually into Texas. They were ancestors of
the famous Texas longhorns. Governor Edward Winslow of
Plymouth Colony brought the first purebred Devon cattle to
New England in 1623. The Shorthorn arrived in 1783.
Cattle raising spread westward as the pioneers
moved across the continent.*
— *World Book Encyclopedia*

It is generally agreed that the BSE announcement, although devastating news to Canada's cattle industry, came at the best possible time of year for ranchers. Cattle movement from the ranch to feedlot is heaviest between September and December; another push occurs in January and February and light shifting in March and April. By May, most cows with newborn calves and one and two-year-old heifers are ready to go to pasture where they will spend the summer grazing in the company of herd bulls.

The feedlot operator did not fare as well as the rancher. Had a few more weeks passed, most of the fat cattle (animals ready to go to the packing plant) would have cycled out of the feedlot. Most finishers sit with a twenty percent capacity during the summer months. This is the time that pens are cleaned and feed is made as the feedlot operator gears up for the fall run. That's when he'll fill his lot with calves as the cycle starts all over again. Of course, there are exceptions to this ideal, but for the most part,

Neil and Shane Jahnke

the laws of supply and demand, combined with North America's 120-year-old cattle cycle, keep the industry moving at a predictable pace.

The cattleman is born into the understanding that he's working within a blueprint he cannot change. The best he can do is plan for the 10-year cycle that divides equally the number of years he makes money, breaks even, then borrows against his equity when the price he receives for his animals doesn't meet the expense of raising them.

October 17, 2004

Yesterday, the weather at home was mild as I set out on a journey to talk to cattlemen about how they've been affected by BSE and the closed border. I already have ten days worth of interviews done and wonder if the producers I've spoken to in Manitoba have a different perspective than those in the west.

This morning, I wake in Qu'Appelle, Saskatchewan, to find three inches of wet snow covering everything in the valley.

Neil and Marilyn Jahnke are expecting me in the early afternoon. I met Neil briefly once back in the summer of 1999 at the Canadian Cattlemen's Association (CCA) semi-annual meeting in Penticton, B.C. I was working as the Communications Coordinator for the Manitoba Cattle Producers Association (MCPA), and knew Neil by reputation. The following year, he was elected vice-president of the CCA, which meant that in two years time, he'd likely become president of this umbrella organization that represents more than 90,000 producers across Canada.

There are people in the industry who are known for the things they say, what they do or the place they run. Neil Jahnke is a real cowboy who is known on all three accounts.

The windshield wipers beat frantically as the roar of the defroster muffles the radio announcer's voice. I pull onto the highway and head south, surprised that I'm alone on the normally busy road. Halfway up the hill leading out of the valley, I see that a tractor-trailer has jackknifed and lays sprawled across both lanes. I churn up snow, creeping past men standing alongside the road wearing ball caps and thick-soled felt-lined boots. They are looking at the wreck, deciding how to clean it up. A long line of cars waits at the top of the hill while a police officer stands in the middle of the road directing traffic. An empty cattle liner has slid into the ditch, too, and had it been full of cattle, this would have been a catastrophe.

Jackknife. *To double or bend from the middle.* That's exactly what has happened to the cattle industry. Everything came to a crashing halt because of one cow, and since then, cattlemen have been navigating a slippery slope. Waiting. Getting by as best they can in a storm of uncertainty that just won't let up.

I spend a few tense hours on the Trans Canada Highway, crawling along snow-packed, polished pavement, hoping a nudge of wind won't cause the car to shimmy into the other lane. I turn off at Chaplin, opting to take the backroads the rest of the way to Gouldtown.

There are few provinces in Canada that elicit more sarcastic, good-natured barbs than Saskatchewan: Easy to draw but hard to spell. This province is considered by most as one gigantic grain field interrupted only by the occasional, odd-named town. But that perception is untrue. The northern part of the province is rich with lakes and forest. The south central region is some of the best cattle land in the country, home to 1.33 million cows and nearly 22,000 cattle producers. This is the second largest beef-producing province.

There is something unspoiled about Saskatchewan that seems to rub off on its inhabitants. The people here have a self-sufficiency that can best be described as resilience from having grown up on the prairies. They are straightforward and helpful. Teenagers here look you straight in the eye.

I'm told that you can travel anywhere in the world and you'll meet someone from Saskatchewan. Drive along the grid roads between the towns Eyebrow and Gouldtown, and you won't meet a soul.

Taking my eyes off the desolate, gravel road long enough to flip through a book I've brought, I read that the town I'm looking for was named for an early pioneer named Mr. Gould. Not a particularly fascinating story.

Flipping back a few pages I locate Eyebrow. It was "named for Eyebrow Lake nine miles from the village. It is southeast of Elbow and the centre of one of Saskatchewan's better hunting and fishing districts."[5] I share a kinship with these folks because I'm from a funny named place too—Vogar.

I grew up in southern Ontario in an area that was considered rural. After moving to the ranch, I came to understand what the word rural means. There were people who would ask why I wanted to live in such a remote place. I'd answer with platitudes about the clean air and absence of crime, but I've since come to realize it lies deeper than that. Somewhere out here, buried deep in the chest of the prairies, is an explanation why so many pioneers came west, and in spite of tremendous hardships, never left.

The Jahnke place is further back from the main road than expected, and just when I think I've missed the turnoff, my eyes are drawn to a line of hydro poles soldiering on to the last place on the road.

Coming up over a rise, I see the Big Coulee Ranch nestled along the shore of the South Saskatchewan River. An inch of new snow softens the look of the frost-withered prairie wool. The river winds through the homestead, deep and blue as the back of a peacock's head. The simple, ranch-style house is on this side; the barn and corrals sit on the other side, with a wooden bridge connecting the two. Settled in 1879 by railway surveyors, the Big Coulee was established with Texas cattle and has been in the Jahnke family since the early 1900s.

The car rattles over a corrugated Texas gate that separates the yard and pasture. Movement in the distance causes me to slow down to watch as a dozen horses crest the hill, galloping playfully, kicking up snow and nodding at one another. They continue toward me until their chests rub against the split rail fence that surrounds the yard. They follow it until they are close enough to the house that a whinny can be heard inside.

As I get out of the car, I wonder about the size of this place. Long ago I discovered that you don't ask a cattleman how many cows he's got. The old-fashioned fellows (and you can never be sure who they are) are insulted by the question. They say this is similar to asking a man how much money he makes, so I never do. I wait for him to offer, or go home not knowing.

I step from the cold wind into a porch filled with warmth and the smell of coffee brewing. The wall is lined with jackets, coveralls and a row of cowboy boots. A gravelly voice hollers to come on in.

Neil is sitting at the kitchen table. His nose and cheeks are wind slapped from two days working cattle. His hair, the colour of ripe grain on a frosty morning, sits flat against his forehead, pressed that way by his cowboy hat. He massages the full moustache that hangs like quotation marks at the corners of his mouth. He takes a sip of scotch, then invites me to sit down. He doesn't remember meeting me and looks troubled by the fact.

Marilyn is at the opposite end of the table. She nods a polite hello, then finishes sorting through a bundle of cattle files. She has striking blue eyes, a quick smile and easy-to-keep dark hair. I notice a gentle rasp in her voice when she offers me a cup of coffee. I accept a sandwich while the three of us make small talk. Marilyn doesn't seem to mind that most of my questions are for her husband.

The Jahnkes aren't ready to settle into conversation yet because their grown children, Shane and Jennifer, are getting ready to leave. They came home for the weekend to help brand and process cattle. Neil is concerned about the weather so he checks the road report on the telephone's speed dial, relaying back that the highway is clear to the west. The kids wave goodbye and tell their parents not to worry.

Neil had no idea in March of 2002 when he became President of the CCA that his outgoing year would be spent battling the worst crisis the industry has ever seen. He remembers where he was on May 20. He and Marilyn were on their way to the CCA head office in Calgary when CBC called his cell phone looking for comments.

"On the 18th I knew there was a suspected case," he says, taking another sip of scotch. "I couldn't tell anyone and didn't sell any animals either. Let me tell you though, I'd be lying if I said it didn't cross my mind."

Within hours of the announcement, the U.S. border slammed shut to Canadian beef. With the industry here depending so heavily on exports, sixty percent to the U.S., the closed border meant that it took only a few days for beef and live cattle to begin backing up. Beef is a multi-billion-dollar industry in Canada—daily losses were estimated at $11 million.

In those first few months everyone was looking for the answer to one question: When will the border re-open?

In other countries that have reported cases of BSE, it has taken up to seven years for international borders to re-open. Producers, especially feedlot operators, grew frantic. Some of the pressure was relieved on August 8, 2003, when the United States Department of Agriculture (USDA) announced that they would allow in boxed beef—boneless cuts from animals under 30 months of age. This relieved some of the pressure off the packing plants, which were now in the envious position of having a market to ship to and an oversupply of fat animals waiting for slaughter.

For the Jahnkes, these months were remembered as a blur of activity. Neil spent countless hours on the phone, in meetings, and travelling between home, Ottawa, Calgary and the U.S.. Because Marilyn was President of the Saskatchewan Stock Growers Association, they were often running in opposite directions.

"We wore out at least two phones," Marilyn laughs. "I'd be on one in here and he'd be standing in the porch talking on the other."

Neil's ice blue eyes soften as he watches her light a cigarette. He opens the pack and lights one, too, saying that 98 percent of the calls they received were from cattle producers pleased with their efforts.

"I had people saying that Saskatchewan producers were getting updates faster than anyone else because the president of the SSGA was sleeping with the president of the CCA," he laughs.

Now each of them sits as Past Presidents of their respective organizations. Not as busy, but still involved.

I ask what motivated them to take on such high-profile positions. They chuckle together and Marilyn shrugs, saying that they did what they had to do.

Neil's grandfather, father and uncles were all active with the provincial cattle organization. He attended his first meeting when he was 30.

"I always say that a person has to take his turn in the barrel so others can shoot at him," he chuckles, smoking his cigarette down to the butt, then lighting another. He doesn't hesitate to voice his opinion about how the situation was handled by government.

With the exception of the CFIA, Neil believes that the politicians, some bureaucrats and industry officials on both sides of the border have worked diligently in the best interest of this industry. He praised Federal Agriculture Minister Lyle Vanclief and Vanclief's successor, Bob Speller. It was level-headed comments by politicians and industry officials in those first few days after the announcement that kept the hysteria down as they stressed this was not an epidemic but just one cow.

"I started calling him 'one cow Vanclief,'" Neil laughs.

Canada is the only country in the world that has seen their beef consumption rise after reporting a case of BSE, thanks to fair reporting by the media and common sense on the part of consumers. Many communities held barbeques and "eat beef" rallies all across the country that helped boost consumer confidence and brought out the competitive nature of prairie folk.

"Every time Alberta had a barbeque, we had a bigger one," Neil smiles, adding that 5,600 people came to a cookout in Moose Jaw. Saskatchewan stood behind its producers the same way they support their football team—unconditionally.

I ask what would have happened if consumers had stopped eating beef.

Neil inhales sharply, shakes his head, then takes a drag from his cigarette. He exhales slowly, blinks hard, then his eyes go to a faraway place.

"It would have been the biggest wreck you've ever seen."

Afternoon wears into evening. I'm offered a glass of rhubarb wine made by local Hutterites. It's both stronger and better tasting than I expect.

The actions of the CFIA are weighing down Neil's thoughts. He recently received calls from a small, producer-owned plant that is having difficulty with them. He cites a doorway being an inch too narrow and an employee wash basin set three inches too close to a door as reasons the CFIA has refused to pass the plant's inspection. Officials at the agency are deliberately making life difficult under the guise of food safety, not because they need to, but simply because they can.

"Another plant could have been killing 700 to 800 cows a day by now, but the CFIA is dragging its feet." He calls this harassment of the industry at a time when fast tracking is needed.

I've heard countless explanations why it is taking so long for the border to re-open to live cattle. I ask Neil if he understands the reason for the delay.

Neil explains that the Office Internationale des Epizooties (OIE) administers plant and animal sanitation rules for health and safety considerations under the World Trade Organization (WTO) agreements, developing a risk assessment code for member countries. It has five categories of BSE risk, ranging from BSE free to high risk.

With the support of the United States and Mexico, Canada began immediately petitioning the OIE to re-write the rules to take into account updated, scientific understanding of the disease. Countries that have taken steps to manage the risk of BSE should not be penalized by having their borders closed because of one or two cases. The guidelines recently changed so that a country deemed minimal risk can have one positive BSE case for every one million adult animals in the previous 12 months, and retain low-risk status. Canada is waiting to be officially declared a minimal risk country.

He is quick to say that the Canadian government does not hesitate to enforce these same rules against others, closing borders immediately upon the discovery of BSE. Some call this an artificial trade barrier, while others say it is a necessary step if a country considered BSE free wants to keep the confidence of other BSE-free trading partners. Neil believes the Canadian government is as guilty as anybody when it comes to playing politics with BSE and border restrictions.

"We did it to other countries and now they are doing it to us," he says.

The fact that the U.S. border did open in September 2003 to boxed beef from animals under 30 months of age is both a credit to the USDA and a compliment to our industry.

"Canada is the only country to ever export to a BSE-free country after only three months of trade stoppage," he says, adding that ranchers saw prices in the fall as high as $1.30 a pound. No other producers in the world have been that lucky. He wants producers to understand that things could have been a lot worse.

I ask where the U.S. producer group Ranchers Cattlemen Action Legal Fund (R-CALF) fits into the puzzle.

Again, Neil blames the CFIA. He explains that strict regulations imposed by the government make it difficult for American producers to do business here. There are two cattle diseases in the U.S.—Aniplasmosis and Blue Tongue—that do not exist in Canada. These diseases are transmitted by insects which cannot survive our harsh winters. Blue Tongue is the more serious of the two because it is considered untreatable and sometimes fatal. Aniplasmosis can be treated with antibiotics and animals usually recover. Neither disease is contagious or a threat to human health, but Canadian regulations mean American livestock accepted into Canada have to first go through rigorous testing and quarantine before they can touch Canadian soil. The CCA has been fighting against these restrictions for years. They want the diseases placed on the annual notifiable list just as they are in the U.S., which allows the industry to take responsibility for managing the risk. Neil believes that if it wasn't for the rigid hand of the CFIA, R-CALF likely wouldn't exist.

He says that for 17 years, cattlemen in the northern states have been watching thousands of trucks filled with our cattle passing through their states, and for the last 15 of those years knew there was no scientific basis for the restrictions toward them. Neil calls this Canada's lesson to start basing decisions on science, too.

"They wanted to trade up here but the costs made it near impossible. So, they got mad and then got organized and now we have R-CALF."

Suspecting R-CALF would find reasons to petition to keep the border closed, Neil shared this fear with the federal agriculture ministers and anyone else in government who'd listen. Again he recommended the relaxation of these import rules and even spoke to Brian Evans, one of the top men at the CFIA.

"I had him cornered on a plane, so he couldn't get away from me," he laughs. "But he still refused to move on it, even after having explained it to him in plain English. Unbelievable, really. I'd rather deal with Revenue Canada than the CFIA."

Finally, with mounting pressure due to the prolonged border closure, the CFIA was forced to address the issue and relaxed the restrictions earlier this year, but the damage was already done.

While on the topic of the CFIA, I ask his opinion about how the McCreas were treated.

Neil scowls and shakes his head.

He explains that the CFIA came to him once, concerned that Mel wasn't going to give up the animals. Neil phoned Mel and they had a long chat and, of course, Mel understood; he was just angry and frustrated. Afterward, Neil phoned the CFIA and told them that there would be no problems at the McCreas.

Neil looks past me, focusing on the wall over my shoulder, rubbing his moustache as he recalls that evening's news broadcast.

Apparently, the CFIA arrived at the McCrea house shortly after they spoke, flanked by RCMP officers, with the media and film crew close behind. Neil hated watching Mel's concern for his cattle being mocked.

"I wouldn't be surprised if Mel never spoke to me again," he says. "After the fact, it looked like I was conspiring with those bastards against him, which I sure in hell was not."

As we settle into our chairs after supper, I ask if there is a business more complex than the cattle industry.

Marilyn raises her eyebrows as she ponders the question. Neil tilts his head slightly and thinks. It appears that nobody has ever asked this before. We debate the complexities of lumber and the auto industry, concluding that dealing in live animals adds a complexity otherwise missing from most big business. In Canada, the beef industry was worth $30 billion to the economy in 2002. Unlike chickens, eggs, hogs and milk, cattle production is not managed by a marketing board. In fact, those two words will quickly raise the ire of a true cattleman.

I need to understand why.

"We regulate ourselves," he replies, explaining that supply management of beef would be the ruination of the industry, because orderly marketing is considered subsidization by trading partners, and huge duties would be imposed on our meat, making Canadian beef and live cattle less competitive. For supply management to work, quotas would have to be established, and that would shrink the industry to half the size in order to eliminate the reliance on exports. Many producers would be forced out of business, resulting in a waste of the natural prairie grasslands that are good for little else. Neil calls proponents of the idea selfish and stupid.

We debate this and other issues long into the night. Marilyn shows me the guest bedroom and it isn't long before I'm tucked under a snug, home-made quilt, listening to the wind outside whistling through the coulee.

The next morning, I wake to the relentless wind and the glow of a sun halfway up. Its reflection has cast everything outside in a silver blue sheen. I emerge from the room to the quiet sounds of morning that begin in the kitchen. A light glows golden and the smell of fresh coffee adds to the cozy feeling of a warm house on a winter morning.

Neil stifles a cough to keep it from echoing throughout the still house. He is standing gazing out the window, enjoying his first smoke of the day.

"Some men have girlfriends or cabins at the lake," he says, taking a sip of coffee. "That's my vice right there. My horses."

I peer out the window to see the animals looking back in at him. Knowing Neil a bit better today, I suspect that these are expensive pure-breds. The stormy northwest wind whips pellets of freezing rain against the window. Two more inches of snow have fallen and it is starting to blow.

We talk about the prairies and why he lives here. He admits that the raw beauty of the place is something he's gotten used to, but it isn't something he ever takes for granted.

"Sure glad we did those cattle yesterday," he says. Most of his life he's made decisions based on gut feeling, and now confirms that once again his instincts were right.

We sit for awhile in silence, then I tell him how much I like their coffee. He brightens, saying that there is a natural flowing spring that supplies drinking water to the house.

Marilyn joins us and Neil offers to make breakfast. Once we've had our fill of coffee, we decide to take a tour of the ranch. As we climb into his diesel pick-up, Neil admits that BSE is not the first hardship that Canadian cattlemen have faced.

He tells me that in 1951 calves were bringing 33 cents a pound, and a year later there was a Foot and Mouth outbreak that caused prices to drop to 11 cents. It took until 1965 before they saw prices around 30 cents again.

Ploughing along prairie trails filled with snow, he shifts into four-wheel drive to climb a steep incline. I hold on as the truck bounces along the rough pasture.

"I went to the banker in 1972 when we wanted to buy the ranch and he told me that we'd never make it," he says, slowing the truck to a stop. The trail ahead continues for another truck length, then the earth falls away. "This here is likely the prettiest spot on the ranch," he says, nodding for me to go out and take a look. As soon as I'm out of the lee of the truck, the wind grabs ahold of me and whips ice pellets against my face. I go only as far out as necessary to glance over the edge. The water churns a few hundred feet below as the snow tries frantically to fill up the valley. I imagine how beautiful this spot would be in the summer.

I climb back into the truck and as Neil turns around and begins following our trail back toward the house, he finishes his story, saying that in the fall of 1973 he was offered 67 cents a pound for his steer calves and 75 cents for the light calves. He figured that price was too low, so he held on to them and wintered them. In February he was offered 38 cents, so he took it and ran, but there were lots of guys who wouldn't. By May, calves were selling for 25 cents a pound.

"We had a couple of really good years, but then that wreck happened. We just dug in our heels and cut back. We didn't hire any help and did all the work ourselves. Marilyn went five years without a new dress or a new pair of shoes."

Neil takes me to the other side of the river where he suspects the cows might be. Sure enough, we find them sheltering in a bluff of trees along a stream that feeds into the river. We sit and watch the cows for a few minutes, beautiful black animals that stand quietly watching us back.

He explains he's expanded numerous times since buying the place from his uncle, and now runs 1,200 cows, mainly Black Angus. A good portion are purebreds. Since he calves on the grass, he uses easy calving, longhorn bulls on the heifers. He claims to have a 95% calving rate and says that "my cows work for me, I don't work for them."

On the way back, I point to a set of four old wooden wagon wheels in the field near the barn. I've been looking for three years for a set to use as ornamentation in the large flower garden along the south side of my house. He smiles at the frivolity of this, but drives over so I can take a look. Once again, I step out into the storm, but am thrilled to find good oak wheels set snug in the rim, and about the size I'm looking for.

I ask if he'll sell them to me as I climb back in, breathless from fighting the snow and wind.

He laughs, telling me I can have them. All I have to do is come back to pick them up. I can hardly believe my luck!

"If I had a dollar for every time I've given that set of wheels away. . ." he chuckles as he swings the truck back onto the trail.

Neil asks where I'm heading as I load my bag and camera into the car. He's standing in the doorway of the garage, with his hands in his jean pockets, stocking feet on the cold cement floor.

I tell him there are people I'd like to see in Swift Current.

"Well, if you get the chance, go and stay at the old Commercial Hotel in Maple Creek. You can't do a story about the cattle industry without going to old Cow Town," he says.

I nod that I will, then wave a quick goodbye as I pull the car door shut and turn up the heat before backing away.

I drive for awhile along the unmarked roads, distracted by thoughts about cattlemen surviving hard times without asking for help. They wear their independence like a badge of honour and if BSE has done anything, it's hurt pride as much as bank accounts.

Suddenly, the sights along the road look unfamiliar. I rifle through my bag and pull out a compass; that helps me get back on track before I drain the tank driving in the wrong direction. I fill up in Herbert, then pull onto the Trans-Canada Highway west.

The clerk at the motel in Swift Current gives me a quiet room along the back of the lot and I spend the rest of the afternoon writing. I make a few calls that evening.

A friend told me more than once that if I go to Saskatchewan, I have to call Bob Switzer. I flip through my book to the page with Switzer's phone number and pick up the phone. A gruff voice on the other end agrees to meet with me the next morning, but says he only has a half hour to spare because he's going to a cattle sale in Maple Creek afterward. I can't believe my luck again! We agree to meet there instead and I hang up the phone, thankful for those moments when things seem to fall neatly into place.

CHAPTER FOUR

Cattle are among the most important farm animals. We eat the
meat of cattle as roast beef, veal, hamburger and hot dogs.
We drink the milk of cattle, and use it to make butter, cheese
and ice cream. The hides of cattle provide leather for our shoes.
Cattle also furnish materials for such useful items as medicines,
soap and glue. In some countries, cattle supply a main source of
power by pulling plows, carts and wagons.
— World Book Encyclopedia, 1991

Driving into Maple Creek is like being transported back in time. The wide streets, false-fronted buildings and quaint atmosphere give me a sense of earlier days. Seasoned trees tower overhead, their golden leaves scattered on the ground, turning moldy black from the snow and cold.

Moving slowly down Main Street, passing by all the businesses that complete a small town: bakery, grocery, shoe and clothing stores, numerous banks, town hall, pharmacy, RCMP detachment and museum. I pull into a parking spot, then find Maple Creek in the name book. It says: "Maple Creek rises in the Cypress Hills and flows north into Big Stick Lake. The town of Maple Creek takes its name from the creek. Maple Creek came into being at freeze-up in 1882, when construction of the railroad halted a few miles east of the present townsite. Instead of returning east, a few of the construction crew decided to winter there. About 12 men made up the population of Maple Creek during the winter of 1882-83. At the present time, generally speaking, the land north of Maple Creek is farmland, and to the south it is grazing land where large herds of cattle still roam. Pioneers in Maple Creek still like to think back to the days when it

LeAnne, Glori, Shane, Austin, Ed and Eric Dalke

was all ranch land and they liked to call Maple Creek, "The Old Cow Town."[6]

It seems that today's sale has brought a lot of cattlemen to town. Not sure where to find the auction mart, I wait until a pick-up truck pulling a trailer passes, then follow it to the east edge of town. The gamble pays off, and within minutes, I'm in the crowded parking lot of the Cow Town Livestock Exchange.

Despite the overcast skies, it is warm outside. I step carefully to avoid muddy potholes as I follow a stream of men and a few women to the auction mart door. Throaty bawls suffocate all other sounds except for the jangle of opening and closing gates, and the occasional "Haw!" from the cowboys on horseback riding the pens. The air is ripe with the tangy smell of manure, urine and damp straw. Cow manure is the least offensive of all livestock waste, especially once baked in the sun. The same cannot be said for "pee-water" that is made worse by heat and nauseates like drying blood or rotting fish.

Driving through a small town is much different than leaving the anonymity of your car and joining locals at one of their events. No matter how hard strangers try to blend in, there is no hiding your foreign self in a small town.

Locals will nod politely, even hold open the door, but will avoid prolonged eye contact with anyone new. Brows knit together as they mouth a silent "who's that?" to whoever they are with. A slight difference is seen in the coffee shop, where sitting in a familiar seat surrounded by friends, with a cup of coffee in hand, gives licence to stare. Some folks will even point. I know because I've done it, too.

So it came as a tremendous relief when I stepped inside the waiting area of the auction mart to see a friend, Ed Dalke, and his teenaged sons, Eric and Shane. Ed and his wife, Glori, own one of the larger feedlots in southern Manitoba, near the burgeoning town of Morden. I first met the Dalkes back in the early 1990s when Mark was a director on the Manitoba Cattle Producers Board. I saw them last just weeks ago.

It's 18-year-old Eric who sees me first. His face turns into a smile as he nudges his dad and points at me in a good way. He is a lanky version of his dad and I guess this must be how Ed looked as a teenager.

They meet me halfway across the floor and we shake hands. We are equally surprised to see one another.

"What are you doing here?" Ed asks. He's a big, friendly man with quick, smiling eyes and gentle mannerisms.

I tell him I'm there to watch the sale and meet Bob Switzer. I ask if

Glori came along.

"Somebody has to stay home and do the chores," he says. Ed told me once that Glori is the best ration mixer and feed wagon driver he's ever seen. The prideful gleam when he speaks about his wife tells me as much about him, as her.

We chat for a few minutes, then we're interrupted by cattlemen who are pleased to see Ed again. They clasp hands and talk cattle, so I slip away to wait my turn to speak with one of the auction mart owners.

Glancing around I see that all the seats are taken around the tables in front of the lunch counter. Women stand behind the half wall, serving hamburgers, chili, coffee and pie. There are a few worn easy chairs, coffee tables and a couch near the door. This area is referred to as "the kitchen," the place where producers will sit and gab about the weather, cattle prices and living with the fallout from BSE. Everyone is holding the sale sheet, a typed page listing all cattle on offer that day. Sellers flip the pages until they come to their calves, then flip back, mentally calculating how long it will be before their calves sell. Nobody wants to be at the beginning of the sale, fearing that their animals will sell too quickly at a low price. Nor do they want to be last when both the buyers and cattle are tired and shrunk from not enough food and water.

Auction mart staff hurry by, glancing at their watches. A man wearing a cowboy hat climbs a few stairs and opens the double doors that lead to the sale ring. He disappears into the sound of uprooted bawling calves, the noise soon hushed by the deliberate closing doors.

Brent Weiss introduces himself and I explain why I'm here. He is a pleasant-looking man. We talk about the border closure for awhile, his dark eyes absorbing my words.

"It shut us down for three months," he says, explaining that those first months put just over 20 part-time people out of work. "We kept paying our six full-time staff though, because in our business you just can't afford to let good staff go—you might not get them back."

Brent explained that usually they had anywhere from 300 to 1,000 head at their regular Tuesday sales, and since the border closed on a sale day, a few hasty decisions were made as cattle stood in the pens with the sale ready to begin.

"We got a call from an order buyer from Swift Current at 9:00 a.m. who said, 'We've got big trouble.'" There was suddenly no market for cows, and calf prices were uncertain. Brent and his partners decided to cancel the sale, which meant calling all the producers and sending the cattle home.

Brent has been an auctioneer for more than 20 years and this was the first market collapse to ever completely shut them down. He owns Cow Town Livestock Exchange in partnership with five other cattle producers, sharing auctioneering duties with Jim Wilson and Gordie Cameron. Brent says the negative economic effect on the area since BSE has been "huge" because so many mixed farmers switched from grain to cattle over the past decade.

"We've seen fat cattle sell for what calves are worth," he says, shaking his head. As an auction mart owner, he's in a tough position trying to do the best job he can for everybody—both the buyers and the sellers.

More than one person is waiting to talk to Brent, so I offer to let him get back to preparing for the sale. He apologizes, suddenly spotting Bob Switzer, calling him over. A heavyset man in a brown jacket and black cowboy hat moves through the crowd. The words "Short Grass Bull Sale" are embroidered in square letters across the breast of his jacket. Bob and I shake hands and chat for a few minutes as Brent disappears through the heavy doors leading to the sale ring.

Bob has a deep yet quiet voice and I have to lean in to hear what he's saying. He doesn't offer much in the way of words, answering most of my questions abruptly. He seems distracted. Sale day is not the best time for conversation as minds are often elsewhere. Bob motions for me to follow him into the arena. My nose quickly adjusts to the scent of ammonia that fills the air and sticks to our clothing. Auction barns are like hospitals—unmistakable in their aroma.

The bleachers are filled with mostly men wearing cowboy hats or ball caps bearing an equipment dealership logo or sports team. They huddle and talk, those sitting on the lower levels leaning away from one another as latecomers, like us, climb between them.

The auctioneer stands in a booth on the other side of the sale ring, where cattle will be herded in by lot number, weighed, then sold. Today's auctioneer, Gordie Cameron, welcomes everyone to the sale, telling a few jokes as the arena turns quiet. He makes special mention of a few people, including me, announcing that I'm writing a book about BSE.

"She's sitting right up there with Bob Switzer," he says, pausing as people turn their heads to look. "Just remember, Karen, whatever Bob tells you, it's probably a lie." This generates a ripple of laughter from the crowd and a full-body chuckle from Bob. I wave and smile. I shouldn't be so surprised that Brent remembered my name and the details about why I am here. Auctioneers make a business out of communicating. Most are quick minded and sociable.

A quick glance at the sale sheet shows that the majority of the cattle on this sale are Black Angus calves weighing 450 to 700 pounds. Buyers have calculated ahead of time how much it is going to cost to feed a calf to a finished weight. The sale begins and it doesn't take long to establish the average price for the heavier steer calves today is 98 cents a pound. Lighter steers sell for around $1.23. Heifers bring five cents a pound less than the steers in every weight class because it will take longer to feed them to butcher weight.

Bob watches intently. He is one of the founding directors of the Red Coat Feeders and knows that some of the animals bought today will be shipped to their feedlot.

He leans toward me and says that he worried for years that Canada was too dependent on the U.S. In a way, it was a sense of foreboding he had that someday things could go wrong, but he didn't tell too many people his thoughts because it would have seemed alarmist—especially in the years just prior to BSE when prices were very good.

"Before BSE, good quality calves like that would bring at least $100 a head more," Bob whispers, as a pen of sixty-nine, 618 pound calves bring 97 cents a pound, or $599 each. There are 24 buyers in the front row bidding against one another, including Ed Dalke.

I watch Ed for awhile and begin to recognize his buying pattern. He's looking for what are called "six weight" steers, calves weighing around six hundred pounds. He watches the auctioneer intently, lifting his wrist ever so slightly each time he bids. Once the bidding hits 98 cents he shakes his head no, then stops bidding. He'll go up to $1.03 for steers weighing 572 lbs. He has calculated beforehand how high he can go, based on how much it will cost to feed them this winter and make a profit. If things go as planned and he makes his margin, Ed will pay his expenses and use whatever is leftover as equity to show the bank. He'll borrow against that, and then next fall will buy more cattle. Today, he buys approximately 600 head, worth nearly $360,000.

I sit through three quarters of the sale, then return to the kitchen area to talk with sellers. Now that people know why I'm here, they will either come over to talk or avoid my gaze.

A few minutes after I sink into the old couch along the wall by the door, an elderly man pushing a cane pauses, then comments on the weather. He tilts his head and cups his good ear toward me. He considers sitting down, but might not be able to get off the low-slung cushion without help, so he leans heavily with both hands on his cane instead. Somebody will get the idea to put blocks under the legs of this couch one day.

I hoist myself up onto the armrest. He tells me his name is Victor Kriwokon. Victor doesn't seem to mind when I ask him to spell it for me as I start a new page in my notebook.

"The only thing we've seen that compares to BSE is when Foot and Mouth hit back in 1950s, but even that was only for a year and affected a small area around Moose Jaw," he says. "Calves were bringing 40 cents a pound back then, but in those days, things cost a lot less, too."

Victor retired in 1987 and now his son, Kevin, runs their ranch south of Piapot. He says they've always been careful about what they buy and try to keep the debt down. He worries about how political the industry is becoming and doesn't favour how the packing plants are gaining control.

He's quiet for a moment then shakes his head. "I'm glad I'm retired."

I ask if they sold any cattle today. Retired in this industry does not necessarily mean free of cattle. Nor does it mean free from work.

He shakes his head no, explaining that he worked the sale ring for 15 years so he feels at home in this place. He likes to come to the weekly sales to keep abreast of prices and enjoys contact with the staff and area ranchers.

"I've been in the business all my life, so the roots are still here."

We chat for awhile longer then he ambles to the door, waving "goodbye, see you next week" anonymously toward the crowded tables. A few wave in reply as he disappears out the door.

I speak with another fellow, Clay Yarshenko. He sold calves today and says that even though prices were up a bit, he won't meet his cost of production.

"But I don't feel too bad," he chuckles, shaking his head. "It's become a habit for producers to lower their expectations. Even though we're losing money we say, 'it's not as much as we could have lost.'"

Clay is a third-generation cow-calf producer who has been ranching alone for the past 12 years. He says this year's prices are similar to what they were in 1996. He sold his best steers for 86 cents then. The problem is that input costs have skyrocketed and the cull cow is worth very little. This situation is causing him to take a harder look at how he makes a living.

"I'm doing some off-farm work now, and let me tell you, it's pretty attractive going to work and getting paid for what you do and having weekends off," he says. "It's going to take at least three years to make up the losses incurred so far. What the closed border has done is forced me to consider long-term what I'm going to do, how much I'm willing to work for."

When the sale is finished, Bob and Ed meet me in the kitchen area after arranging for trucks to deliver cattle to their feedlots.

It is customary after cattle are sold for buyers and sellers to sit down and share a drink. A buzz starts that a hospitality room is set up at the Commercial Hotel, so I invite myself along.

"Tomorrow we'll tour the feedlot and round up some cattle," Bob says. "I already called Gail, so she's expecting you to stay with us tonight." Friends from Alberta are visiting the Switzers so Bob has to go home. He gives me sketchy directions to the ranch that include "you can't miss it" before hurrying toward the door.

"Supper at Hazenmore?" he asks the group I'm standing with. He points first to me, then to Ed and the boys.

"We can't, we've left Glori home long enough," Ed says. He would enjoy a sit-down meal but will likely settle for a burger to go.

"Oh, c'mon dad," Eric says, giving Ed a nudge.

"It's on your way," Bob coaxes. "They've got the best steak in western Canada—"

Ed wavers but shakes his head no. Bob nods, then he's gone.

The Commercial Hotel is easy to find; it towers two stories over everything else nearby. At street level, it looks like most other rural hotels. Stand back, then look up, and you'll wonder what might bring enough people to Maple Creek to fill all the rooms that look out onto the street.

The Dalkes meet me in the hotel lobby and wait as I soak in the community's history, told in photographs lining the walls. A heavy wooden desk, switchboard and leather-bound chairs from the original hotel give the lobby an old west ambiance. Sleek marble floors and open hand-cut ceiling beams whisper the building's age. Built in 1883, it is one of Western Canada's older businesses, and certainly the first one established here.

I'm told that the hotel was built by a wealthy Montana firm and has undergone numerous facelifts over the years. During prohibition, the bar was converted to a bank, and then, once the liquor ban was lifted, changed back again. The bank vault became a beer cooler that is still being used today. I read that this is the only place in town that still has hitching post rights, so if a cowboy on horseback were to wander into town, he'd have a place to tie his horse. Some say that the old hotel is haunted—I shiver at the idea as we take the open, spindle-railed staircase to the second floor. Our footsteps are absorbed into the heavy brocade carpet and the subdued atmosphere makes us lower our voices.

The hospitality room is situated right at the top of the stairs. The room is full so we join others lining the hallway. I listen as the men talk cattle and am introduced to most who walk by. Some nod and continue on.

Others stop and lean against the wall beside us and chat for awhile. Ed speaks tactfully about the day's prices.

"I come here to buy calves because of the cattle quality," he says. "These guys make their living raising cattle, and it shows." He says that in the fall of 2002, he paid $1.51 a pound for six weight calves. The same ranch sold today and he bought calves again, this time paying 98 cents.

I'm introduced to industry veteran Jim Wilson, who is part-owner of the auction mart. He remembers well how the first stockyards consisted of a few pens and an open-air ring in the field just across the street from the hotel. That changed in 1997 when newer, modern facilities were built east of town.

Like most of the pioneers in the area, Jim's dad immigrated from the U.S., settling 15 miles southwest of Maple Creek. In 1972, Jim bought up part of the historic 76 Ranch, a deal that included the brand and the Angus cattle.

"Maple Creek is likely the mildest place in Saskatchewan to raise cattle," Jim says. Most years ranchers don't have to begin feeding until mid-January and they stop by the end of March; 2004 was the exception and most fed for nearly six months.

Jim says that back in the early 1900s, his father found the Hereford feather-neck cattle most desirable, but that changed during the winter of 1916. It was remembered as one of the worst winters in the area's history. When the cattle were rounded up in the spring, not many had survived and the ones that did were of the Angus breed. From that day on, the Wilsons ran Angus cattle.

Jim describes ranching as a nice way of life, but notes that young men starting out now have a tougher time making a go of it than their fathers.

"Young guys now need a lot of financial help," he says. "It used to be a man could buy land and pay for it, but now, you can give a young guy the land and he still has to spend carefully."

A thin man in his sixties extends his hand to Ed, thanking him for buying his cattle.

"My pleasure," Ed replies, introducing me to Manly Magnusson. Manly hands Ed a drink.

Since changing his lot over to mostly Blacks, Ed buys the majority of his calves in Maple Creek. He says that he bought Manly's calf crop last year and they did real well for him, so he sought them out again this year.

The comment makes Manly smile. In a soft, gentleman's voice, he replies, "If he's happy, then we're happy."

Like Jim Wilson, Manly has been in the area his whole life. His father was a streetcar conductor who came from Iowa in the midwestern U.S., settling nearby after buying a quarter of land for $13 in 1913, then seeding it to grain. Manly was born on the farm.

"Dad started picking rocks in 1913 and we quit in 1992," he says, adding that is when they switched to cattle.

He explained that in 1992, the Provincial Farm Rehabilitation Association (PFRA) encouraged farmers in the area to re-seed land back into forage crops because the rock-infested hills were poor grain land and, as Manly says, "never should have been cultivated in the first place." PFRA paid farmers $72/acre for a commitment of 22 years. The incentive worked.

He says that they were worried this summer after hearing rumours that calves would bring only 50 to 60 cents a pound in the fall, admits that he can live with prices in the 90 cent range. He calls BSE an "eye-opener" and believes that Canada has to have its own packing plants so that the industry can gain some independence from the U.S.

I spend nearly two hours at the hotel and much of what was said rolls through my mind as I step out of the cozy lobby onto the windy street. The town is quiet now, except for the occasional passing car. The wind cuts through my fall jacket, hinting I should wear a heavier coat tomorrow.

As I wait for the engine to warm, I study the directions to Bob Switzer's house, then look for clues in the road atlas sitting on the front seat. The town of Aneroid is south of here and farther east than I expect. Flipping open my name book, I turn to page 8. Aneroid is described as: ". . . situated in the southern part of the province on a CPR line that runs from Weyburn west to the border, and owes its name to a lost article. Aneroid marks the spot near which a survey party lost an aneroid barometer."[7]

I hesitate for a few minutes. I'm tired from a long day of talking and reluctant to leave this intriguing hotel. I calculate a two-hour drive and glance at my watch. It's too late to meet Bob for supper, but to stop for a meal will take too much time. I remind myself why I'm here and pull away from the curb, heading back to the Trans Canada Highway. I set the cruise control at 110, gambling that Bob's wife will feed me a sandwich when I arrive.

Rural hospitality. I'm counting on the long-standing tradition of the west that travellers are always offered a place to sleep and never sent away hungry. So far, my luck has been good. In late September I spent an after-noon at the Dalke's feedlot in Morden, Manitoba. I arrived there on a sunny, warm day right as they were trying to decide how many cattle to buy that fall.

Glori, a striking woman with a confident smile and eyes that listen, was just finishing off the afternoon feeding. Ed and their four children, Eric, LeAnne, Shane and Austin were hand picking sweet corn to sell in town. I climbed into the truck cab just before Glori backed up to the feed bins. Reaching out the window, she pressed a button and a mixture of bar-ley and corn augered into the mixer box. She moved ahead, then pushing a button on a panel at the grain bin, added a protein supplement. Then she flipped a switch in the cab that set the giant auger behind us in motion. When the mixture was even, she pulled up to the feed bunks and began driving slowly along as the feed spilled out into the trough. The hungry calves lined up and waited for her to drive by.

"You know they are getting enough when a third are hungry and come to the bunk, a third will turn their heads and watch as I go by and the rest pay no attention at all," she said.

I asked if the protein supplement they feed is free of animal by-prod-uct and she said that it is. I also wanted to know if they use medicated feed.

Glori explained that they feed a series of six rations, each one geared toward a calf's age and growth stage. Adding antibiotics to feed is costly and, most of the time, unnecessary.

Cattle are robust animals that require little intervention by people to stay healthy. Like humans, they are susceptible to disease, so ranchers and feedlot operators will vaccinate to prevent an outbreak of disease.

And like humans, stress will cause a myriad of problems in cattle. By far, the most stressful time in an animal's life occurs when it is weaned, sep-arated from its mother, then shipped from the ranch to a feedlot. Unfamiliar surroundings cause the calves to go off feed and water, and their resistance lowers. A common problem amongst newly weaned calves is "shipping fever," a pneumonia that will wear a calf down over the period of a few weeks, eventually killing it. For this reason, most feedlot operators will give all calves a subcutaneous injection of a long lasting antibiotic when it arrives at the feedlot. This gives the calves a boost, and in 80 percent of the animals this is the only antibiotic they will receive. The other 20 per-cent, usually calves that have unhealthier constitutions, will need another shot. Death rates sit at around three percent—usually calves that were chal-lenged as newborns or compromised in some way.

Medicated feed is sometimes given to the young calves after their first shot if their physical condition weakens. It is a less labour-intensive way of treating sick calves and usually done for a short period of time. While there may be some operators who misuse antibiotics, it doesn't make sense to over-treat, so producers like the Dalkes keep injections to a minimum.

I mentioned that some people favour the idea of eating completely natural beef and ask her opinion.

Glori is confident the meat they produce is safe and nutritious. Strict regulations by the CFIA and regular meat monitoring programs that analyze thousands of samples a year in Canada back up her belief.

"Nobody eats more beef than a cattleman and his family," she said.

We finish feeding the last pen and she parks the truck off to the side. Ed brightened as we stopped at the cornfield to cut short the afternoon pick.

"I'm getting too old for this," he laughed, placing a handful of cobs in the box at his feet.

We walked to the house and I waited while they cleaned up. We spent the evening sitting in the dining room talking about their operation, the industry and the future. The boys were sent to town to pick up pizza and soft drinks. They returned less than an hour later and we all sat down to eat.

"In Biblical times during celebrations, people consumed flesh from the fatted calf," Glori said, as we discussed the importance of food and how it relates to the human experience. "Today, we have a barbeque."

I'd asked how she feels about raising animals for slaughter.

She thought for a moment, then explained that humans are natural meat eaters who crave protein. People have always hunted and killed animals for food. The difference today is that people have become disconnected from hunger and find animal slaughter distasteful, but it is a reality of meat consumption.

She took a bite of pizza and chewed thoughtfully, while everyone digested her words. "When I'm out there choring in a blizzard, I take pride in the fact that we're producing food," she said. On average, Canadians eat 49 pounds of beef in a year. Taking a calculator, Glori figures out how much meat is on a steer carcass and multiplies it by the number of animals they put through the feedlot in a year. "We feed about 40,000 people a year, and I'm quite proud of that."

The day BSE was announced, Dalkes had ten loads of fat cattle ready to go to a U.S. packing plant; in fact, the trucks were booked for the next day. Once they got over the initial shock of the announcement, they rationalized that the situation would be quickly resolved because of Canada's solid beef trade relationship with the U.S. They kept feeding the cattle, hoping the border would open. The border closure backed everything up. The Canadian plants were suddenly inundated with offers for cattle. Normally the national kill capacity is 55,000 head a week. All at once the demand rose to 90,000 head. Even if the plants could keep up to the kill demand, there wasn't enough cooler space to hang the meat. With no way of getting cuts to their customers stateside, the packing plants dropped the price they'd pay for live cattle.

With virtually no packing facilities in Manitoba, Ed and other feedlot operators here found themselves at the back of the line. Had they shipped a week before BSE, their animals would have brought between $1.05 and $1.10 per pound.

Rumours were that prices would go down to 80 cents a pound. Ed had paid an average of $1.35 a pound for calves ($810 each), then fed them for eight months, so at 80 cents he'd lose hundreds of dollars a head. In fact, prices went down to 50 cents and by the end of July, animals weighing 1,500 lbs. were selling for 35 cents a pound or $450 each.

"That's why there was talk of industry collapse," Ed said. "Feedlots across the country were facing unrecoverable losses."

Dalkes put their cattle on restricted rations and held onto them until the end of September. There was a slight rebound in the cash market and they had only hours to decide what to do. They sold for 70 cents a pound, and although this was still slightly below the breakeven point, the losses were manageable with assistance from the provincial fat cattle program. They bought calves in the fall of 2003, but sold for a huge loss the following spring.

Like so many cattlemen, the Dalkes found the scope of the situation difficult to grasp those first few months. At first they were in denial, not fully believing that this could happen to them and their industry.

What seemed to wear on them the most was the hurt. Mostly they felt betrayed because they'd been fair traders, building relationships with staff at the Swifts plant in Grand Island, Nebraska. They also had a nutritionist originally from Texas who'd worked for them for five years. He was indifferent to the Canadian perspective, which made it easier to part ways when they had to cut expenses.

So often during our discussion, Dalkes called the fallout from BSE a "war." And like in a war, it's the young people who are the casualties. I asked Eric and fifteen-year-old Shane their plans for the future.

"I'll be honest; at one time I would have said that maybe yes, I want to be in cattle, but now it's hard to see a future in the business," Eric replied.

Shane agreed. "I thought of myself taking over the feedlot after dad. Eric and I have talked about options like a meat shop or grassing cattle, but now I stop and ask myself, 'Do I want to be worried all the time?'"

I remember how Ed's shoulders slumped and Glori was blinking hard. She glanced at her husband and quietly sighed. It's been impossible to keep their kids sheltered from the uncertainty they feel every day.

Now, they are trying to decide whether or not to buy calves again this fall. If they don't there will be no way to make up earlier losses. Talk that the border will open in the spring tempts them.

"The focus this whole time has been on the money," Glori said taking a sip from her glass, "and that's only because it's what we need to survive. Raising cattle is about more than money." Then she chuckled and shook her head. She can't put into words what it is about cattle that keep her going out into the storm.

Ed agreed. "It's more than a job. There's a responsibility to the animals and the rest of the industry."

I asked how they've coped under the stress of knowing that being forced to sell into a volatile market could put them out of business for good.

"I pray," Glori said. "Other adversities like illness and weather have been easier to handle because that's when I get strength from God. This is different though; it is man-made, and we feel as though we've been wronged."

Ed placed his hand on her shoulder and squeezed.

"We try to stay positive, but that's not easy," he said. "A neighbour put it to us like this—to try and remember that when you're driving a team of horses and you hit a wet spot, you don't holler 'whoa.'"

CHAPTER FIVE

He embodies the history of the ranching west, he's a man of
obvious courage and principle, he's tough and resourceful and
not the kind of man who will take any nonsense from anyone.
He's courteous, nevertheless, and pleasantly old-fashioned.
— description of a cattleman by Allan Anderson in *Remembering the*
Farm: Memories of farming, ranching and rural life in Canada.

If you took a map of Saskatchewan and drew with closed eyes a line
from east to west, the end result would look something like Highway #13.
Straight in the east, jagged in the middle, then falling off at the borders in
the west. But what you can't see on the map are the hills. Like the long
stretch on a tame roller coaster track, the highway to Aneroid rumbles up
and down for a distance long enough that I start hoping for the flatlands
that define this province.

Pulitzer Prize-winning author, Wallace Stegner, gives life to the
Palliser Triangle in his book, *Wolf Willow*. Stegner spent ten childhood
years in Eastend and writes of the area as: "Desolate? Forbidding? There
was never a country that in the good moments was more beautiful. Even in
drouth or dust storms or blizzard it is the reverse of monotonous, once you
have submitted to it with all the senses. You don't get out of the wind, but
learn to lean and squint against it. You don't escape sky and sun, but wear
them in your eyeballs and on your back."[8] I recognize the desolation he
describes as I pass through Admiral, Cadillac and Ponteix—all settled about
ten miles apart.

This part of Saskatchewan is cow-calf country. As soon as the border
closed, rumours began circulating that if it wasn't open by fall, there would

be no market for calves since the feedlot operators were threatening bank-ruptcy. Everyone saw the equity in their operations drop overnight. Commercial cows that were valued at around $1,200 pre-BSE were now worth only $200. Since bank loans are tied to equity, operators with 300 cows suddenly saw paper values drop from $360,000 to $60,000. Land and machinery is only worth what someone else is willing to pay, so many cow-calf men knew that on paper they suddenly owed more than they were worth. If the financial institutions panicked and started calling in loans, all but those who were virtually debt-free were vulnerable.

It is dark by the time I pull off the highway at Aneroid. I switch on the interior light and dial Bob's home number, mildly surprised to find there's cell service here.

Bob's teenaged daughter answers, telling me that her parents just left to have supper at Hazenmore, the next town.

I pull back onto the quiet road. In the surrounding blackness there's no telling where land and sky meet. Stars overhead outnumber the lit homesteads by a million to one.

In the distance, a fast-moving light coming from the south tells me a car is approaching the highway. It slows to a stop and my lights linger on it long enough as I pass to recognize a dual-wheeled truck. I watch in the rear view mirror as lights follow me into Hazenmore. This is a small, small town so the only restaurant is easy to find.

"Perfect timing," Bob hollers over as I get out of the car. A light dust-ing of snow has settled on the ground already and I shiver as my boots punch through a thin layer of ice near the sidewalk. Quick introductions are made under the hazy light over the restaurant door.

Basic is the word to describe the Red Coat Inn. The bar, with pool table and television, is to the right of the door when coming in and a large, but mostly empty dining room is to the left. There is nothing fancy here with standard issue, square vinyl seated chairs and arborite tables. I rate a restaurant by the quality of its Caesar salad, and this looks like a boxed croutons, artificial bacon bits kinda place.

Bob's wife, Gail, sits across from me. She is a pretty blonde who smiles shyly each time we make eye contact. We watch Bob, captain of this ship, counting seats and inviting people to join in. He seems at home here and proud of the place, almost as if he owns a corner of it.

The long table fills up with people whose names I promptly forget. The banter begins immediately as a teenaged waitress hands out menus and takes drink orders. A big, nearly bald-headed man named Bob Prestage announces, "Anyone who orders chicken can damn well pay for his own supper."

Gail laughs and orders it anyway. I ask what's good and Bob replies "everything." By now, my hunger has subsided, but I know it will return at 3:00 a.m. if I don't eat. I order a small steak.

The plates arrive heaped with food. It reminds me of the time I helped organize a cattle meeting. When discussing the meal, there was concern over how much we'd need. I suggested that the caterer double what it took to feed "normal" people and then add even more.

As the evening wears on, the room fills with casual laughter and shaking heads as we talk cattle, BSE, the U.S. and the future. Bob disappears into the bar a few times to check the score of the world series baseball game on tv.

We stay for a few hours until both Gail and I are stifling yawns.

"How was the food?" Bob asks as we prepare to leave.

I've had better meals, but not by much. Bob was right—they grill an excellent steak and I tell him so. He smiles and nods, satisfied it is time to go. The meal is paid for but I'm not sure who to thank. Nobody seems concerned as they pull on their jackets and drain their glasses. Next time, it will be someone else's turn.

Gail rides with me to the ranch, and I'm glad for the company. We're both tired so our conversation is minimal and quiet. Though I can tell we are different in many ways, we understand one another. We share the bond of being ranch wives with husbands with similar ideals.

We allow each other to vent for awhile and wonder out loud what we worried about before BSE left us feeling so strapped for cash. We talk about the stress on our husbands and the effect we're seeing in our communities. I confess feelings of helplessness because I live too far from town to get a job. Gail agrees. Both of us and most of the ranch wives we know are needed at home.

Guilt. Sometimes I feel consumed by it for wanting back the little luxuries I've grown accustomed to being able to afford after 25 years of work.

Gail understands. Like us, they renovated the house just prior to BSE. She doesn't want to stop taking their daughter, Bailee, to rodeos because of the expense any more than I want to tell my son he can't attend University next fall. All both of us want is for life to return to normal.

As we step into the entrance way, I see that Gail and Bob's renovations are similar to ours. The entrance way was expanded to accommodate the boots, coveralls, hats, coats, gloves and shoes and keep them out of sight.

Their kitchen is large and inviting, making it the perfect gathering place to eat, drink coffee or talk. This is the most used room in every ranch house. It's where the rancher will sit in the middle of the night playing solitaire while waiting for a cow to calve. He'll number ear tags, update calving records and sort receipts for the annual visit to the accountant, or go through equipment brochures—all from his chair at the end of the table.

Tonight, Bob sits sharing a drink with their friends from Alberta, two of the men who joined us for supper. I say good night as Gail shows me to the spare room. I realize as I climb into bed that while I've spent half a day with Bob, we've shared little conversation. I hope for more talk tomorrow.

The smell of fresh coffee greets me as I open the bedroom door. I find Gail in the kitchen quietly preparing breakfast. Bob is outside, so I use the opportunity to begin talking with the fellows from Alberta as they come into the kitchen one at a time.

Walter Byers is a Backgrounder from Camrose. He buys calves in the fall and feeds them to between 900 and 1,000 pounds, then sells them to a feedlot as "short keeps," usually in August. Thinking the border was going to open, he bought calves in the fall of 2003, selling them for only 62 cents a pound the following August.

Unfortunately, backgrounders like himself can't benefit from the government financial programs, specifically the newly announced "set-aside," because you have to own cattle to qualify. He can't afford to buy calves this year due to the hit to his equity last season. That means he'll have to swallow those losses in an industry where, traditionally, a negative margin one year can be recouped the next. For him, it means a decision whether to stay in the business or get out. He's nearing retirement age and isn't sure how much more risk he's willing to take.

Walter believes that eventually the border will open and the industry will turnaround, but the more ominous problem producers face is increasing input costs. He says that calves in the early 1960s in a low market sold for 30 cents a pound but expenses were much lower.

In 1962, he bought a new Chevrolet half-ton truck for $2,350, or thirteen, 600 pound calves at 30 cents a pound. Today, a basic used truck would cost approximately $30,000, or fifty 600 pound calves at $1.00 a pound. Back then, $100,000 would finance a 500-head feedlot, pay all the bills and secure another rotation of cattle. Now, $100,000 won't buy a load of calves. Fuel in the 1960s "wasn't even a concern," but now it is a major farm expense, burning up the profit margin.

Bob Prestage shuts off the television to join us at the table. He holds up his cup as Gail nears with the coffee pot. Everyone calls him by his last name, likely because there are too many Bobs here. He is gruff and loud, and I discover through the banter between him and Walter that he's the same man who bought our supper last night.

Prestage works as an exporter of livestock genetics. He understands Walter's plight because he knows how it feels to work a whole life with hopes of an equitable retirement.

When BSE was announced, Canada Livestock Services Limited had 1,200 animals "on test." He explains that in the business of exporting live animals, cattle must be subjected to numerous health and disease tests before they are permitted to enter another country. His company buys the cattle conditionally, then requests that the CFIA go to the farm to do tests for diseases like tuberculosis, brucellosis and blue tongue. If the animals pass the test, they are then paid for and put into a 30-day off-farm quarantine.

"We knew by 8:00 a.m. the industry was in trouble. The biggest challenge for us was to contact our buyers and tell them to stop buying cattle on our behalf," he said. Prestage says that Canadian cattle are some of the best in the world so they were always exporting.

They had a sale for two boatloads (3,000 animals) to China. There were 1,200 animals being tested in Saskatchewan and Ontario and 250 animals already quarantined. As it turned out, of the 250 head his company owned when the border closed, none could be exported, so they lost upwards of $375,000 overnight. Animals normally worth $2,000 were worth 25 cents on the dollar.

I ask Prestage his opinion of the CFIA.

"They only understand the dairy industry," he growled. "I know guys who've been in the business for 50 years, but the CFIA refuses to sit down and simply won't seek counsel from them. Because of that, they constantly agree to protocols that are unworkable."

Prestage says that during a conference call in July 2003, he was asked what is the one thing that should be done in Canada to strengthen our export position once the BSE issue is resolved. He replied that the cattle industry must take over the rendering industry and stop feeding mammalian tissue to any animals.

"How else do we get the confidence of the world?" he asks, implying that the current ban is not working. "Just ask a feed mill how they keep the different feeds separate."

He says that feeding animal protein is not necessary, that there are processes that will bump up the quality of low-grade protein in soybeans, canola and peas. He believes Europe will not take Canadian meat until mammalian proteins are removed from feed to all animals.

"In business the customer may not always be right, but he controls the finances," he says.

He also believes the Canadian industry needs to stop worrying about what the Americans are doing. He cites the National Cattle Identification System as just one way that Canadian standards are ahead of the U.S., and will meet the demands of European customers. He wants to see the industry take a more pro-active approach and stop "tagging onto" our American cousins.

Prestage drains his coffee cup then points to Walter. "His dad, Laurie Byers, and I were good friends. He died of a heart attack in 1970, but I remember he used to always say, 'When everybody's running, you walk, and when everybody's walking, you run.'"

I ponder the meaning behind the words then agree it makes good sense.

"Switzer's a good example of that," Prestage says. "Now there's a boy who gets things done. I remember the first time we pulled up to that restaurant, I thought Switzer was out of his mind. Hazenmore isn't even a town, just a wet spot on the road."

He pauses then explains that Bob was the big push behind getting the feedlot up and running and how the economic spinoffs helped revitalize Hazenmore, a quiet fact that makes Bob proud.

The door opens and the sound of boots being released onto the cushioned floor echoes up the hallway, halting our conversation. In that moment I understand the foundation of admiration these friendships are built upon. Footsteps hurry into the kitchen.

"What kinda lies are those two telling you?" Bob smiles. He rushes past the table, picks up some toast, and drinks a quick cup of coffee.

"If we're going to see the ranch and the feedlot, we'd better get moving," he says. Bob already has arrangements made to meet the others later at the pasture where the cows will be trailed home.

I gather up my overnight bag, notebook and camera. Within fifteen minutes, Walter and I meet Bob out by the truck. Again, it is overcast outside. The air hangs moist in a frozen fog, softening the edges around everything. We hurry through the immaculate yard to a building at the far end. It's a new, enclosed sale ring that the Switzers built to host their annual bull sale. I'm both surprised and impressed. Most purebred breeders I know join together with other breeders on sale day and rent a local auction market.

Bob says they've always had their sale on the farm and decided to build a proper facility for it. The building doubles as a shed for their seasonal equipment.

Their sale is called the Short Grass Bull & Female Sale and it's been held the third Saturday in April for the past 27 years.

"April 2003 was our best sale ever," Bob says, explaining that they had invested in new bloodlines and it paid off. "We've never had a floor price at our sales. A bull will bring $800, $2,000, $3,000. If you get a good crowd, people will tell you what they are worth."

The Short Grass sale is the largest, oldest, privately owned Black Angus Bull sale that Bob is aware of. As he opens the door to the small office and we step inside, he says the sale in 2004 was better than expected, but they noticed the absence of the U.S. buyers, some who were long-standing customers, producers who usually took home 10-15 percent of their bulls. Bob speculates that even if the border does open, the purebred industry won't return to normal for a while. There is talk that no breeding stock will be allowed across, only calves and spayed heifers.

The office walls are plastered with posters and photographs of hundreds of smiling customers and friends. A signed poster of Patrick Marleau, a local boy who played with the NHL San Jose Sharks, is tacked to the wall.

"I coached him between 6 and 10 years old," Bob beams as he pulls the office door closed as we leave.

On our way back to the truck I notice the Canadian and American flags in the yard. I ask how he feels about the U.S.

"I'm not anti-American, that's for sure," he says. "I've got lots of friends and customers there. Can't blame them for this."

Bob says that he's been worried about our dependence on the U.S. for many years, and has lost patience with the Canadian government's inability to help the industry be more proactive.

He says our biggest problem is insufficient slaughter capacity, and that two decent-sized plants for cattle over 30 months are needed. He's annoyed that the government appears to be doing nothing to fast track the plans.

"When are they going to build them, next spring? Government programs aren't going to help for long. Sooner or later we have to get the animals killed. Build the goddamned things and get it over with."

Bob's frustration is shared by producers nationwide. While slaughter capacity is slowly increasing, a year and a half has passed with little progress been made. When BSE hit, the only large, federally inspected processing plant for older animals in Saskatchewan was XL Beef, located at Moose Jaw. XL was a cow plant until the border closed, then it switched over to processing fat cattle. The capacity of the plant is expected to nearly double early in 2005 when expansion of the coolers is complete.

In 2004, a group of cattle producers began construction of a 1,200 head per week facility near the town of Neudorf, with hopes of having it up and running in the spring of 2005. They plan to process approximately 25,000 cull cows and 25,000 natural cattle—animals that meet the standards of their branded beef program. This will also be a federally inspected plant, meaning that meat processed here can be shipped anywhere in the world. Most small abattoirs only carry a provincial licence, which means the meat cannot move across provincial borders.

I climb onto the back seat of the crew cab as Bob puts the truck in reverse. As we drive the back roads he points out the boundaries of their land. He turns off the gravel and bumps across a field toward a group of heifers a half mile away. He slows to a stop and I roll down the window to get a better look.

Back on the road he slows to a stop again on a corner where the cows have gathered by a gate. All heads turn to watch us.

Bob tells me how years ago, people said that he'd never be able to breed and sell black bulls around here, that nobody would want them. Undaunted, he went to Ontario and visited with purebred breeders there to find out why. Back then, Blacks were short, dumpy and the genetics needed some work.

"You've got to raise cattle they want," he says, as we sit watching the cows watch us. Desirable traits include a good mothering ability, lots of milk, strong legs, calving ease, plenty of muscle and length. He's built his herd up to about 450 cows. I'm not a cattle expert, that's for sure, but to me, these black-eyed beauties look about as good as they get.

Then Bob explains how the Red Coat Feeders feedlot got started. Thirteen people within a hundred mile radius got together to discuss the idea of building a feedlot. They chose the site near Hazenmore because it was ideally situated—close to feed, water, power, the highway and access to natural gas. The land is on top of an aquifer with a well that provides 125 gallons of water a minute. Now there are 220 shareholders in the operation, including 10 from the U.S.

They built the 10,000 head lot with expansion in mind. Construction came in $40,000 under the $3 million budget and the place was a tourist attraction when it first opened.

"The contractor built it on a handshake," he smiles. "That's the cowboy way."

Custom feeding means the feedlot does not actually invest in the animals, but feeds them for a set price or per pound of gain. Profit is built into the daily feeding cost, which makes for a profitable venture if enough cattle can be attracted to the lot. Some of their customers are from the U.S., but nearly 60 percent are from Ontario.

BSE has helped the feedlot because those who bought cattle in the spring and put them on grass had no place for them to go in the fall, so they came in to the lot as custom cattle.

"Some guys held on, speculating the border would open in 2004," Bob says. "Like I said, it's been good for the feedlot, but it's the people who own the cattle who've paid the price."

Further down the road we get out of the truck to look at Bob's watering system. He explains that he has figured out a way to capture natural run-off through the hills, which saves pumping into waterers from underground wells. Listening to him explain the details, it's here, through the camera lens, that I really see Bob for the first time. On his land talking about things that matter most to him.

"The boys want to ranch so we're helping them get started," he says. Just before BSE they bought two ranches worth more than $1 million in land alone. His youngest son, Kyle, 22, is managing the one nearby while Beau, 25, is on the ranch at Lac Pelletier, southwest of Swift Current. Both boys are working out right now to earn a little extra income. Bob also has a 20-year-old daughter, Jane, who is in her third year of Commerce at the University of Saskatchewan in Saskatoon.

He quietly tells me that his first wife, Sandra, died of a brain aneurysm when Beau was 9. Bob spent four years by himself raising the kids until he met Gail and Bailee, and their families blended.

We climb back into the truck and drive toward Hazenmore. The Switzers have lost money just like everybody else, but Bob says he isn't going to go "crying" to the government. He's also not going to forfeit his independence. Bob's put a lot of pride into the belief that Saskatchewan can feed cattle as well as Alberta—and he's not about to back down now.

I wonder out loud what it is about this lifestyle that presses a man to work so hard, to take so many chances.

He says it takes guts to go to the banker with ideas. Men like Bob are always putting their reputations on the line and though it seems hard to believe, it's the everyday cattleman who is financing the industry.

"Honestly, the banker thinks you're nuts half the time," he chuckles.

As the restaurant comes into view, I ask him for a few final thoughts on BSE. He thinks for a few minutes, then replies, "When this is all over we might find it's made us into better people. Once we deal with it and move on, the industry's going to be stronger."

Despite his initials, there's no "B.S." in Bob Switzer.

Once we arrive at the restaurant, I know the interview with him is over. After lunch, the horses are brought by trailer to the pasture near the highway where the cows are corralled. Bob and Gail mount their horses and as the gate opens, the cows take off in the wrong direction, as cows are prone to do. The riders get them turned around and pointed toward the road. Soon the cows are settled, the lead animals push to the front and the rest of the herd falls in behind.

Bob and Gail take up the rear position, nudging a few reluctant cows along. We don't really say goodbye, just wave from the road. I snap a few last shots, zooming in on them one final time as they pull back on the reins, keeping the horses steady. A final wave, then I sit and watch for awhile as side-by-side they follow the cattle up the road.

It is a romantic thing to see, really, and makes me long for the days when life was supposedly more simple. Seeing husbands and wives working together is still a common sight out here on the prairies. The trials either bind you together or blow you apart.

Bob and Gail Switzer trailing cattle home

CHAPTER SIX

The Norse settlements in Iceland are fascinating because they
reveal so many interesting dichotomies. The Norse settlers were
remarkably healthy; their remains show an absence of nutri-
tional deficiencies and much better general health than groups
on the Continent. They ate almost entirely meat and dairy
products. Their lives were based on livestock keeping, hunting
and fishing. The Vikings, with their emphasis on cattle, were
like other cattle cultures in that women were much the equals of
men, with much more standing and freedom than in
crop-growing patriarchal societies.
— *Cattle: An Informal Social History*, page 56

Late spring. There is no time quite like it on the ranch. That short
spanse of time between the end of calving and the start of haying season is
the beginning of a new year. It is liberating when calving and winter feeding is done and the grass is lush enough that the cows and calves can be
turned out to pasture. The ground is soft and the air carries warmth, the
days grow noticeably longer. It's too early for mosquitoes, but late enough
that snow from an unexpected storm won't stick to the ground long. This
is perfect weather for fixing fences and planting crops once the pastures and
fields are dry enough to navigate. It's the circumstances that will define next
year and the hope that it will be good keeps the rancher going.

I've been thinking about getting ice cream since crossing the Alberta
border. The red and white DQ sign up ahead prompts me to quickly
change lanes. A Skor Blizzard® will hold me for the rest of the afternoon.

Erik Dunsbergen

I think of how shortly after Mark and I married, every time we'd take a day and go somewhere, it would end with us getting ice cream for the ride home. I discovered that this ritual was established when he was a boy and ice cream was still considered a treat. The Dairy Queen is our favourite place to stop.

Turning back onto the highway in Medicine Hat, I follow the arrow sign pointing to Lethbridge. I'm confused for a moment, when the bypass veers north. Soon the winding street crosses over the Trans-Canada and turns into Highway #3 west.

In the first months after BSE was discovered, consumers began asking fast-food restaurant chains where they bought their beef. Saskatchewan teenagers Rhyann Duffey, Stephanie Adams, Brett-Lyn Bossence and Megan Nash discovered that Dairy Queen used only Canadian beef and that prompted them to investigate the other chains. Their protest outside a Burger King restaurant in Moose Jaw threw a spotlight on the issue. At the time, Burger King Canada bought half its beef from Australia and New Zealand, but was already in the process of dropping their foreign suppliers in a public race with A&W to wholly support the industry at home. Pressure was put on all fast-food restaurants to do the same.

The McDonald's restaurant chain didn't need to change their buying practices since they already were the largest buyer of Canadian beef in the country, purchasing around 43 million pounds annually, or 70 to 80 percent of their beef buy.[9]

Grocery stores and steak houses came under the same scrutiny. Superstore (Westfair Foods) and Costco said they buy only Canadian beef. But the grocery chain Safeway and The Keg restaurants admitted they were having a difficult time accessing the product because some cuts were becoming impossible to find.

That's because it was the middle of barbeque season, so the more expensive cuts like steaks and ribs were in high demand. Because these cuts make up only a quarter of the animal, they were selling faster than the secondary cuts. Before the closed border, those cuts were exported to the U.S., so distributors were overflowing with secondary cuts taking up freezer space and that slowed the cattle slaughter in Canada. This left some businesses with no choice but to import demand cuts. Soon, distributors to the fast-food chains were finding it almost impossible to source enough domestic hamburger to fill its orders. Cows, which supply most of the ground beef, were not being processed because there was no space in the Canadian plants.

Provincial organizations like the Alberta Beef Producers saw an unprecedented number of calls from restaurants and retail outlets asking for publicity materials and information sheets to help promote the industry. Kelseys Restaurant chain introduced three new menu items: a beef wrap, Asian Stir-fry and a Steak Caesar salad. Branigan's restaurant in Winnipeg spearheaded a barbeque in support of the industry at Portage and Main Streets that attracted 10,000 people. Proceeds were donated to the city's food bank, Winnipeg Harvest. In Ontario, Norwich Packers donated 5,000 lbs. of hamburger to a Waterloo food bank. Similar acts of generosity were seen in cities all across the prairies. Consumption skyrocketed to levels the industry hasn't seen in 30 years.

This was all wondrous support toward cattlemen who were still in shock over the BSE announcement.

I'll be staying with Mark's uncle and aunt in Lethbridge. Wayne Johnson is the Member Relations Representative for the United Farmers of Alberta (UFA) Cooperative. His wife, Jan, is a real estate agent with Coldwell Banker.

They are situated on the southeast part of town, so finding their home is easy. I arrive to discover that they aren't home, but have left a message for me that a key is hidden outside. Having experienced their generosity before, I am not surprised and am reminded of the significance of small kindnesses.

When Mark was four years old, his parents bought a farm in the Icelandic farming community where we now live. It is only three miles from where his mother, Jonina, grew up. Her parents and younger siblings were still living there, so the families spent a lot of time together. This was back in the days when parents worked long, physical hours and the older children did chores while the younger ones played the day away.

Mark told me about one summer afternoon. He was walking through the pasture along the small lake on his grandparent's farm, helping Uncle Wayne bring the cows home for the afternoon milking. Wayne was seven years older than Mark who would be starting school that fall. Because Icelandic was spoken at home, Mark couldn't speak English. Between swatting the mosquitoes that landed on the six-year-old's back and lifting him over the watery low spots in the field, Wayne taught Mark the English alphabet. It is fond memories like these that keep family together, even when physical distance forces us apart.

As I switch on the lights in the recreation room where I'll be staying, I see they have a wall unit filled with family photos. Their son looks so much like ours that they could easily be mistaken for brothers.

My thoughts are interrupted by the door opening in the entrance upstairs. Wayne and Jan are home; we exchange hugs and settle in for the evening.

Wayne gives me a long list of people willing to talk about how they've been affected by the closed border. I'm immediately overwhelmed. That night as I lay in bed, too tired to think solid thoughts but unable to shut off the stream of worries running through my mind, I stare into the darkness and wonder how many sleepless nights BSE has caused.

In the mid-1800s, as the land in the northwestern United States and Western Canada was being settled, cattle were trailed up to graze the seemingly endless miles of grassland stretching north to the 55th parallel. Men have always battled one another for the rights to use land. Cattle owners were no exceptions. As they moved into Canada, they were pitted against the farmer trying to eke out a living, and together they battled the Indian population and buffalo for rights to live off the land.

Generally speaking, the cattle baron is remembered as a wealthy risk-taker whose eye was continually on the bottom line. The men who worked for him, the cowboys, were seen in an entirely different light. While the cattle baron had the money, it was the cowboy who got the job done.

Romanticized in novels and immortalized on the movie screen, cowboys became heroes to generations of young men and heartthrobs to women. Brave, ingenious, strong but gentle—the proud cowboy always did what was right, even if it meant sacrificing himself.

Not so romantic a picture was painted of the average farmer. Noble, but not necessarily book smart, the farmer worked the land for reasons only he could understand. He was inarguably the hardest working person in the world, next only to a black slave, submitting himself to a master almost as unforgiving—his own land. The farmer was seen as a man of simple needs.

There is no question that history has seen its share of generous cattle barons, cowardly cowboys and educated farmers, but to the general public even today, these stereotypical beliefs prevail.

It comes as no surprise when I wake up the next morning that the sky is bright and clear. The skin of frost that covers everything outside disappears quickly as the sun rises up over the buildings, warming the cool shadows and invigorating the day.

With an Alberta map and a list of contacts on the front seat, I weave the car through the city, turning north toward Picture Butte. Places seem to hold the energy and feelings of its inhabitants, and here, out on the highway where the sky is big with possibility, it's easy to understand why people love Alberta. Driving a half day in any direction puts you in a whole different world. From the dry rolling hills in the south to the lush fields and streams in the north, the badlands in the east and Rocky Mountains in the west—Alberta has it all.

This is a province rich in oil and progressive to the extreme. Critics of the strong Conservative government say it is exploitative and narrow, but you won't hear many cattlemen complain.

The saying, "Lead, follow, or get the hell outta my way" likely originated in Toronto, but the person who uttered those words has moved to Calgary. Alberta is a magnet to the like-minded and a repellant to everyone else.

In 1987 there was a shift in the cattle industry that saw expansion of the feeding industry here and the construction of two major packing plants. The cow herd grew by 67 percent when the Crow Rate grain subsidy ended and free trade agreements were signed with the U.S. Over the next 15 years, beef exports grew to the point that Canada became the third largest exporter by 2002.

Right here, in Lethbridge county, you'll find the highest concentration of cattle in all of Canada. The pre-BSE feedlot capacity of feedlot alley, that 200-kilometre strip running north from Lethbridge to Brooks, was around 700,000 head. Accounting for 39 percent of the Canadian herd, Alberta is home to approximately 35,000 producers who own 2.23 million breeding beef cows and heifers.

Within a year of the BSE announcement, Cargill Foods announced a $32.5 million expansion to its facility at High River. Gradually, processing numbers inched their way up, and by the fall of 2005, the plant will be capable of processing 5,000 fat cattle a day.

Lakeside Packers (Tyson Foods) at Brooks is the second largest processor in the country. When the borders closed, Lakeside was also processing cows, but that stopped, resumed, and then stopped again when U.S. protocols demanded that animals over thirty months of age could not be processed on the same line as those under thirty months of age. When their expansion is complete in the fall of 2005, Lakeside's numbers will also be up to 5,000 a day.

XL Beef in Calgary is a cow plant that was processing cows pre-BSE and continues to move approximately 900 mature animals through its plant a day.

All these numbers are backed up by a fiercely protective provincial government, which means that Alberta owns Canada's cattle industry. It's something the rest of us are loathe to admit, but when BSE hit, we were quietly thankful for Alberta's straight-talking, no nonsense approach to the crisis. The rest of us had no choice but to let them lead.

Alberta politicians wasted no time, taking recommendations from industry leaders along with the promise of financial support to the Federal Government. There was a surprising lack of partisanship in those first few months as politicians of all stripes worked together for the common good of the industry. Those who pushed their own agenda, mostly MPs and MLAs in the opposition, lost the cattleman's respect.

Picture Butte is a tidy, compact town that spills down a hill in all directions. The UFA gas station sits near the crest of the hill. I pull in and park off to the side, then begin organizing my notes as I prepare myself mentally for the day ahead.

I'm keenly aware that I'm not an Albertan and suspect that the folks I meet today are going to be disappointed by the fact that an interloper is here to write about their industry. Also, I'm a cow-calf producer smack dab in the middle of feedlot alley. I've been around cattlemen long enough to know that there is a certain level of animosity between cow-calf producers and feedlot operators. Then we have the middlemen, the cattle buyers. Ranchers will tell you he paid too little for his animals; the feedlot operator will say he paid too much. Packing plant owners fit into a whole separate category, outnumbered by producers near ten thousand to one. When all are thrust together, they smile politely and keep their thoughts mostly to themselves. The animosity they feel stems from the belief the other sectors do not understand their business and the fact that higher profits for one sector means serious losses for the other.

Besides cattle, the one thing all these men have in common are rubber boots. My pair is in the trunk. I remind myself that we're all cattle producers as I pull open the gas station door.

Paul Shimek recognizes me immediately from the flyer Uncle Wayne sent out advertising my plans. We chitchat for a few minutes, then he hands me another list of names.

As he's giving me directions to the first feedlot I plan to visit, the door opens and a lanky fellow hurries in. Paul introduces me to Erik Dunsbergen—owner of the Picture Butte Auction Mart. Erik agrees to meet with me when he's finished running errands. He points out the window to the long building less than a mile away. I go there to wait.

If purebred breeders are the artisans of the industry, then auction mart owners and auctioneers can be called the peacekeepers. Their livelihoods depend upon positioning themselves between the buyers and sellers while keeping both happily prospering.

Erik meets me in the parking lot and motions to follow him inside. I find a seat at one of the long tables in the kitchen area and wait. He returns a few minutes later carrying his four-year-old son, Mitchell—a quiet, well-behaved boy who leans his head against his father's chest.

"What do you want to know?" Erik asks with a smile.

I ask about his business and how he's been affected by BSE.

He says that he bought the business in 1991 after being on the payroll for more than 20 years. He grew up in the area and delivered pigs with his dad to the auction mart when he was a boy. He started helping the owner, Jim Juris, when he was ten years old. Over the years he did everything except office work and when Juris was ready to retire, the two men made a deal.

I can tell by the way he speaks that Erik is a religious man. I also sense that he makes his decisions based on what is morally correct, not necessarily what earns a profit.

Erik says that in the first year he put a lot of improvements into the place, and by the second year the books were in the black. Then BSE hit, and everything he knew as truth in the business changed drastically.

He is only seeing 60 percent of the normal cattle run and they have lost some customers to the competition because now everyone is more price conscious. He deals mostly with producers who run small herds as a sideline, those with mixed livestock and small backgrounding lots. These customers are simply not buying anymore and some are in fact liquidating their stock.

Erik finds that sellers are less predictable, too. In the past, they would book a sale date and bring in the animals. Now, they are hesitant, worrying about market fluctuations or getting caught selling on a bad week. Buyers are equally conservative, wanting to pay the least amount possible.

"Any rumour or speculation that's negative stops movement altogether," he says, as his son slips off his lap and goes to the open door. "Everyone is constantly watching what the big guys are doing—are they buying or pulling back?"

Most of the buyers he sees are small feedlot operators who have grown far more selective, no longer willing to gamble on an animal that might be problematic or won't bring them a profit in the end. He understands their position since they are feeling more pressure from the other end.

It's the cow-calf producer and backgrounder who are paying his bills right now. He's lost equity just like everybody else, feeling discouraged, but also beginning to wonder if opening the border is the answer.

"I know people don't want to hear it, especially those who are really hurting, but in the long run it might be best if the border stays closed," Erik says. He believes we should be processing our own cattle and selling straight to countries like Japan and China.

He's troubled by the fact that some of the independent feedlot operators who used to feed their own cattle are being forced to custom for others because they can't afford to finance a full lot themselves. American investors are trying to capitalize on this by buying up cattle, placing them in Canadian lots, with hopes of turning a huge profit when the border does open. Unfortunately, those profits will likely leave the country.

What Erik seems to find most upsetting about the market squeeze is how some people he's known most of his life have changed.

"I've seen the uglier side of people who, because of the bottom line, are being forced to deal in ways they normally wouldn't," he says.

We are momentarily distracted by a truck rumbling past the window through the parking lot, toward the loading chute. Instinct causes me to look for his little boy.

Erik jumps up and hurries outside. He returns a few minutes later carrying Mitchell. I ask if his wife is at work.

He tells me no, that his wife, Rita, is a homemaker and kept busy caring for their eight children. As a member of the Netherlands Reform Congregation, he sometimes wonders if the world's ills aren't brought on by deteriorating values and rejection of God's commandments.

We discuss this for awhile, then I ask him: If there is a God, is he punishing the beef industry for ignoring the rules of Leviticus that govern what man should and should not eat? That it is unclean to feed cattle back to cattle?

Erik's eyebrows raise and I assume by his look that he hadn't thought of this before now. But maybe he is thinking something else.

We discuss God's role in this mess and, of course, come to no solid conclusion. We smile at one another, knowing this is a conversation that could continue for the rest of the afternoon. Neither one of us has time. Our parting handshake is friendly and I assure him we'll meet again.

PART TWO

BARGAINING

CHAPTER SEVEN

*Farmers are now members of a capital-intensive industry that
values good book work more than back work. So several times a
year almost every farmer must seek operating credit from the
college fellow in the white shirt and tie—in effect,
asking financial permission to work hard on his own land.*
— Andrew H. Malcolm, *Murder on the Family Farm*, 1986.

The request for financial assistance came almost immediately. Feedlot operators were in desperate need of help. They had cattle ready to go to the packing plants, but an oversupply of meat that was usually exported meant the plants weren't taking the animals.

Federal Agriculture Minister Lyle Vanclief suggested government guaranteed loans would be an immediate solution to help producers through the crisis. They could hold onto the cattle, continue feeding them, but still pay their bills.

Calling the situation a disaster and requesting that it be treated like one, Neil Jahnke said the loan offer was, "kinda like throwing a rock to a drowning man."

Rural Liberal MP Paul Steckle was the chairman of the House of Commons agriculture committee. As the representative for Huron-Bruce in Ontario, he spoke to the House on behalf of cattlemen, saying, "These people don't make a habit of asking for help. They don't come to us unless they are desperate. When they ask, they deserve our attention."

There was very little opposition or debate amongst politicians over whether or not help was needed. Once everything shook out, details of the "BSE Recovery Program" were announced in mid-June. Ottawa offered

$276 million as their 60 percent, with an additional $184 million expected from the provinces in the 60/40 cost share. Thirty million dollars was offered to packers to clean out their freezers of products Canadians normally do not eat, which would open up freezer space and allow packers to begin buying cattle again for the domestic market.[10]

They also announced work-sharing agreements to help specific companies affected by BSE. An agreement worth $9 million was signed with Lakeside Packers in Alberta to help avert the layoff of 900 employees. In Saskatchewan, an agreement worth more than $400,000 was signed with Heartland Livestock Services, owned by Nilsson Bros. Inc., to help avert the layoff of 53 employees.[11]

There was no financial help offered to small business owners like Erik Dunsbergen who rely heavily on the cattle industry for income, or to the many truckers suddenly out of work. Eyebrows were raised at the government's decision to assist the packing industry while businesses supporting cattlemen were largely ignored.

I follow directions to Larry Nolan's feedlot just a few miles from Picture Butte. Like most feedlot operators, his home is situated near the road and the business is in behind.

Larry's wife, Mary Ellen, answers the door and offers me a seat at the table in their spacious kitchen. Larry appears, freshly showered, carrying two phones—a portable and a cellular. One rings as I'm introducing myself. He talks for awhile to his son-in-law, the lot foreman, until the other phone rings and he discusses prices with whoever is on the other end. More calls interrupt us, until finally he shuts off the cell phone and abandons the other in the hallway. We both laugh, and I decide immediately that I like Larry Nolan.

He's not a big man but his voice booms as if he were. He pulls out the chair at the end of the table and sits down. I can tell he's been thinking about what he wants to say, and I have to ask him to slow down. I want him to tell me what he finds the most difficult aspect of trying to make a living in the current environment.

"That's easy," he says. "Since BSE we've absolutely lost all our market signals and the ones we are getting are false."

Larry explains that being in the feedlot business now has nothing to do with how good a manager you are; it is all about cash. Under normal circumstances, to be profitable, a feedlot owner has to be able to make fast decisions and handle the stress of a big money business. One month a feeder can be on top of the world and then out of business the next if he makes a few irresponsible management decisions. Now, he's at the mercy of circumstances that he has no control over and they seem to change every day. It has been impossible to plan.

"In order for me to still be here when the border opens, I have to have inventory to sell when it does," he explains. "I'm trying to maintain an inventory level without jeopardizing my equity even further. It would help if we didn't have to keep giving money to the packer."

Larry has been feeding cattle since 1968. His operation consists of two lots with a total capacity of 18,000 head, mostly yearling heifers. He turns the animals over twice a year. When BSE hit, he got caught with 16,000 animals on feed.

He explained that Alberta feedlots were already hurting because of the previous year's drought. He had to import feed corn from North Dakota and Minnesota, adding to his feed expense. The first quarter of 2003 was looking good though and the lot was beginning to show a profit, and then everything fell apart. This trade disruption is the worst thing to ever hit the cattle industry.

"Everything else you can work around, but not this," he says. "The market indicators disappeared. You can't market on luck for very long, lots of us made decisions that later on turned out to be wrong, and it cost us."

I ask if the financial programs helped.

He says that all the money from the first program went to the packers. I've heard this before and ask him to explain.

The program was designed so that when feedlot operators sold their cattle at a presumed loss, the operator would absorb ten percent of the losses and then the government would pay a declining percentage of the difference between a fair market value and what the packers were paying.

Larry searches his pocket for a pen and begins writing on a paper napkin. He outlines the program logic using the figure of $1.00 as a reference price (pre-BSE values) and 70 cents as the amount the government expected packers to offer. The government would pay 85 percent of the 30 cent difference, or 22 cents a pound, totalling $220 for a 1,000 pound animal. If the price went down to 50 cents a pound, the government would pay 71 percent of the 50 cent difference, 35 cents a pound, or a total of $350 per 1,000 pound animal.

What the government didn't anticipate was the packers dropping the price to 30 cents a pound. At a 60 percent slide, the government had to come up with 42 cents a pound per animal. The program was quickly cancelled.

Larry explained that in order for producers to qualify, they had to sell the animals at the discounted price and apply to the government for the difference. Smaller operators were relegated to the back of the queue as packers favoured their larger, regular customers. Feedlot owners who couldn't get their animals into a plant or those who decided to wait rather than dump, were left out altogether. The program was re-tooled and other plans were introduced so that eventually money began flowing where it was intended.

Larry is alarmed by the growing trend of packers owning cattle. He explained that calves are bought and either fed in a custom lot or in yards owned by the packer. The fear is that if this course continues, packers will control too much and alter the free-market structure of the industry. The potential exists for packers to squeeze producer margins even tighter by simply slaughtering their own when fat cattle prices go too high for their liking. Some say this is already happening—that packers already own kill numbers exceeding 90 days.

When the first government program was announced, packers bought fat cattle, but also slaughtered their own at around 30 cents a pound and applied to the government for the difference.

Of the $400 million in BSE compensation given out that first year, Lakeside Farm Industries Ltd. at Brooks received $32.9 million and Cargill Foods Ltd. of Calgary received $8.99 million—two of the top three. Both plants are U.S. owned and, based on Larry's calculations, each making a million dollars a day in profit.

"That's why everyone says the packers have got all the money," Larry says, lamenting that he didn't apply quick enough to the first program. "The CCA warned the government that the program wouldn't work and they were right. Why the feds went with it I don't know."

Larry was able to get help through the Alberta-funded programs that followed. One required that the cattle be "set-aside," meaning they were put on a diet and kept off the market for eight weeks.

"I called those my 'Jenny Craigs'," he says, adding that while this helped regulate supply, in the end, producers whose cattle were held too long were docked $250 an animal by the packing plant if the animals were overweight.

In theory, all of the programs were designed to help feedlot operators pay their bills, move cattle out of the lot and give them enough equity to buy calves in the fall.

"I know the cow-calf man doesn't like to hear this, but whether he likes it or not, the money has to be given to the top," Larry says. "Give it to me and I guarantee the cow-calf man will get some of it, because the only way I can make money is to buy calves—and that's what he's selling."

I nod in agreement. The price calves brought in the fall of 2003 proved Larry right.

"The key is," he says "we have to keep that money out of the hands of the packers."

Larry and Mary Ellen invite me to stay for lunch. We move to a small table along a wall of windows that looks out into the front yard.

I ask Larry's opinion of the Canadian Cattlemen's Association.

He thinks for a moment, then replies that he likes the idea of having a single voice, but believes the organization hasn't communicated well enough with the feedlot sector during this crisis. He believes that the CCA is too cautious when dealing with the U.S. and that the industry leaders view feedlot men as "too radical." Larry is not afraid to upset the U.S. and is growing more impatient by the day. He's one of more than 100 producers named in the legal suit filed against the U.S. government under Chapter 11 of the North American Free Trade Agreement (NAFTA). They are suing for more than $300 million citing protectionism and unfair trade practices.

Larry doesn't say exactly how much money he has lost, but it's enough that he's worried for the future of his feedlot.

I wonder out loud how much bounce back is left in Alberta's feeding industry.

He finishes swallowing a bite of sandwich, then takes a spoonful of soup. He looks out into the yard at nothing in particular as he formulates his answer.

He says that feedlots can't afford to lose more equity, so the American border has to open soon. He'd like to see two more major packing plants built—one in the east and the other in the west. He's concerned that if the border stays closed and financial support for the feedlot sector wanes, Canadian feedlot operators won't be able to compete and will be forced out of business. That will leave the door open for American buyers and the packing plants to take control of the industry.

"If that happens and things continue in the direction they're going, instead of having a couple hundred buyers bidding on your cattle, you'll have only a few." We sit in silence for a long while, letting the scenario wordlessly unfold between us.

When lunch is finished, I ask him to show me his feedlot. Larry's face brightens when he asks where I live. As we walk slowly down the driveway, he tells me he buys calves from my area.

I back my car out of the way, then follow him past the processing shed. He turns down the wide main alley, then pulls off to the side. I meet him in front of a pen filled with tan-coloured heifers.

These cattle look much like what we raise. The heifers back up slightly, then stop as we approach. I can't help myself and search for Mark's printing on the hand-numbered tags. As we stand quietly talking, curiosity brings them close again.

Larry believes that if we can all stay in business long enough to turn the industry back around, the potential exists to expand into other parts of the world since foreign countries like to deal with us. Larry has travelled around a bit and knows this firsthand.

He pauses for a moment and looks into the pen of heifers, extending his hand slowly toward their noses. They lift their heads slightly, then stretch forward to smell his fingers.

"We've got the best cattle in the world right here," he says quietly, turning to face me. "And everybody knows it."

There is little a cattleman appreciates more than a person who tells it like it is. He may not always like what he hears, but prefers to respect a man than to like him, and sometimes genuine fondness will sprout from a seed of honesty.

There was a sense in those first few months that everyone was being honest. Producers were telling industry leaders what they needed. The industry took those concerns to the government. Politicians replied with unabashed concern. They believed, based on talks with counterparts in the U.S., that the border would open to live cattle that fall. Saying so gave everyone hope.

When Japan discovered a dairy cow with BSE in 2001, Canada closed its borders to their beef. The Japanese reacted by introducing a ban on the use of rendered beef in feed and implemented a rigorous testing program that turned up seven more cases. To allay consumer fears (consumption plummeted in that country after the discovery), they now test every animal destined for human consumption.

In spite of Japan's efforts, Canada still does not accept Japanese beef because they are not classified as a minimal risk country.

So, it came as little surprise to producers when Japan refused to reopen their borders to us. Japan even put a September 1st deadline on the U.S. to provide country of origin labelling, to ensure no Canadian beef would be included in their exports. The U.S. didn't want to lose $8 million in sales to Japan, but because the North American cattle market was so integrated, it would be near impossible to guarantee.

Effective July 24, 2003, all specified risk materials were removed from all Canadian cattle aged 30 months and older, and testing of animals for the disease were amplified.

There was a growing undercurrent of thought that politics and protectionism were slowing down the border opening, but the truth was the U.S. was simply following protocols established by the Organization of International Epizootics (OIE)—the same protocols Canada has followed in the past. In all honesty, it was too soon to be calling the U.S. protectionists.

The push from our industry was to have those rules reviewed by the OIE, and changed, so that Canada and other countries with only a few instances of BSE could be declared minimum risk countries.

In a letter to Saskatchewan news editors, MP and former agriculture minister Ralph Goodale blasted Canada's trading partners. Frustrated by the time it was taking to get the rule reviewed, he said the international bans on Canadian beef were not based on science.

"It's painfully obvious: You cannot count on science or fairness, so you better not test your cattle and you better not report any diseases because the results will be devastating," he wrote. He warned the OIE that they should be worried that every other country will adopt the "Triple-S" approach to avoid animal health issues: "Shoot, Shovel and Shut up!"[12]

Goodale issued an apology the next day, but it was muffled by the cheering from ranchers across the country. What Goodale did was convey in simple, straightforward language the feelings along the countryside. Cattlemen were being punished for their honesty, and the very real risk existed that Canadians could adopt the Triple-S attitude, too. Many believe it already exists in the U.S.

Knowing the cost of BSE to their families, neighbours and communities, I heard producers say, "I sure as hell wouldn't want to be the one who took in that sick cow."

Producers started asking why Canada continues to import beef at a time when we have an oversupply in the country. Under the World Trade Organization (WTO) rules, Canada is obligated to import 76,409 tonnes of offshore beef tariff-free each year. Supplementary permits were allowing in at least that amount again, until the CCA petitioned to have that stopped. The permit meat consisted mostly of lean, cow-type meat.

It wasn't long before cows became the focus of everyone's attention. Producers began asking that plants be built to accommodate cows, and at the same time rumours of a mass cull began circulating. The benefit of such action? To destroy animals born before the 1997 feed ban and eliminate the risk of finding another cow with BSE, and to lessen the burden on producers who could not afford to feed an old cow until he could find a facility to take her.

The problem? With no hook or freezer space in the slaughter plants to accommodate old cows, a mass cull would mean destroying the animals and the meat would be either buried or burned. With a 10 percent national cull rate per year, that would mean 700,000 animals equalling 800 million pounds of carcass weight. Cattlemen would never agree to such waste. If legislated, the government would then be obligated to pay a pre-BSE average price for the animals. Cowboy math rounds that out to $420 million. A lot of money for a whole pile of waste and a mess of public outrage.

According to Neil Jahnke, the CCA didn't support this option. More than one producer said, "Whoever digs that hole had better not stand too close to it, because he'll be the first one in."

This idea appeared in the media a few more times, but in the minds of cattlemen, it was a dead issue. And that's because even though this whole problem focuses on finances, at the grassroots, it's about more than the money. Like Glori Dalke, most cattlemen take great pride in feeding the nation. They'd rather give it away to consumers than see it go in the ground.

For some, BSE became a secondary issue in July. A forest fire was burning out of control in the cattle region north of Kamloops. Producers lost their homes, buildings, winter feed, fences and some livestock.

Parts of Manitoba were suffering the worst drought in recent memory. Pastures were barren by mid-July and cattle were eating leaves to keep from starving. Producers were haying every bit of grass they could find, knowing that they would never get enough. The thought of going into debt to buy feed for animals that might have little value made no sense, but to let them starve? Normally, producers would sell down their herd in times of drought, but with the market at is lowest, this was not an option.

With the fall run only a few months away, the rumour ran wild that calves would be worth less than 70 cents a pound in October. This caused the cow-calf man, who was already nearing the end of his operating line, to panic. Some looked this devil straight in the eye, made a budget and took it to their creditor. The banker was swamped—extending loans, terming out operating lines—preparing their customers for the worst-case scenario.

The less confident producers waited for the banker to call them, preferring instead to take the uncertainty to bed with them each night. The pressure of it was tremendous—bringing cattle producers in from their razed fields and into the media spotlight.

And then, like a cooling summer rain, came the August 8, 2003 announcement that the U.S. would begin accepting meat from Canadian animals under 30 months of age. Days later, Mexico partially lifted its ban as well.

Cattlemen rejoiced, seeing this as the first step toward getting the border open to live cattle exports.

CHAPTER EIGHT

"This is not the end. It is not even the beginning
of the end. But it is, perhaps, the end of the beginning."
— Sir Winston Churchill, following the allied forces first victory
at El Alamein, North Africa, during World War II

Criticizing the media has become a near reflex reaction for people.

When asked, some cattlemen will shake their heads in disgust at the mention of how the media has reported the BSE/closed border story. Probe deeper, ask for examples, and producers will backtrack, even agree, that for the most part the media continues to be fair and thorough when talking about the cattleman's plight.

Early on, the latest on the Mad Cow Crisis could be read every day, heard every hour. The term "Mad Cow" was a bit of an irritant but was gradually replaced by BSE.

Well-meaning reporters called everything "a cow," which left cattlemen scratching their heads. While this did no real harm, it did cause confusion that fueled rumours, especially when referring to slaughter capacity, proposed border opening rules or promise of financial help.

Reporters travelled to small towns to hunt down stories, and for some, BSE became their beat. This helped build rapport and gave the newsperson a better understanding of the issue.

The announcement that the U.S. would begin taking beef products from Canada shifted the media focus away from the battered beef industry toward other newsworthy topics. The general public started to believe that the beef man's worries were over.

It's not the media's responsibility to get out someone's message. Their

The Templeton family

job is to report news. When cattlemen fall off the front page, it's because there is nothing new to report. Still, it is disheartening for cattlemen to know that the industry is still struggling and yet the average person living in urban Canada believes the situation is resolved.

In a way this is like experiencing the death of a loved one. Once the initial shock begins to subside and sympathetic understanding begins to wane, life for everyone else returns to normal. It feels unfair, inconceivable that the disruption to our lives means little to the rest of the world. But that is just the way it is.

All cattlemen can do is be thankful that the anti-meat agenda is not gaining ground, and that the stories making it into the news are objective and mostly sympathetic. Being ignored is much easier than being criticized, especially by the ill-informed who offer simplistic solutions to a very complicated issue. On one talk radio program, a listener who was tired of hearing our worry recommended that cattlemen "stop complaining and get a job." Letters and editorial comments followed, reminding folks like him that running a ranch is meaningful work, and that anyway, the last thing he needed was a hardworking farm lad to move to the city to compete for his job.

I'm told that the weather is unusually wet this fall in Lethbridge. The bit of snow that fell last night has made the gravel roads around the next nearest town, Coaldale, wet and messy.

I'm on my way to the XTC Hereford Farm to meet with cow-calf producers Byron and Carolyn Templeton. I turn at the sign and drive past a house to find them processing cattle out back.

The road to the pens is a soupy mess. I pull alongside a patch of grass and get my boots out of the trunk. I slosh through the water and follow the sound of bawling cattle toward a series of pens and a processing shed. Byron and Carolyn see me and wave. I've come at the perfect time. They've just finished processing a load of calves to go into their backgrounding lot, where freshly weaned calves are fed to up to 900 pounds.

They wipe muddy hands on their coveralls before extending them to me. The wind has a cold bite today, so they are dressed for it in lined jackets and toques.

We agree to meet back at the house. Carolyn rides with me while Byron finishes up a few things. She holds her boots carefully on a stack of paper towels as I drive a half mile back down the road to their yard.

Two dogs, a black and white border collie and a shih tzu, jump off the deck and run barking toward the car. We navigate around them and step into a porch that is filled with boots, jackets and farm clothes. Their three daughters, Roberta, 18, Jocelyn, 14, and Rosie, 12, just got off the school bus. The girls smile and nod politely through introductions, then attack their mother with questions. Carolyn answers each one thoughtfully as she begins tidying the kitchen. In that moment, I know Carolyn feels the same way I do, arriving home after being out all day to find everything standing where it was left in the morning, a reminder of how much still must be done.

Housework is never ending on the ranch. Because our whole lives revolve around home, everything here is used more. Things wear out, become dirty, messes are made. Housework is seldom caught up, especially when the wife doubles as the hired man.

The children's evenings are consumed by school projects, sports practice, 4-H meetings and socializing. The distance from town means they must be driven everywhere. Homes like this don't see a silent moment until the kids are grown and gone. Then life becomes much too quiet.

With the pressing issues resolved, Carolyn pours two cups of coffee and joins me at the kitchen table. Their house has a simple, southwestern layout and flare that reflects her down-to-earth style. I chuckle at how frazzled she looks and she smiles back, running a hand through her fine, blonde hair. She has a wholesome, girl-next-door look—my guess is she's an animal-lover who at one time could climb trees as easily as a boy.

Carolyn grew up on a mixed farm near Rosebud, east of Calgary. She's always been interested in the farm, and when she and Byron met more than 20 years ago, they hit it off immediately. He graduated from university and did some travelling, experiencing five years of life off the farm before the pull brought him home.

I ask how they've been managing through BSE.

Carolyn says they are reasonably well established in a diverse operation and doing fine, but had BSE hit fifteen years ago they would be in tough shape.

The Templetons sell Hereford seed stock and grow some cash crops. They've been backgrounding cattle for a while now and in addition to feeding their own calves, custom feed for others. Four months before BSE, they sold some cattle and bought 60 purebred cows at a dispersal sale to bump up their genetic quality a notch.

I ask what is the worst thing she's seen since the border closed.

"The worst thing we've witnessed is seeing perfectly good virgin bulls that would normally sell for $3,000 have to be shipped to the packer because there is no market for them," she explains. "If you can't sell them, what do you do? The meat will still grade double A, but they are only worth $300—if you can get them killed." Buyers were tentative at the 2004 sales and with the loss of American buyers, there were just too many bulls on offer. The Canadian market became saturated with breeders who before then didn't compete much with one another.

"We've been lucky," she says. "Our customers are faithful and so far we have sold every breeding bull and heifer up for sale."

She tells me that not all American producers are happy that the border is closed, handing me a printed sheet with comments from one of their North Dakota customers who asked to remain anonymous. It reads:

> "I am unable to buy bulls in Canada as I have done for the past ten years. The bulls that I bought here cost me more money and were of lesser quality. It also forced me to have to try to establish a relationship with a breeder that I am comfortable with. The breeder in Canada that I had been dealing with had treated me with complete fairness and honesty to the point that I knew that I was going to be satisfied with my purchases every year. I am hopeful that we can go back to that relationship soon."

We discuss the importance of a good breeding program, then I ask what is the best thing she's seen since the border closed.

"The Canadian consumer," she says quickly. "The way the consumer stood behind us is tremendous; quite honestly, I don't know what we would have done if they hadn't."

I mention the sad fact that there are people, mostly from within the industry, who are unsympathetic toward those in financial trouble, saying that these people were likely overextended before. I ask her opinion.

Carolyn shakes her head in disagreement, explaining that circumstances are so different from operation to operation that it is unfair to label anyone. She explains that the drought in western Canada hurt a lot of good managers, so when BSE hit, it put some out of business. Producers struggling now are victims of circumstance, especially the newly established operator. Many decisions, including expansion or opting to breed heifers, seemed right at the time.

The door opens and we pause, listening for the sound of boots on the floor. A few moments later, Byron steps into the kitchen. His nose and cheeks are pink from the cold. We finish our conversation and he listens for a few minutes, grabs a coffee, then joins in.

"I just hope the banks have the vision to see everyone through this," he says. "We need every link in the chain to be healthy. If the feeders keep losing money, then the cow-calf guy should be getting nervous."

Byron believes that there are many producers who have come to the end of their risk tolerance and predicts there will be plenty of producers who will retire given the first opportunity. Many of the smaller, recreational cattle farms are already starting to disappear.

"Everyone in the industry stood around for the first six months and didn't really do anything," he says. "A lot of money went into band-aid programs, and while it was necessary at the time, we need a long-range plan."

He agreed the number one priority was to get cash to the feedlots. Now he'd like to see the industry working toward killing a greater percentage of its own cattle, marketing to more than just one customer, increased processing capacity and a stronger vision for the future.

"My dad always said that debt is a great motivator," he smiles, shaking his head. "Cattlemen are getting pretty motivated right about now."

Byron's biggest worry is that if the border doesn't open soon, producers might begin to lose hope.

I ask what they've done to preserve their optimism.

Byron says what works for them is to keep focused on the big picture. They make a point of paying attention to the small things that bring joy, and concentrate on what makes them feel thankful. They are careful not to get pulled into the vortex of doom and gloom. When the bad news stories start dragging them down, they shut off the radio.

"Everything we've worried about all these months has turned out okay, so now I just try not to worry," Carolyn says, adding that if she was really concerned she could go back to teaching, but doesn't feel the need to do that since they are still supported by the farm.

Byron is an optimist who believes that now is a perfect example of the importance to maintain a positive attitude. He believes that optimism will prepare the industry so that when these circumstances turn around, cattlemen will be ready. "A poor attitude will just wear you down."

"I heard that there were more farmers in England who committed suicide than people who died from CJD," Carolyn adds. "We don't need for that to happen here. This shouldn't be the end of anybody."

Byron says he's concerned for the young people who want to make a life for themselves in agriculture. Both he and Carolyn are 4-H leaders and they've been trying to keep kids enthusiastic about the business; at the same time, they're making a point to not let their own children become overly worried about BSE.

"If we're not careful, we can lose a whole generation," he says. "I see this as being not much different from a war, in that the ramifications will carry on long after it is over."

Byron and Carolyn are encouraging their daughters, who still feel optimistic about the industry. Roberta is enrolled in the University of Saskatchewan's agriculture program for the fall of 2005. She believes BSE is a short-term crisis that will be over by the time she graduates. Jocelyn and Rosie both plan to seek careers in agriculture as well.

But they admit that staying positive hasn't been easy. The worst time for them was June 2004. Like so many others, they were disappointed when the border didn't open that spring. Fortunately, they snapped out of the short-lived funk and woke up one morning with the resolve I'm seeing now.

Carolyn insists that I stay for supper and I accept, asking where she keeps her plates so I can help set the table. She apologizes for the simple meal that's been simmering in the slow cooker all afternoon.

I laugh, telling her that I'm just happy to eat. Not having to prepare the meal is the bonus. We sit down and begin eating. Halfway through the meal, Byron makes a confession.

"When I heard someone was coming out to talk to us, I wasn't too sure what to think," he says. "But then when I saw you walk up wearing your rubber boots, well, then I felt a whole lot better."

I ask about their brand and why the farm is called XTC.

Byron says that his dad enjoyed raising cattle so much he named the place X-T-C—three letters whose full meaning is best understood when repeated out loud. We laugh at this, agreeing that a life is lived happiest when a person enjoys what they do.

Just before I leave, they tell me that early this past summer they decided to take a break. They jumped in the truck and drove to Williams Lake, B.C., to visit with acquaintances.

"We had a great time," Carolyn confesses. "We just left all the worries behind, and to be quite honest, it did us a world of good. I can't think of anything I'd rather do. There's nothing we like better than sitting around the table visiting with cattle people."

She smiles, turning to her husband, letting her eyes rest on him awhile. It's the sort of look that spreads their destiny out in front of them.

By summer's end, the rush to put up winter feed is pretty much over. Hauling hay home takes weeks of work for those who feed all winter. The bales are piled in strategic locations by the pens where the cows will be kept sheltered from the wind and driving snow.

Many producers also feed grain, as a supplement, most often to the heifers or older cows that need an energy boost. Some cow-calf operators make silage, but this feed source is used mostly in backgrounding and feedlots. Silage is made by chopping and piling rows of grain, forages or corn into great mounds. Depending on the growing season and price, producers will either grow and harvest their own or buy in enough for the winter's supply. Before the feed dries, the piles are covered with plastic, which helps seal in moisture causing the mixture to ferment, preserving its quality and giving it a sweet, yeasty smell.

In the fall of 2003, offers for free straw came to the drought-stricken ranchers in Manitoba. While straw is a nutritionally poor feed substitute, it can be fed with a supplement. A handful of potato growers also donated two million pounds of off-grade potatoes, a somewhat unorthodox choice of feed, but it has the same feed value as barley and is a natural product that cows will eat.

The provincial government was lobbied for financial assistance by the Manitoba Cattle Producers Association and other producer groups. Reeves and councillors from nine municipalities met with Agriculture Minister Rosann Wowchuk on behalf of the 32 municipalities that declared themselves disaster areas, and asked that the province do the same. They reasoned that this might make them eligible for federal disaster relief, but they discovered that unlike flooding, drought and forest fires are only considered a disaster by those affected.

The provincial government did agree to reimburse producers for costs incurred to bring in hay or straw from other parts of the province. Producers who benefitted from the program (those living the greatest distance from available feed) were thankful for the help, but by no means considered this a windfall. They still had to pay for the cost of the feed or the expense of running equipment to bale the straw.

And like the producers in Alberta did the year before, some Manitobans adopted out segments of their herd to producers in areas where there was available feed. This, of course, came at a cost—adding more debt and worry.

CHAPTER NINE

*Security is a feeling that there is a larger and more enduring
life surrounding, appreciating, upholding the individual, and
guaranteeing that his efforts and sacrifice will not be in vain.*
— Charles H. Cooley, *Social Progress*, 1908.

Farmers have always owned cows, and growing up on the farm meant
that you learned how to milk at a young age. The family "milk cow" would
supply the house with enough milk to drink, and cream that was turned
into butter or cheese. The milk cow's calf was raised to butcher weight,
adding beef to the winter store of venison, mutton and pork.

As urban populations grew and the need for milk products increased,
farmers started milking cows to supplement their income. This continued
until about the 1970s (dates vary by province), when the business of milk
went high tech, and the introduction of quotas made farmers choose
between crops and cattle because there wasn't time to do both. Dairy herds
either expanded or became beef herds, and those who didn't like working
with bovines made the switch to grain. The past twenty years has seen a
renewed interest in raising cattle by the farmer, as prices and demand for
grain fluctuates wildly on the world market. Encouraged by agriculture
departments, the grain farmer was told to diversify into cattle, which was
considered a complementary, sure investment.

Animosity has always existed between the farmer and the rancher, and
in some places it continues to this day, likely because they compete for the
same land. The word "farmer" is used to describe agricultural producers in
Manitoba and Ontario; "rancher" predominates among cattle owners in the
west. To call a western rancher a farmer is considered an insult, and to call

John Deere dealer, Alan Fabro

yourself a rancher in the east is the same as putting on airs. It's no wonder the general public just lumps everyone together and calls anyone who owns more than an acre of land a farmer. Unfortunately, the word is sometimes said in a derogatory tone.

The fact is ranchers and farmers today are more businessmen than anything else. It is a label most of them quickly reject, probably because the businessman is not considered altruistic. We are taught to believe that money is the root of all evil, and the implication exists that people who have a lot of it must have done something underhanded to obtain it.

Years ago, the businessman was the fellow in the community who had more than everyone else. The jaded view is that he became wealthy from buying low and selling high, by taking advantage of customers and exploiting his workers. The stigma still exists today. As much as rural Canadians believe in capitalism and technology, there is an underlying resentment toward business owners. We crave their products and services, but are suspicious—even jealous—of the success needed to continue bringing these products to us.

It's difficult to pinpoint exactly when farmers and ranchers became businessmen. The evolution began around 40 years ago when raising food became capital intensive and computerized. The scales were once tipped heavily toward the ability to perform long hours of backbreaking, mind-numbing work, but now the ability to effectively plan and manage resources, including money and manpower, is the weighing factor. Today's full-time farmers and ranchers are not on the land by default, but by choice.

John Deere Equipment dealer Alan Fabro sits across from me now, behind his desk, leaning forward in the chair with his hands folded neatly on the blotter. I am in his office at McKay Brothers in Lethbridge. I am surprised by how tastefully decorated this office is, considering the trademark green and yellow colour scheme. The place is spotless, too. It is immediately apparent that Alan is a better-than-average salesman, a vibrant businessman with a strong social conscience. There is no edge to his voice and I have his full attention.

I ask how his business has been affected by BSE.

Alan tells me that so far, things have gone better than expected. Sales figures are down from previous years, especially on balers and forage harvesters while producers make do with their old equipment for another year. But because his company, McKay Brothers, isn't wholly reliant on the cattle industry, there is still equipment moving in and out of the lot.

Before the border closed, plans were underway to expand the business onto a larger lot, but that was put on hold. Alan says that fortunately no employees were laid off, although a few left on their own and weren't replaced. The parts and service end of the business remains strong, keeping their 22 mechanics working full-time, as producers choose to fix older equipment rather than buy new.

Alan is originally from Kimberley, B.C. He began working for John Deere Ltd. after obtaining an Economics and Math degree. He came to Lethbridge in 1984 and when the opportunity arose to invest in McKay Brothers, he jumped at the chance. Now he works as the General Manager. There's no regret as he explains he can't see himself in any other business.

"I couldn't imagine working with customers outside of agriculture," he explains. "It sounds cliché, I know, but these really are the best people in the world to deal with."

It is obvious he's given this some thought as he compares Alberta's feedlot sector to a locomotive, at the forefront, pulling along related industries like trucking, manufacturing and feed. He says the feedlots here are so solid that he seldom sees a dishonest customer.

When the BSE announcement came, there wasn't one cancelled order—an amazing fact considering most deals are made on a handshake. Alan tells me he can't think of another collective group of business people with the same inherent sense of pride.

He describes the cattlemen he deals with as mostly young, enthusiastic visionaries whose only backing when starting out is a tremendous work ethic and ability to take charge. Because the industry has seen so much growth over the past 15 years, regular ups and downs within the market have caused financial difficulties for most of these entrepreneurs. One thing is for certain though—they always make arrangements to pay their bills.

He says that Alberta's cattlemen seem to have a closer tie with the U.S. than producers in other parts of the country, and he believes they were hurt as much by the broken relations with their neighbours as they were by the financial losses they faced.

"This is really bothering them to feel suddenly on the outside," Alan says. "We are so impacted by U.S. decisions, and to have our closest neighbour and biggest customer suddenly behaving in such a self-serving, protectionist manner is a real shock to some of these guys."

Alan says it is stress of the unknown that's wearing some of these men down. Alan is an optimistic, focused individual, even he understands how hard it is for producers to stay positive when they don't know which way to turn next.

Alan says that he has not lost a moment's sleep over BSE, not because he doesn't care, but because he's living his life exactly how he wants and is exactly where he wants to be. This makes him surprisingly upbeat, even reflective about the industry's future.

"I have full confidence that the entrepreneurial spirit is still alive in these feedlot owners and they won't be down for long," he says, explaining that a stint as a professional baseball player with the Pittsburgh Pirates taught him alot about learning how to focus on a goal. He says that for him, success in the sport might have come a bit too easy. He was a young man who loved baseball, but wasn't focused and that likely cost him a spot on the Pirates team.

"I didn't realize it at the time," he explains. "And if I can say anything to producers, it's just that. If you are exactly where you want to be, then don't lose focus. Don't take your eye off the ball."

The drive to Milk River is a welcome break from days of interviewing and note taking. The highway rolls out in front of me to the southeast, like a spool of ribbon atop vast fields, swept clean by harvest, waiting for the quiet stillness of winter to settle in.

With the road pretty much to myself, I use the opportunity to catch up on a few phone calls. My message box is full. The last voice message is from Shirley McClellan. She was the provincial agriculture minister here when BSE hit. She says with polite sincerity that she doesn't have time to get together. I can tell by her tone that I'd like her, that she'd have so much to add to this story. But it's all over the news that Premier Ralph Kline is expected to call an election within days.

As the meaning of this missed opportunity settles over me, a twinge of self-doubt starts to rise up—maybe I can't do this. The day I decided to do this, I made a list of the people I wanted to see. McClellan was one of them. I push away thoughts of what too many negative replies will mean.

The orange, green and white United Farmers of Alberta (UFA) sign at the Milk River fuel dealership comes into view. I slow down, then pull of the road that leads into town. There is one car at the pumps in front of the small service station. Five rows of cardlock machines sit empty at the far end of the sprawling lot, designed for tractor-trailers. Fuel is a volume business so it's obvious that Jan Spencer's dealership is hurting.

I pull open the door and the young woman behind the counter greets me with a cheery hello. She says that Jan will be off the phone in a few minutes. I walk around the convenience store, then use the washroom.

The first thing I say to Jan when we are introduced is how refreshing it is to step into a clean, nicely decorated bathroom. I tell her it's obvious a woman owns this place.

She laughs as she extends her hand. "You'd be surprised how many men comment on it, too."

I look around her crowded office and can't help but smile. She reminds me of a good friend who also owns a gas business. Every day means balancing the pressures of business against being a wife and mother. Success means making decisions that are often tough and unpopular; what is expected of a man is seen as harsh from a woman.

Don't be fooled by the no-nonsense exterior, though. She cries when nobody is looking and feels things so strongly, it's like her heart might explode. She's generous to a fault and the people who love her can't understand why others don't.

I feel I know Jan before she even says a word.

As we sit and chat, Jan tells me that she was raised in Coutts, a small town southeast of here that borders Sweetgrass, Montana. She speaks fondly about growing up with one foot in the U.S., playing with kids across the line and walking to her uncle's house on weekends. It seems that life here is a rather unique existence where families and countries are intertwined.

Jan remembers never being asked for identification because everyone knew who she was. Back then, she called the customs officers by name. Now, she can't take her grandchildren to visit her brother who lives in Sweetgrass unless providing written permission from their parents to border officials.

"Everything is just so much harder," she says. The weariness in her voice tells me it's not the first time her world has been turned upside down.

In 1994, her husband, Lloyd Bellew, died from cancer. They'd been high school sweethearts who married when she was 18. They had four children, so she spent the early part of their marriage at home raising them. In later years, she worked at the border as a custom's broker.

After Lloyd's death, she took over his gas business, reasoning that her husband put in 14 years for her and their family, and she wasn't ready to let go of such a big part of their lives. She became one of only two female UFA agents in the province. Jan is proud of the fact that hers is a family run business, noting that she's hired many family members over the years and that her son-in-law, Derek Smith, works at the station and son, Lane Bellew, drives the fuel truck delivering to their agricultural customers. She is also proud of the fact that Lane has taken over the family farm—a piece of history she'd hate to see disappear.

In 1999 Jan remarried, then in 2002 recorded a banner year showing the largest volume increase of any UFA dealer that year in Alberta. Life was feeling good again. Then BSE hit.

At first she couldn't believe what was happening. Her station is one of the last stops before the border, so a lot of cattle liners would fill up on the way down to the U.S., then stop again on their way home. Since the border closure, she's lost a huge percentage of her customer base—truckers.

"It was like a great big tap was suddenly shut off," she says.

Most of her remaining customers are agriculture producers. At one time, dealers held their customer's receivables, but now, the debt load is carried by head office. If a customer falls behind in their payments, it's up to the discretion of UFA whether or not Jan can continue delivering fuel to them.

She says turning down a customer is the most difficult reality she's had to deal with through all of this. She knows her customers well and is passionate when she says that if they've fallen behind, it's because they have no choice, that their pride is taking a beating as well. She has come to a customer's defence more than once with UFA, but putting in a good word is all she can do.

All around, life just isn't like it used to be. Jan says she began to notice tension between countries shortly after September 11, 2001, when the twin towers in New York City were blown up. Border regulations tightened, suspicions grew. "I don't make jokes with the customs officers anymore, and they rotate so often, I'm lucky if I see someone I know."

Jan says there is an inherent difference between Canadians and Americans that residents around here have always understood. Until now, those differences never really mattered. The war on Iraq and the border closing to cattle has caused hard feelings to sprout and grow, changing life in these border towns—possibly forever.

Her second husband, Ed Spencer, is an American working as an agricultural banker in Conrad, Montana. Both kept their respective homes after marrying and commute to see one another on weekends. Long lineups at the crossing have turned her hour-long drive to Conrad into an ordeal. She can't transport beef across the border, not even in the form of a sandwich or stew for supper. With so many of her family members making a living from either cattle, fuel, or trucking, she feels a tremendous amount of pressure for life to return to normal.

Ed has more than 30 years' experience working in farm credit, so he understands the plight of the Montana rancher well. When they sit down together in the evening, Jan says there are subjects she and Ed simply can't broach. Each is dealing with the grassroots everyday and agree it isn't a case of one side being right and the other wrong. A way of life is being threatened and good people on both sides of the border stand to lose their livelihoods. It's fairly obvious talking to Jan that she isn't going to feel any relief until the border opens. We chat for awhile longer, then she checks her watch. She has a function in Lethbridge she must attend.

Jan Spencer

I fill the car up with gas, then pull onto the highway that takes me through the town of Milk River. Soon I am on the road again where the landscape is open and rolling. Narrow streams cut through the hills, gurgling into the Milk River. It isn't easy pushing thoughts of Jan from my mind as I follow the twisting, turning directions over the Coffin Bridge onto a gravel road.

If the sky was not blurred by an overcast veil, the sight ahead would be spectacular. The River Road Hutterite Colony sits spitting distance from the border, up high on a ridge surrounded by grain fields. Behind the long barns and row of grain bins, an eruption of snow-crested mountains rises up as a backdrop to the south.

I follow the long driveway toward the row housing, surprised to find the place looks deserted. The community is spartan and clean. Only 20 years old, this colony is an offshoot from Coaldale and home to 18 families.

Jake Entz is one of the foremen here and the colony's financial manager. He's agreed to meet with me. I have no idea where to go, so I pull up beside an older woman who is sweeping the sidewalk. She hurries over in greeting, inviting me in the house to wait while she fetches Jake, who is across the road working on renovations to the large communal kitchen. She offers me a seat at the kitchen table then disappears out the door.

Their home is silently relaxing. The utilitarian surroundings tell me there's nothing here they don't need. Light coming in through the windows sparkles off the immaculate ceiling and floor. The house smells of nothing but cleanliness.

I wonder what it would be like to live in a community like this. After marrying Mark, I told an acquaintance that we would someday move to the farm. "How could you live there?" she'd asked, clearly disgusted that I was considering such a move. Of course, I could never understand why she'd stay in the city when she could live in paradise, like us. I suppose Hutterites feel the same way.

My thoughts are interrupted as the door opens and Jake steps inside. He is from that generation between my husband and my father. As he introduces himself, his accent reminds me of the German immigrants who farmed where I grew up.

He apologizes for making me wait.

I explain the project I'm working on and he says he's not sure how much he can contribute. They don't have beef cattle here, just dairy.

I ask him to explain how the dairy operation has been affected by the closed border.

Jake explains that overall, the colony has not felt much of an effect because their diversification provides food for the colony and supplies marketing board quotas for a 400-sow farrow-to-finish pig operation, 12,000 laying hens, 300 turkeys and 4,000 broilers. They have a 300-head dairy herd, which means they milk 90 cows at a time. With no market for cull cows, they now destroy the older animals on the farm.

Calves are a by-product of milk production. They are conceived so that the cow will produce milk. Normally, dairy producers sell newborn bull calves to ranchers who adopt them to a cow whose calf died. Since BSE, this market has dried up. The rancher isn't as willing to pay for a dairy calf since it will bring substantially less than weaned beef calves in the fall. It's no longer worth the effort it takes to adopt.

Jake excuses himself for a minute, then returns carrying a thin stack of papers. He thumbs through, then turns the page so I can see.

In January 2003, he fed five steer calves up to 1,200 lbs. and received an average of $1,350 a piece. In December 2003, after BSE, he sold five steers of the same weight for $495 each. Pre-BSE, cows sold for $658 each and afterward, for only $128.

"It just doesn't make good economic sense to keep old cows," he says.

I ask what they feed the dairy herd and feedlot calves.

He explains that they buy canola oil for $190 a metric tonne and mix it with micronutrients, barley, wheat or corn—depending on what they can get for the best price. They don't buy feather meal because even though it is high in protein, he says it doesn't convert well, so the animals don't gain or maintain the weight they should. He says their animals do really well on the homemade mixture, adding that their 90 cows online supply 83,900 litres of milk each month.

Again, I'm being told it's not necessary to feed animal by-products. It takes a me a few moments to digest this bit of information.

I ask if he has noticed any tensions living so close to the border.

He says that they have no trouble going across and that dealings with the colonies in Montana have not changed. He says it's unfair to blame producers in the U.S. for the mess we are in.

"We have supply management in dairy and poultry, so think it through," he says, explaining that Canadian agriculture has protectionist sectors, too.

Jake believes the industry would be better off if it focused on building packing plants and creating employment. He thinks we should rely less on the U.S. and begin aggressively chasing the Asian markets.

He would like to see a more even exchange on the Canada/U.S. dollar, saying it would be better for everyone over the long-term, especially if the processing sector is strengthened. He also thinks the cull animal plants that are popping up across the country will be successful as long as the border stays partially closed. They will have a difficult time competing with the larger U.S. plants if the border does open again.

"We had two nice plants in Lethbridge close down when everything started going south," he says, referring to pre-BSE times.

I ask if they have ever considered setting up a plant to process their own animals.

Jake tells me that it would have to be a licensed facility and they aren't prepared to make that kind of investment, mostly because they don't have the manpower to run it properly.

He offers to show me the work they've done on the kitchen.

I walk with him across the parking lot. Jake tells me that his father was the financial manager here before him.

"I don't know how he got along without a fax machine," he says, opening the door at the end of the long building.

We walk through the renovated laundry area, past the commercial-sized washers and dryers, down a long ceramic-tiled hallway. He opens the door to a walk-in freezer, where pallets of food bought in bulk sit along the far wall.

Jake explains that the young people are cycled through the different jobs in the community as they mature. Natural ability and enjoyment for a task is a factor that is considered when deciding each person's life work.

We step into the brightly lit dining room where a half dozen people are working. They look up and smile politely, but then return to plastering and spacing white tiles across the ceiling and walls as Jake explains what each person is doing. A woman in her mid-20s works alongside a man who I guess is her husband.

Jake shows me the creative flair they've incorporated into the arched doorways before taking me into the kitchen. Industrial-sized stoves, ovens and specialty machines will be hooked up once the walls and floors are finished.

Two women come in through the back door carrying ice cream bars and homemade matrimonial cake. Some of the workers stop to take a break, but others continue working. I reach for a small piece of cake, but they insist I take a large chunk, smiling as they wrap it in a plastic bag before handing it to me.

Jake walks me to the door, saying it's time to get back to work. I thank him for his time and wish them luck.

Climbing into the car, I'm overwhelmed by the warm feeling that they allowed me to see snapshots of their private world, educating and mothering me all at the same time. I'm halfway back to Milk River before it strikes me that I should have asked to see their dairy barn.

I must be missing home. I was more interested in a run through the kitchen.

CHAPTER TEN

"We've distanced ourselves so much from the source of our food that we no longer consider its biological origins. And when you get that far away from something you lose perspective."
— David Suzuki

It would take until September 10 before Canadian meat was allowed across the border. The Canadian Food Inspection Agency (CFIA) and United States Department of Agriculture (USDA) hammered together a set of protocols that would ensure that no cross-contamination between mature cows and cattle under 30 months of age occurred in Canadian packing plants. By this time, the Canadian industry had lost an estimated $1.18 billion dollars and around 5,000 jobs.

One half-million head of cattle were backed up in the Canadian system, even though weekly slaughter numbers had doubled since May 20, up to 60,000 a week. A kill rate of 85,000 would help clean up the backlog, then once that is done, Canada would need to process 75,000 a week to stay even.

A cross-country barbecue organized by the Kinsmen and Kinettes put Canada into the Guinness Book of World Records when 1.2 million people ate their way through 380,000 pounds of beef on the Labour Day long weekend. Cargill Foods donated most of the beef, while Son's Bakery of Calgary and Wonderbread donated the buns.

Still unsure about the future, cattlemen just weren't spending any money. Manufacturers of farm equipment, ATVs, vehicles and other big-ticket items noticed another quarter of lower earnings, and began asking their retailers the reason for the sales slump. Rural businesses were begin-

Betty Hinton signs the side of Timothy Wishewan's truck.

ning to suffer and municipalities were predicting that cattlemen wouldn't be in to pay their tax bill that fall. The other meat commodity groups grew increasingly nervous that support for the beef industry would mean reduced sales for them. Chicken and lamb reported steady consumption, but sales of pork, bison and other exotic meats were down.

Former Prime Minister Brian Mulroney offered to do whatever he could to get the cattle trade moving south again. A proponent of open borders, Mulroney was in office when Canada signed the North American Free Trade Agreement (NAFTA).

A rally on Parliament Hill saw hundreds of cattlemen and politicians in the Opposition call for Prime Minister Jean Chretien to lead an all-party delegation to the U.S. to ask George W. Bush to open the border. Chretien was being criticized for failing to meet face-to-face with the President. A mediocre rapport between the two leaders was being blamed for the lack of a resolution. That same day, a cattle liner driven by Timothy Wishewan of Edmonton arrived in Ottawa. It was decorated with the signatures of more than 500,000 Canadians in support of the beef industry.

Motion sickness usually prevents me from looking out the window when I fly, but today my eyes are drawn to the snow-dusted mountain tops, partially hidden in the clouds. I'm on my way to Kamloops to talk with producers in British Columbia.

I enjoy flying and always bring along a few things to read so that time doesn't drag, but today there is much to think about, my notebook and research materials lay zipped in a bag underneath the seat.

Early yesterday morning I sent an e-mail to Shirley McClellan's office. I explained the project in detail, assuring her that this would be a favourable portrayal and asked again for a few minutes of her time. I offered to extend my stay in Alberta. Drive to Edmonton if I had to. It was the closest I've ever come to begging for an interview. The terse reply came from her assistant later that afternoon.

"Ms. McClellan is unavailable."

The words hit me like a hammer. No apology or explanation. Usually when someone grovels like I did, the person on the other end has the decency to at least sound apologetic.

I have just finished reading, *Portrait of a Burger as a Young Calf: The story of one man, two cows and the feeding of a nation,* by Peter Lovenheim. He is a journalist from Massachusetts who was troubled by the disconnect humans have toward the food they eat, and wondered how producers can work so closely with animals and then send them off to slaughter. In an effort to better understand all of this, he purchased two dairy calves and followed their lives with the intent of having them slaughtered once grown.

Lovenheim wrote in what seemed to be a fair, unbiased way about milk production after spending nearly two years raising the calves. By the end, there was no sense he'd lost respect for the farmers he spent time with; in fact, his appreciation for their lifestyle grew. He decided, however, to ship his full-grown animals to Farm Sanctuary Inc., a non-profit shelter for farm animals. He did this because he'd grown close to the animals and hated the thought of having them killed.

I understand how he feels. We'd have a difficult time shipping calves after raising them as pets for two years, too. That's why livestock producers are careful not to grow too attached to the animals they own. The same cannot be said for cats and dogs or anything else that finds its way into the house. Ask any farmer about the day he had to put down an aging horse after decades of faithful use and companionship, and he'll tell you it was near the hardest thing he's ever done.

More than one of our teenaged nieces have told us that raising animals for human consumption is cruel, saying that chicks, calves and piglets are cute—but they continue to eat meat. Baby ducks are cute, too. I remember once, Mark saw our male duck in the final moments of pecking a little yellow duckling to death. Grabbing a fish net, he chased the drake to separate it from the duck and her remaining ducklings. The ten-minute chase half running, half flying through the garden, then around the back of the house, wore Mark out enough that by the time he caught the duck, his anger had softened. The quacking bird was placed in solitary confinement until the ducklings were grown.

We experience contradictions every day that complicate the animal rights activist's theory that livestock producers are heartless. They imply that no caring individual could, in good conscience, raise animals for slaughter. My experience is such that cattlemen and women are some of the kindest people I know. Men and women who will at great expense and personal sacrifice take whatever course necessary to save a cow or calf.

My thoughts are interrupted by the ping of the "Fasten Seat Belt" sign overhead and it takes me a few minutes to orientate back to the present. The time it takes to deplane is enough to refocus my thoughts and I become excited about the prospect of seeing friends, Margaret and Hugh Sutherland.

The Sutherlands lived in Manitoba from 1988 to 1991. We became instant friends while Hugh was stationed at the RCMP detachment in Ashern. Margaret is a dentist who practised for a short time in the Interlake until the desire to return home took them back to Kamloops. We've kept in touch over the years and they have offered to let me use their home as a base.

My bag is the first to appear on the carousel and it feels like some sort of victory over all the times it has circled around last. I swing it over my shoulder and make my way outside where the skies are overcast and the air is cool. A heavyset young man wearing a ball cap drops his bag on the ground beside me. We nod at one another, then make small talk. I ask where he's from.

"Regina," he says.

I smile. Both Neil Jahnke and Bob Switzer told me to start paying attention to the mystery that no matter where I travel, I'll meet someone from Saskatchewan.

A truck pulls up a few minutes later and I recognize Margaret. Two of their children, Rorie, 10, and Mairi, 6, are in the back seat. Margaret tells me their thirteen-year-old son, Allistair, is with Hugh. We drive to their home in a residential area on the east side of town. The house is nestled along a mountainside, and from their living room deck, we can see the South Thompson River.

We spend the evening and the next day catching up on the last five years. Later that afternoon, I go through my notebook, highlighting the names of producers I hope to contact. With only five days set aside to cover B.C. I will begin interviewing in earnest tomorrow.

British Columbia's cattle industry began after gold was discovered along the banks of Tranquille Creek near Kamloops. Prospectors from California followed the gold rush fever north, landing at Victoria in 1858. Not long afterward, cattle from the northwestern states were trailed north to B.C., crossing the border at Osoyoos. The herds expanded to meet the needs of miners, but as the gold rush waned, so did the demand for beef. By the turn-of-the-century, population once again began to grow, but this time the people who came, stayed, increasing the need once again for beef.

There is no place in Canada where the history of the ranch is held so tightly to the chest. There is a strong sense here that the folks living within the 240,000 square kilometres of ranchland in the south central part of B.C., are cow men and women to the core. They ride horses and wear western gear with a confidence. There is no gimmicky edge to their cowboy hats, boots and buckle.

It is said that a cowboy's hat is guaranteed to make his face at least 50 percent more handsome, and I believe this is true. I also know that a man's hat is something you don't mess with. It is considered bad form to ask a cattleman to try on his hat. Many have a custom fit so a bigger head will stretch it out, rendering it useless afterward.

Women especially should avoid the temptation, unless her heart is set on a certain cowboy. Little excites a man more than a sassy woman wearing his hat. The saying "You wear the hat, you ride the cowboy" has caused many an unsuspecting woman to blush.

When not being worn, the cowboy hat should be placed on its crown, in a place where it won't be sat on or kicked accidentally. Some say it is bad luck to lay the hat on a bed. Most cowboys have a special place near the door for their favourite hat.

Here in B.C., they have kept many beliefs and traditions about the cowboy lifestyle alive and relate superstitions with a quiet assuredness, even though this is one of the smaller beef-producing provinces, with six percent of the national herd, totalling 290,000 head, grazing in the mountains and hills of the interior. Nestled in these valleys, you'll find historic ranches where four and five generations of the same family have lived, prospered, died, or gone broke. What they lack in sheer numbers they make up for in tradition and pride.

The summer of 2003 was a time that Betty Hinton will never forget. She is the Member of Parliament for Kamloops, Thompson, Cariboo, representing about 45 percent of the cattlemen in B.C.

The first time I saw Betty was during a televised parliamentary BSE debate. She spoke with genuine passion about the issue and how ranchers in her riding have been affected by recent hardships.

She is in Ottawa this week, so I won't be able to meet her in person. We arrange a telephone interview instead.

I ask what made her venture into politics.

Betty tells me that she's been politically active most of her life, sitting on the Kamloops school board and doing municipal work. The decision to run as an MP in 2000 was not an easy one, but a natural progression after a stint as a mayor, alderman, school trustee, regional district director and activist. She's always believed it is important to try to make a difference. Sitting in the House of Commons is the most challenging yet interesting work she's ever done.

And while her past business and political experiences prepared her for the political challenges ahead, nothing could ready her for the emotional challenges she would face during the summer of 2003.

Betty was visiting her daughter in Idaho at the end of July looking forward to the birth of her first grandchild, when she received a panicked phone call from her constituency office. They told her to come home right away because the riding was on fire.

Betty boarded a plane immediately and arrived back in Kamloops just before Transport Canada began diverting flights to other airports in B.C. as a safety precaution. Thick smoke filled the air and she immediately knew the situation was very serious.

Betty and her husband, Jamie, knew they couldn't help fight the fire but wanted to be useful, to do something to help, so they went to work volunteering at the local evacuation centre, and continued there over the next few weeks. She'd always heard that tragedies like this could bring out the best in people, and here she saw first-hand as so many people came together to help.

Life became a blur of activity that meant little sleep and plenty of stress. After the fires were finally extinguished in September, the year would be remembered as the worst fire season the province has seen in more than 20 years, with at least 255,000 hectares burned. Almost half of that was in the Kamloops region.

Once the fires were out, Betty set to work, travelling into the affected area to find out what help was needed. She was saddened by what she found.

Burned-out livestock producers were left with no place to turn.

"It was heartbreaking," she says, explaining that before the fires, producers had endured two dry years and were already cash-strapped when the fires swept through. Some livestock were killed and corrals and buildings burned. Those who managed to save their animals now had no pasture for them and some producers lost all their winter feed. The situation was tragic, compounded by the closed border, but overshadowed by the industry's preoccupation with BSE.

She spent weeks meeting with ranchers and came away with a better understanding of the people she represents. Betty describes ranchers as down-to-earth folks who at first were reluctant to ask for help. With some coaxing, she was able to get enough facts to help her understand and appreciate the lifestyle. She says that while she doesn't pretend to understand all the intricacies of the industry, she knows one thing for sure—that cattle people are honest about their needs. She immediately went to work to find financial help for the burned-out producers, only to discover that fencing materials and hay didn't fall under any compensation program. She made a number of phone calls and it took until the following spring before some ranchers received help through the Community Futures Program, which hired unemployed people to go in and help the cattlemen repair fences. At least 148 kilometres needed replacing.

"Our whole riding was turned upside down," she says. "This hurt agriculture, the tourist industry, forestry, and we're still hurting."

She says it was tragic seeing ranchers weighed down by circumstances beyond their control. In one case, she visited a rancher who had lost animals but was unable to prove how many because the fire was so intense it even burned the bones.

"These are people who have made a real contribution to society and to hear a fourth-generation producer say he might not carry on, that's really frightening," she says. "But having said that, there still is a lot of hope out there. A lot of people believe in this industry and aren't about to give up."

CHAPTER ELEVEN

*"Start a new terminology for these gals that work so hard and
do so much for us, and that we so often take for granted . . . I,
as a mother, consumer, rancher and general human being,
think we would do much better if we referred to
and marketed these gals as Mother Beef."*
— Faye Street, Jaffray, B.C., Letter to *Cattlemen Magazine*.

Debt. Most cattlemen have it. The days are long gone that a man can afford to buy a piece of land, raise his cattle and live a simple, debt-free life. Comfort levels vary between ranchers and feedlot men. A debt load that would strangle one man with worry might be an accepted reality for his neighbour.

Along with debt comes a responsibility to creditors, meaning cattlemen are more beholden to the banker than ever before. Submitting budgets, performing annual reviews and preparing monthly financial statements are taking up more of a cattleman's time than ever before.

Payday on the ranch comes only a few times a year. Traditionally, when calves are sold, producers make loan payments, pay off their operating line of credit and still have enough money left over to cover household bills and run the ranch for a good part of the year.

After surviving drought and then faced with the closed border, cattlemen are seeing their operating lines reach unprecedented levels. Cheques from their calf crop and cull cows no longer cover it all. The difference, or loss, has to be termed out, creating more long-term debt. Maintaining a healthy cash flow is a huge problem for producers right now, even those who have an excellent debt/equity ratio.

Larry and Wayne Jordan, auctioneers at the B.C. Livestock Co-operative

The B.C. Livestock Co-op sits not too far from where I'm staying. After breakfast, I make a few calls, then borrow Margaret's car and drive to the auction mart. Apparently there is a sale on today, but as I pull off the highway, discover there are only a handful of vehicles in the parking lot. Gathering up my notebook and camera, I follow the cement walkway to the front of the building, which looks more like an office than an auction barn. Pulling open the front door, I find myself in what looks like a mini-mall. There is a vet supply, trucking firm, restaurant, and the B.C. Cattlemen's Association (BCCA) office at the far end.

Inside the office I find the air is warm with the smell of copier ink— someone is finishing off a large job in the photocopy room. I introduce myself to Becky Everett in the front office. She directs me to David Borth, the Association's General Manager.

Having worked for the Manitoba Association for a few years, I can well imagine what the past 18 months have been like here. David says his staff hasn't seen a moment's rest since May 20th.

"This has certainly been the most demanding experience of my professional career because we've been challenged like never before," David says. There is an edge to his voice that I recognize, and sense that he's just received a distressing call from a producer who is looking for answers David can't give. Their office acts as facilitator to some of the provincial assistance programs, so they receive a lot of questions and take flack over circumstances they can't control.

"At the provincial level there is only so much we can do," he says, adding that 90 percent of the time they are able to help by just listening. Sometimes all producers need is a place to vent their frustrations.

I'm curious how the crisis has affected board dynamics and the relationships between provincial associations.

"Well, it's much like herding cats," he says. Cattlemen are so independent they don't always go in the same direction." He says the organizations have gotten along surprisingly well, considering the serious nature of the issue, and the fact that needs vary considerably between provinces. David defends the industry leadership, saying producers have never been more critical of what is being done, while the leaders have never worked harder.

David is originally from Kansas, having moved to Vanderhoof, B.C. when he was 12. He worked for the Ministry of Forestry for 14 years after obtaining his Agriculture Degree from the University of British Columbia. He began working for the BCCA five years ago.

The B.C. board consists of 28 directors and includes a seven-person executive. Directors represent 17 regional associations and 56 local groups. The Association's annual general meeting was held just days after the BSE announcement was made, so B.C. was thrust front and centre at the beginning of the controversy. Both Neil Jahnke and executive vice president of the CCA, Dennis Laycraft, were at the meeting, so there was a lot of media attention.

I ask how cattlemen here are coping.

He takes a deep breath. "They are such a self-reliant bunch it's not always easy to tell," he replies. "Pride gets in the way with some of them." David says he is recommending that everyone sign up for the CAIS program and apply for all government assistance offered, because whether producers want the help or not, some of them really need it.

When the border closed, there were approximately 15,000 fat cattle ready for the U.S. market. Because there was virtually no processing capacity in the province, feedlot operators stood in line to have their animals sent to the Alberta plants. Thoughts were that it could take up to seven years to get the border open to mature cattle, so talks began almost immediately to turn the mothballed Blue Mountain Packers plant at Salmon Arm into a cow and bull plant. It took more than a year before the federally inspected facilities were up and running. By the end of 2004, there were 50 head a day moving through the plant.

David directs me back down the hallway, steering me away from the auction barn doors toward a boardroom. There are a dozen men sitting around two long tables, watching a giant screen mounted on the far wall. I slip quietly into the dark room, finding a chair near the door. A few of the men glance over their shoulders at me, nod, then turn back to the screen.

They are in the middle of an auction sale via The Electronic Auction Mart (TEAM) based in Calgary. It doesn't take long to figure out who's buying and who's selling and that the men in the white hats are auctioneers. Using computers and phones, they are buying and selling cattle over the Internet. I've never seen anything like this before.

When the sale is finished, I meet David and Bob Haywood-Farmer, cousins who ranch together at Savona, about 60 miles west of Kamloops. They sold a few lots of steers today, but passed the heifers because the price was too low. We chat for a few minutes, then they invite me to come out to their ranch, saying they will have time to talk after dinner.

Auctioneer Larry Jordan introduces himself, offering to visit over lunch, so I walk with him to the restaurant, explaining why I'm here.

"Well, that sounds great," Larry replies. "There is a lot written about ranching history, but not much about today's cattle industry. This will be something for the young fellas to read and look back on and say, 'I was there for that.'"

We agree these years won't conjure up too many pleasant memories. Larry shakes his head. "It's a heck of a thing, isn't it?"

We order lunch and make small talk. Larry has a way about him that makes whoever he's talking with believe they are the only person in the room.

I ask how producers here are coping.

Larry says that the border closure has forced more ranchers to take logging jobs or to start driving trucks, and that wives are looking for work in town. A number of older ranchers, who'd likely planned on owning cattle for the rest of their lives, have given up and sold out.

"They just can't take it no more," he says, explaining that the financially strapped hobby farmers are using RRSPs and old-age pension cheques to keep things going. In some cases, ranchers have drawn the line and said no, refusing to compromise their equity levels further. Some have sold their cattle and left the business. At least four herd dispersals have come through the auction mart because of BSE.

Larry also blames the economic crisis for a number of divorces and for all the stress families are feeling.

"It takes a pretty good husband and wife team to lose $30,000, money they don't have, and still stick together."

Larry is troubled by the perception outside the industry that because producers control such large pieces of land, they are rich beyond hurt. He shakes his head, explaining that with input costs so high, none of these men are wealthy. He tells me that some of the old timers here were raised with strong memories of the depression in mind, so they don't trust the banks or the government. They pay cash for everything and are not accustomed to the paperwork involved in running a ranch today. He believes that because of this, producers most in need are the ones least likely to fill out government aid forms.

"The CAIS document, it's 80 pages long," he says, shaking his head. The Canadian Agricultural Income Stabilization Program replaced the Net Income Stabilization Account (NISA) in 2003. It is supposed to help producers during low income years, but the initial set-up of each individual farm and ranch requires five years of historical data. Any producer will say it is a daunting, time-consuming process and that government programs are written in a language all their own.

"It's not like applying for the family allowance where you call up and tell them how many kids you have. CAIS is just way too much for some of these guys. They get discouraged just looking at the dang thing."

Larry has been the auctioneer in Kamloops for 35 years and in that time he's seen a lot of changes. Before, buyers would travel out to the ranch, take a look at the cattle and make the owner an offer. The construction of auction marts in strategic locations like Kamloops, Williams Lake and Okanagan Falls helped consolidate selling, bringing more buyers into the market. The fact this particular business is a co-operative means producers share in the Association's profits, if there are any at the end of the year.

Some cattlemen still like to sell the old-fashioned way, so Larry must travel around, take a look at the cattle and give the producer an idea how much the animals might bring at the following week's sale. It has become difficult for Larry to predict because each time an announcement is made or something about the BSE situation hits the news, prices fluctuate up to 15 cents a pound.

The TEAM method of selling has added an option that never really was needed before now. Because the cattle aren't physically brought to the auction yard, the seller can pass if he doesn't like that day's price, with no need to truck the cattle back home. It's a high-tech spin on the traditional way of selling cattle.

Auctioneering is a stressful job even during prosperous times. Now, with need even greater, there is a lot of pressure for cattle to bring a good price. In spite of this, Larry says there is no other life for him. He tries to lessen the anxiety by maintaining a good sense of humour.

"And sometimes my wife and I, well, we just take off for a few days to find some time for ourselves," he says.

Listening to Larry is like inhaling a gust of fresh air. He is so passionate about the industry and cares about his customers unconditionally. To him, the person with three or four head is just as important as the guy with 500.

He tells me it is his job to stay optimistic and I wonder out loud how much counselling Larry is doing on the side.

"I get calls," he chuckles. "More now than ever. There used to be a time I could get away from the phone, you know, on these long drives to go look at cattle, but not anymore, not with these cell phones."

It's time for me to leave for the Haywood-Farmer ranch. Larry insists on buying my lunch. I ask to take his picture before I go, but he refuses, saying that he doesn't want to be in the limelight. If I want, I can return on Tuesday and snap a shot of his son, Wayne, selling cattle during the regular sale. I ask him for a business card.

"I don't have one," he chuckles. "Everybody already knows how to get a hold of me."

He takes my hand and shakes it hard.

"I've see it in the faces of the people," he says. "They are hurting. Believe me, the hurt in this goes around the whole wheel."

Christopher Haywood-Farmer waves. Photo by Santiago Salazar, Vancouver, B.C.

CHAPTER TWELVE

*"Only the stockman, among all of God's people, has remained
constant in preserving his heritage against the forces of both
man and nature's vagaries. It is as though his knowledge and
way of life had been designed as part of the Master's original
plan, a plan that could never it be destroyed nor greatly
improved upon."*
— Glen R. Vernam, *The Rawhide Years*, 1976.

Directions to Savona take me west of Kamloops and into the mountains where coniferous trees spike up in all directions. Try planting a tree here between the rock crevices into a bit of dry clay and sand, and the tree would surely wilt and die. And yet, the native pine will sprout up on its own, defying tremendous odds, growing to heights they never should, in numbers that defy reason.

Hundreds of feet below the winding highway, the South Thompson River snakes its way west. A person has to look really hard to see it is autumn here. It certainly isn't felt in the temperature, which hovers at a sunny 10 degrees. The heartier flowers continue to bloom and there are still leaves hanging ready to abandon the trees. Plastic jack-o-lantern bags filled with grass clippings remind me there are only a few days left until Hallowe'en.

As I turn off the highway just before Savona to make my way south to the Haywood-Farmer ranch, I am reminded of the first fall I spent in Manitoba. Mark and I were living in Winnipeg and made weekend trips out to the farm. One crisp October morning stands out in my memory and when I think of it hard, I can almost smell the morning breeze wafting in through an open slit in the bedroom window, the sound of bawling cattle saturating the air. The day before, the men had separated the cattle because it was weaning time. The cows and calves would bawl for two, maybe three days, cows standing on one side of the fence, calves on the other. Instinct kept them pressed together like this until the stronger instinct to eat and drink took over. Gradually they forgot one another and by the following weekend, the pens were quiet and peaceful again.

Turning off Tunkwa road, I follow a winding driveway halfway down into the valley. There a house sits, backed up against a hill as if asking for its protection, surrounded by shrubs and trees. A truck is parked beneath a giant willow that rises up along the edge of the front yard. Opposite the house is a machine shed, barn and stable. There are people, dogs and move-ment everywhere.

I park the car and step out into the sound of not one, but two diesel engines. A young man jumps down from a tractor, then heads toward the house while another man tries to coax a big, yellow dog into the cab of a semi-truck parked at the edge of the yard. Two other dogs run to greet me, both border collies, one noticeably slower and older than the other. A horse stands with his head over the stable door, whinnying at the sight of me.

David Haywood-Farmer is standing on the deck at the side door. He has the look of a cow man—rugged and serious—but a few minutes into conversation with him and it's easy to see that he's not stern at all.

Two young men are piling split wood from a trailer onto the ground near the walkway to the house. David waves for me to come inside.

One of the young men follows me up the deck steps. David introduces me to a younger version of himself, his 21-year-old son, Stephen, who nods a polite hello, then asks his dad a question before hurrying away. It's a busy time of year as they press to get the fall work done before it's time to bring the cows home.

"That's my daughter's horse," David says, nodding toward the stable. He tells me that Becky isn't home and the horse misses her when she's gone. He invites me into their comfortable, clean, ranch-style kitchen, and apol-ogizes that his wife Bonnie isn't here. She has gone to a community funer-al, he says, as he offers me a homemade tart—baked especially for the funeral lunch. I gladly accept and joke about how mom isn't allowed to leave the house carrying baking unless she leaves some behind.

Glancing around and listening, I'd say the Haywood-Farmer family is a fair representation of cattle producers in Canada. Their lifestyle, man-nerisms and priorities fit what cattlemen are all about.

We sit at the table for a few minutes, but soon decide it will be easier for David to explain their set-up while touring the ranch. We pull on our boots, pushing past the dogs who are up again and hoping to come along to do some work.

"We still have two hired men," David says as he climbs into the truck and pulls the door shut. "BSE did a number on our cash flow, but it did nothing to lessen the workload."

He puts the heavy diesel in gear, then slowly backs up. He pauses for a moment, looking as though maybe he has forgotten something, then shrugs. Whatever he was supposed to do will be waiting when he gets home.

The truck rumbles up the steep driveway and he turns onto the main road. He says that producers in B.C. work three types of land: deeded, leased and permit. He points to a long, narrow strip of alfalfa saying that deeded land is owned by the producer and the core of the ranch. It is the land that usually contains the hay base, outbuildings and house.

Grazing leases are 21-year contracts with the Crown and these provide a good portion of the fall grazing land. Summer grazing is done on Licence or Permit land, which is rented out annually at a per animal per month cost.

In this part of the country, the average producer needs 25 to 30 acres of grazing space per cow/calf pair. A ton of hay per cow will get them through the 100-day winter feeding period. This year, David's irrigated land produced four tons of alfalfa per acre—a tremendous yield, and he's glad for it.

He explains that years before BSE, ranchers in B.C. were being squeezed. There is unyielding pressure from provincial agriculture, forestry and tourism departments for ranchers to manage their lands in a responsible manner. Today's producer is having to atone for abuses in the past, and even the responsible cattleman is expected to take part in programs. David has spent countless hours developing range plans that focus on sustainability with a heavy emphasis on rotational grazing and wildlife management. He believes in the concept, but says everything takes time and money to implement. Pressure to comply comes from the fact that tourists are flocking to the land in record numbers, expecting to see wildlife and the environment in its most natural state. Native land claims are ongoing and urban sprawl has resulted in an alarming amount of ranchland being taken out of production—and there is nothing the cattleman can do to stop it.

"We're seeing people from the coast selling out, buying land here and building themselves beautiful homes," he says. "We just can't compete with the prices they are willing to pay."

David says that making a living right now is really tough. He is not consoled in the knowledge that if times get tougher, he can always subdivide some of the deeded land and sell it off.

"A person gets attached to a piece of dirt, you know. It's hard to let it go," he says quietly. "And besides, once it's gone—it's gone."

Hearing this is discouraging and I'm filled with a shattering sense of desperation. Like me, the urbanites who come here simply want to experience B.C. ranch country as it once was. Unfortunately, they just don't realize they might be the undoing of it all.

David has been ranching his whole life and has watched land prices and input costs skyrocket. The cost of a new baler jumped from $10,000 fifteen years ago to $40,000 now. Maintenance on machinery is escalating and fuel bills are the highest they have ever been.

"We're in a cash squeeze right now," he says, explaining that they declined selling their heifers today because 80 cents a pound just wasn't enough. He was disappointed with the price the steers brought as well; $1 a pound is about 20 cents below the cost of production. "But we've got bills to pay just like everybody else, so we had to sell."

Before the border closed, producers had more options. Cows or bred heifers could be sold, cutting back the herd, resulting in overall lower expenses, and in effect riding out difficult times. Now, with no market for these animals, the value of cows is so low that it's not worth selling them. The only people in the market wanting to buy are cattlemen and most don't have the money or desire to do so. There are speculators still willing to invest money in cattle, but even they have been burned by the delays in seeing the border open.

We have been driving for a long time, so I ask David just how big this ranch is. He says it is about 30 kilometres in three directions but difficult to estimate exactly because the mountains mean nothing is square.

I look out the window at the vast area and can see dots on the landscape that look like cattle. I wonder out loud how they manage such a vast piece of land.

David says they have at least 100 kilometres of fence that needs tending, a job they do as they ride the range over the spring and summer months while checking the cattle. Their cows are a Hereford and Red Angus cross and they use Beef Booster bulls. He says the exotic breeds don't do well here, but the British animals can travel long distances and keep their condition on sagebrush, shortgrass and the dryland grasses that grow on the range. The cattle are branded so that if some do get mixed in with cows from the neighbouring ranches, they can be easily sorted.

Within the next few days they will begin the task of bringing the cattle home. It will take them two weeks on horseback to round everything up, unless the weather takes a bad turn.

"Snow is the best cowboy there is," he chuckles. "They seem to know winter means it's time to come home, so that's when they start to migrate back on their own."

David decides to turn back now and asks if I have time to go into the mountains to see the Tunkwa Lake reservoir. He explains area producers irrigate from this reservoir using gravity, by opening the dam to let the water trickle down when needed. It is a system that works well and pretty much assures them a hay crop.

I ask him if this was a particularly dry summer. Many of the trees along the winding road up the mountain look dead, but not charred as you'd expect to see if a fire came through.

David tells me that the dying trees are the result of an infestation of Mountain Pine Beetles that have descended upon the province in unprecedented numbers.

"They are the most damaging thing I've ever seen," he says as we wind our way up the mountainside. So far, the infestation has resulted in upwards of 300 million cubic metres of dead timber. Because of the beetle, the forest is being aggressively logged in an effort to stop the spread and salvage the wood. The result is an oversupply of lumber on the market and depressed prices for logging rights.

David is hoping I've brought with me a little bit of Manitoba winter. He says that two weeks of really cold temperatures is the only thing that will permanently kill off the beetle.

He slows as we round a curve and meet a few cows on the road. Further on, I see a part of their herd grazing a small field. We stop a few times along the way so I can take pictures of the cattle.

I get out of the truck at the reservoir and, as I stand looking out over the shimmering water, let the wind fill my ears. A few men fish along the bank not too far away.

God, this is a beautiful spot. It's something He already knows.

We travel in silence for a long time before I ask the origin of their unusual last name.

David tells me his grandfather, Charles Haywood-Farmer, came with his family to the area from England in 1933. The family name honours a promise made by Charles' father, whose last name was Farmer. He was business partners with a man named Haywood who had no family and worried that after his death, there would be no one to carry on his name. The two men came to an agreement that Mr. Haywood would pass on all his assets to the Farmer family if they would adopt his name. The agreement was made and is honoured to this day.

David is the third generation to ranch this land, and given the chance, Stephen, Christopher and Becky will be the fourth. He worries most about their future.

"We love this place—" he begins, voice catching as he looks out the window. It takes a few minutes before he's ready to finish the thought. "B.C. might not be the best place in the country to make a living raising cattle, but for us, this is home."

With the ranch tour over, Dave drives me to see his cousin Bob and wife Kathleen who live in the same valley along the Tunkwa Road, approximately seven kilometres south. They have been ranching together since 1975.

As we turn down the steep driveway, I am warmed by the rustic beauty of this place. Everything here is built from wood. The house has the look of a mountain cabin, sitting up high on a ridge overlooking a handful of outbuildings and a large corral system. The most striking feature on the place is an unusual log barn that we pass on our way up to the house.

David parks the truck not far from the backdoor, slides out and sticks his head into the porch. He hollers for Bob, but there's no reply. We stand outside chatting, enjoying the remains of this sunny, windy day while we wait.

It isn't long before Bob emerges from his workshop and, in a purposeful way, comes up the driveway toward us. His border collie trots just a few feet ahead, pausing occasionally to look back to see if he is still coming.

Bob's face turns into a warm smile as we meet again. Together we walk back down the hill and they show me the corrals and system they have set up for processing cattle. The calves they planned to sell today were brought in from a nearby pasture a few days ago for weighing. In 1990 they installed an electronic scale that eliminates the guesswork from knowing calf weights at weaning time. It is a slick set-up that most cattlemen would love to own.

The calves they didn't sell at today's sale will stay out on grass for awhile longer, but the ones that sold will be rounded up again and brought back for weighing and shipping, once the buyer gives them a date the truck will arrive. Someone from the auction mart will be here to verify the weights.

David checks his watch, saying there are a few things he must do before dark. They decide that Bob will drive me back later for my car.

As we amble toward the house, I ask Bob to show me the barn.

He smiles at my interest as if to say: I was wondering when you'd ask.

"It's pretty unique to the area," he says in a relaxing drawl. "All hand cut, dovetailed corners and hand split shakes from douglas fir trees with straight grain. Dad had an old Swede working for him and he's the one who built it."

Bob swings open the wide door and we step inside.

Light shines in through the six-paned rectangular windows spaced neatly along the front and back walls. Horseshoes, tack and thick blankets hang on pegs over a workbench at the front. Stalls line the length of both walls, and Bob points to the two widest sections, saying they were reserved for his father's team. Bleached skulls from animals I can't identify sit on the window ledges, a collection considered appropriate for decoration in the west. I am pleased by the echo of my boots on the rough hardwood floor that runs in long planks from end to end. A catch of wind blows in from an open window, churning up the dusty smell of sun-cured grain. I decide that the Swede must have been short because the ceiling is unusually low.

Bob seems to enjoy my fascination with this relic he's known his whole life.

I pull out my camera and attach the flash. It's then I realize I'd forgotten to turn it off last time and the batteries are dead. I don't have any more with me.

"That's all right," Bob says heading for the door. "What size? Double As? We've got a box of them at the house. How many do you need?"

While he's gone, I wander around the barn, looking at his stash of vastly interesting old things—tobacco cans, antique bottles, metal hinges and hand-forged nails.

I have read that buildings and land hold the energy of the people who live in them. Somehow, life's happiness, disappointments, joy, sadness and even hate will find its way into the walls where we live. If that is the case, this barn has seen more good days than bad. Chances are there were hardships here, but this place harbours no tortured souls—human or otherwise.

Bob returns with four batteries in hand. I plunk them into the flash and take a few pictures of him standing in the barn. He waits until I've had my fill of the place before suggesting we leave.

As we step outside, his wife, Kathleen, and their 16-year-old son, Mark, drive up in an old, two-seat half ton truck. By now the wind has picked up and a thick bank of dark clouds have brought a chill into the valley. We hurry to the house where I hang my jacket on a hook and step over an old dog sleeping on the porch floor. I'm offered a seat at the kitchen table across from Kathleen as Bob offers to make us hot chocolate. The house has a warm, rustic feel and it's the sort of place you don't want to leave.

I estimate Kathleen's age around 50. She is slim and strong looking, likely in better physical condition than most women half her age. She has a straight, boyish haircut that she dresses up with gold hoop earrings. She and Bob have the look of a couple who have been married a long time—a comfortable way of being together with mannerisms that have grown more similar over the years.

She tells me that she is originally from Vancouver and came here via Toronto after meeting Bob. She loves the ranch, and prefers working outdoors on the land, or with the cattle, to being cooped up indoors. Her voice is soft and words thoughtful. If she ever had a rough city edge, all signs of it are gone.

I ask how they've been managing through BSE.

"Well, we signed up for every program in sight," Bob replies from the kitchen counter. He has three mugs in front of him. He dips a spoon into one and starts stirring. He says the last few years haven't been easy because they expanded the ranch just before BSE, and not long before that, had to buy out other partners. Lower calf prices have resulted in their operating line creeping up higher than expected.

"It's tough wondering how we're going to hold this all together," he says, shaking his head.

I ask if the government programs helped at all. The most recent is a program dubbed the "set-aside" that pays cattlemen a portion of the feed costs to keep their animals longer and sell them at intervals to keep from flooding the market.

"Some programs were better than others," he says, dipping the spoon into the second mug. "The set-aside is good for the guys who keep their calves over and background them, which we do with some of our calves. If you've got your own feed, then maybe, but not if you have to put them in a custom lot."

They are concerned that the set-aside program will create an over supply of yearlings next year because it is based on the assumption that the border will open.

We discuss how it has become an accepted practice for cattle producers to have at least the husband or wife working out to supplement the ranch income. The trend is disturbing, especially when the workload at home is enough for two but only a paycheque for one.

"Our operation is such a size that we can't work out," Bob says, stirring the last mug. He brings Kathleen and me each a cup, then returns carrying his. He pulls out the chair across from me and sits down.

Kathleen takes a sip. "I can't get a job that would make it worth the expense to go every day," she says, her voice tinged with guilt. Covering the shortfall in a large operation takes more than an outside job can cover. "Besides, Bob needs me here."

They tell me that Mark is their youngest and they have three other children away right now. Their eldest daughter, Christy, is in her last year of medical school at the University of Ottawa; a 23-year-old daughter, Jane is studying social work at the University of Victoria, and their 19-year-old son, Ted, is in first year Engineering at UBC.

It's no surprise they are feeling financial pressure.

Bob says that when times get tough, ranchers need their herd to be more efficient. But since BSE, they've watched their herd grow older and less productive because there is no market for older cows. A heifer calf will bring between $500 and $700, so producers are selling younger animals to

Kathleen, Mark and Bob Haywood-Farmer

service debt and pay bills while keeping the older, less productive cows with no market value, hoping to get a calf from them in the spring.

He says since they have no way to increase income, they plan to lower expenses this year by cutting back on pregnancy testing and treatments such as topical insecticides that help prevent parasite infestations. They don't like skimping on herd health, but feel they have little choice right now, but say they will keep up their vaccination program.

"I was so surprised to hear that people ship downers," Kathleen says, referring to the publicity over the fact the first cow with BSE was having difficulty standing by the time she reached the abattoir. "We ship old cows long before they get to that point. We would never, ever ship an unhealthy cow." She is already worried about what lies ahead for some of her favourite cows who have names like Spice and Betty.

"And you'd think with all this extra meat, the consumer would be rewarded with lower prices after standing behind us like they did," Bob says, slowly shaking his head. "It's just not being spelled out how the beef producers are still suffering, the consumer is still paying high prices and someone else is making all the money."

We finish our hot chocolate and talk for awhile longer. They tell me that there was one bright spot for them during the summer of 2003. A call came from a production company asking if they would be willing to allow a film crew to come onto their land and shoot a movie in the yard. Nothing would be required of them—all they had to do was agree.

For six weeks that summer, a group of 200 actors, actresses and crew filled the little valley with trailers and other equipment.

They point out the window to an old frame home that sits near the barn. It is the house where Bob's mother lived for more than 50 years. Many of the buildings, parts of their yard site and, of course, the barn were featured in the film.

"Real nice folks," Bob says, "especially that Morgan Freeman fellow. We went riding together once and I really liked him."

Bob went on to describe Robert Redford as intense and quiet, but always polite. He couldn't remember the lead actress' name. He described her as "a real nice girl—the one who has had all that man trouble."

Kathleen searches her memory, too, but can't recall a name. She jumps up just as Bob asks her to go find the picture. She returns a few minutes later carrying a large photograph taken on the last day of the shoot. The cast and crew of "An Unfinished Life" are all lined up.

"There we are," Bob says, pointing to the centre of the photo. Sure enough, he and Kathleen are standing right in the middle of it all.

I take a good look at the faces, recognizing actress Jennifer Lopez.

"Yeah, that's her," Bob smiles.

We talk a little more about how interesting it was for them to see a movie being made. Even though it was boring at times, they say it was still fun to stand around and watch. This was an experience they'll never forget and a pleasant distraction from the turmoil surrounding BSE. They expect the movie will be released in September 2005.

"Do you want to know the best part?" Kathleen asks in a near whisper.

I wait, watching her eyes light up and a sly smile lift the corners of her mouth. "We were expected to join them for meals. I didn't have to cook the entire time."

Now I am impressed. To have someone else do the cooking for six weeks? Ranch-wife heaven.

A glance out the window tells us the sun has long disappeared behind the mountain west of here. The sky has turned slate grey, muddying the outline of everything outdoors. Soon it will be dark. Kathleen invites me to stay for supper, but I reluctantly decline. I still have to stop in to meet David's wife Bonnie, and then drive back to Kamloops where Hugh and Margaret will be wondering where I am.

Bob takes me back to David's house and I am invited inside.

David introduces me to Bonnie who asks me to sit for awhile and have something to eat. I tell them I can't stay long. I'm tired and Bonnie looks that way, too.

My eyes are immediately drawn to a large family photograph on the wall behind the table. Mountains serve as the backdrop as David, Bonnie and their three children, mounted on horses, line up in a lush green field. The sky is the same soft blue as their denim shirts.

The photo was taken as part of the "Ranchland Heroes" beef promotion initiated by the Canadian "ABC Country Restaurant" chain. Based in the west, ABC is known for its hearty, wholesome meals. The BCCA suggested the Haywood-Farmers would make a suitable poster family, and the restaurant's marketing department agreed. This photo was a gift for participating.

Bonnie disappears into another room, then returns carrying a long cylinder. She rolls out a large poster for me to see.

"It feels really strange walking into the restaurant and seeing that," David chuckles.

Looking closer I recognize that the denim shirt, canvas vest and cowboy hat he is wearing in this photo are the same he is wearing today. This tells me more about him than he might realize.

What you see is what you get.

It is the most endearing characteristic of ranch people. The Haywood-Farmers are exactly what you see, and two families I'll certainly never forget.

Everyone was predicting that the border would open to live cattle exports early in 2004, including Lyle Vanclief. North Dakota State University cattle expert Harlan Hughes told 250 producers at a meeting in Rosetown, Saskatchewan, that the logical date for an open border was January 1, 2004. He advised producers to hold on to their cattle and market them after the border opened, adding that there was potential to make fairly decent money by doing so. His comments were reported in the *Western Producer* farm paper. Within a week word had spread like wildfire across the windswept prairie.

In October, fat cattle prices in Alberta jumped to 93 cents a pound, up 14 cents from the previous week. A group called the Disciplined Marketing Initiative took credit for the increase. These feedlot operators joined together in an effort to regulate weekly cattle numbers being offered to the packing plants. The group said that even though the border is partially open, prices of fat cattle were still depressed and they weren't yet able to recoup any of the previous five month's losses. Fearing reprisal from the packing industry, these feedlot operators asked to remain anonymous.

On October 31, the USDA issued a proposed rule to amend its BSE regulations to establish a new category that would recognize countries considered at minimum risk of introducing the disease into the U.S. If passed, the rule would allow live Canadian animals under 30 months of age into the country. A 60-day comment period followed, giving both Canadian and U.S. groups the chance to file reports.

Although the date of January 1 now seemed overly optimistic, all signs indicated that the U.S. border would likely be open to young cattle before the start of the next calving season. It's generally believed that this fuelled optimism in the industry that saw feedlot operators pay more than $1 a pound for good calves, prices similar to 2002. They competed with each other and buyers from the U.S. who needed animals to replenish their feedlots.

On November 14, former federal finance minister Paul Martin became Prime Minister of Canada, and speculation was high that Lyle

Vanclief's six-year term as agriculture minister would soon end.

Vanclief defended the Agricultural Policy Framework (APF) as a good farm program but couldn't convince all provinces. As of mid-November, it still wasn't implemented because Ontario and Saskatchewan hadn't signed on. Vanclief suggested that Ottawa and western farmers couldn't agree because farmers were not listening to the message.

"It comes down to communications, and communication is a two-way street. Somebody talks and somebody has to listen," he said, suggesting that despite Martin's vow to end the rift between the national government and westerners, Vanclief's successor should not expect much thanks from farmers.

"It's a reality," Vanclief said. "I farmed for 25 years and I've never heard a farmer say federally or provincially that a government has done enough for them. I know farmers well enough to know that's not going to change."[13]

Cattlemen were left wondering if Vanclief was talking about them. In an article in the same paper a week earlier, he sounded equally frustrated when discussing plans for the cull cow program. Few cattleman I've spoken to complain about the help they've received; actually, they are thankful. Their criticisms surround the fact that the government was so busy trying to devise programs that producers couldn't abuse, that they ignored the advice of the CCA and let the packers take advantage of them instead.

Before the programs were announced, Neil Jahnke and the CCA warned Vanclief what would work and what wouldn't. When it comes to helping ranchers, if anybody wasn't listening, it was the Minister.

In early December, the MP for Haldimand-Norfolk in Ontario, Bob Speller, was named the new Federal Agriculture Minister. Hopes were high in the west that recent changes in the government would add a positive momentum in the drive to get the border open.

Speller's first test would come just 11 days later. On December 23, 2003, a BSE-infected dairy cow was discovered in the United States and traced back to a Canadian herd.

CHAPTER THIRTEEN

A big ranch is a miniature society. Its demise has the impact of
a bankruptcy in a small town: another hundred people out of
work and a big chunk of the town's business is suddenly gone.
A ranch offers more than jobs; whole families are taken in, their
needs attended to: housing, food, schools, even a graveyard plot
for those who died on the job or liked the place so much
they wanted to be buried there.
— Gretel Ehrlich, *The Solace of Open Spaces*, 1985.

Many a cattleman's best ideas come while he's sitting on the tractor.

This is the place where he goes to work, but also to consider things. A lot of thought is put into what improvements he needs to make to his operation so that it might prosper, grow and be more efficient.

By autumn, he's searching his mind for the mental notes made during the last calving season. Now is the time to clean up and get ready for winter. He'll put himself and the hired man to work fixing pens, corrals and chutes. He'll make adjustments to the barn set-up and check the watering system, fixing or replacing what isn't working anymore. He'll also decide how much time he has to spare and balance that off against what he can afford to invest in this year.

Hauling manure from the wintering pens is one job that must be done. This is a weather-dependent task, which means a wet spring delays cleaning until fall. Whether a company is hired or the producer decides to do the job himself, he is looking at thousands of dollars in cost, or weeks of work and fuel expense to haul and spread the manure across the fields.

In Ontario, where the feeding space is intense, and in Manitoba,

Doug Mervyn and Bronc Twan

where the season is long, producers have more manure to move than in the west. Because of this expense, producers are always looking for ways to minimize the concentration of cattle waste and maximize this valuable fertilizer.

Ranchers are being encouraged to develop manure management and environmental farm plans that are designed specifically for each operation, so the producer can see how he might do things differently to save money and protect the environment in the process.

The weather is dreary this morning as I set out; a mixture of rain and wet snow makes the road slick and keeps the windshield wipers beating steadily. I'm travelling the Trans-Canada Highway west to Cache Creek. There, I'll turn north toward Williams Lake, where I have interviews set up with three ranchers in the Cariboo region. It's a five-hour drive, and as I climb higher, I dread the thought that the roads might begin to freeze.

Not far out of Kamloops, as the car chugs to the top of a mountain, I am awestruck by the scene out the passenger window. The valley below is mostly lake except for an outcrop of about three hundred acres of land. A small herd of mixed cattle stand grazing the damp grass as the wind swirls around them, flattening the rippled water that glistens atop cadet blue depths.

The sun must be shining somewhere, because a wide rainbow has sprouted from behind the mountain ahead and is growing brighter each time I blink. It arches up over the trees, falling onto the small pasture, fading onto the backs of the contented cows. I want to slow down, to take in this scene, but the car is already being dwarfed by a tractor-trailer whose grill crowds into the rearview mirror.

There is a rest stop a few hundred feet ahead, so I pull off the highway and scramble out of the car with camera in hand, but by the time I reach the railing, the moment has passed. I stand for a few minutes in the sleet, holding onto the image in my mind and wondering if we'll ever see the day again that cattle are at the end of our rainbow.

The Alkali Lake Ranch is situated 50 kilometres southwest of Williams Lake, down a rough, winding road. It snowed here this morning, so in spots still shaded by the mountain, the road is snow-packed and slippery. In places where there is full sunlight, the road is slushy and potholes are filled with mud. This is turning into a longer drive than expected, and I'm beginning to regret the decision to venture so far off the highway.

I'm on my way to see Robert ("Bronc") and Liz Twan. Liz warned me, but at the time I reasoned she thought I was a city slicker unaccustomed to gravel roads. Her description of it was better than accurate, and I wish right now for a four-wheel-drive truck.

Finally, the town of Alkali Lake comes into view. As I descend into the valley, I catch sight of a scattering of rooftops almost hidden from view. A hairpin turn takes me down a steep lane, and then suddenly I'm driving into what looks like a miniature town on the edge of town.

Established in the 1850s, the Alkali Lake Ranch is recognized as B.C.'s first cattle company. During the gold rush days, this ranch and others like it doubled as stopping houses for optimistic miners travelling north, as well as the disillusioned bound for home. Now, this ranch employs an average of eight full-time employees.

I pass by corrals, a barn and a few small buildings, the remains of the blacksmith shop, the old store, post office and bunkhouse. Modern, red metal roofing has replaced the old, asphalt tiles, so these buildings should be around for decades to come.

Bronc is standing alongside the road. He motions for me to park the car in the driveway beside his truck, then greets me with hand extended. He invites me inside so I follow him along the path to their quaint house, through a small yet abundant flower garden. The porch entrance is surrounded with creeping vines, and little ornaments peek out from behind the nearly naked bushes. Stepping into the kitchen, I feel instantly embraced by the homespun feel of potted plants, braided rugs and a warm stove.

Liz is standing at the sink peeling vegetables.

Tonight Doug and Marie Mervyn, owners of the ranch, are hosting a Hallowe'en party. A few of the neighbouring ranchers have been invited to attend and Liz has volunteered to help with the meal.

"Don't mind me," she says, filling a pot with water, then setting it on the stove, while Bronc and I take a seat at the table. "I've got to get this done."

I've heard that Liz is a writer, and a damn good one at that. Her creativity shows through in her garden and throughout her home. I wish there was more time for us to sit and talk about writing.

Bronc is the manager here. He tells me that the Mervyns bought the ranch nearly 30 years ago from the von Riedemann family. The Mervyns were business owners in southern B.C. who had roots that nudged them toward country life. When the ranch came up for sale, Doug and Marie decided to buy it, investing themselves wholeheartedly in the enterprise.

Bronc's father, Bill, was a long-time employee here, the cow boss, and his mother worked in the early years as the Wynn-Johnson family's nanny. Bronc grew up amongst the cattle, cowboys and horses. With a nickname like Bronc—Spanish for wild, rough or an unbroken horse—it's a fair guess he spent more time kicking up dust in the saddle than spitting stones from the seat of a bicycle. When Bronc was a young man, he left the ranch to rodeo now and then, but he continued to work at Alkali. He married Liz in 1978.

"There's no other place quite like it," he says, explaining that he took over as ranch manager after his father retired. He has been the manager for at least 15 years now. It's obvious that Bronc Twan is the closest thing to a real cowboy I'm ever going to meet.

The ranch itself is one of the largest in the province with 37,000 deeded acres and at least that again in grazing leases and permit land. They run commercial Hereford cows that do well on the semi-arid desert lands in the summer, but can adjust to temperatures that drop as low as -20 degrees Celsius in the winter. They don't get a lot of snow here, although this fall has been the exception. Bronc says they've seen more moisture in the past two months than what is normally recorded in a year.

In 1996, the ranch was presented with the B.C. award for Environmental Stewardship, which recognized their friendly, sustainable practices. Bronc says the days are long gone that cattlemen grazed the land with impunity. The men still in business today are the ones who think of the future.

Like the Haywood-Farmers, he is concerned how the pine beetle is affecting the forests, saying that if the beetle continues to spread at the current rate, there will be no pine trees left in a year.

I'd heard that the ranch and a company called Rodear Meats supplies meat to local restaurants and that Bronc is the man in charge. I ask how they are doing in this venture.

He's modest and quick to downplay how much business they might have pinched away from others. He explains that for many years, the Alkali Lake Ranch has sold both grass and grain-fed cows and finished animals (including smaller bulls) to Rodear Meats at Beaver Valley. Rodear is a provincially inspected plant owned by Dave and Sarah Fernie that took between 50 and 70 animals a year from the ranch. The fallout from BSE prompted Bronc and the Fernies to discuss the prospect of cultivating a larger piece of the local market. They hired a salesman, Willie Crosina, who was bored with retirement and looking for something to occupy his time. Willie is well known to the area so his visits to the local grocery stores and restaurants meant that orders soon followed.

The Fernies run the day-to-day business while Bronc sources the cattle. They've seen business increase all around, selling sides, ground beef, stew, sausage, jerky and hamburger patties, all at a reasonable price.

Locally there is a lot of understanding toward the ranchers so many people are supporting the venture. By 2004, they more than doubled sales from the year before.

"It's a lot of hassle and the profits are slim, but it's a way to move cattle," Bronc says, adding that before BSE they sold mostly prime cuts, but now the focus has turned to hamburger.

There's a quick rap at the porch door, then it rattles open and a man steps inside. Bronc introduces his boss, Doug Mervyn, who nods in greeting, then sits silently at the corner of the table with his back to the window I've been glancing out over the past hour. He listens as Bronc finishes explaining the meat business and how Doug was one of the first cattleman in B.C. to add value to his animals by finishing calves himself instead of sending them to a feedlot. Fattening cattle has always been a bit of a gamble, but now it's like playing the lottery.

"We know the person who owns cattle when the border opens is going to do well," Bronc says. "All we're trying to do here is operate as per usual." He leans back slightly in his chair and glances at his boss, who's carefully watching me.

Doug is a reserved man whose silvery hair adds dignity to an already handsome face. His intelligence is obvious and he seems not all that interested in talking with a stranger about his business and private life. He has far too much pride to complain. If Doug Mervyn is feeling his back against the wall, I suspect it's for the first time.

I ask him a few questions and he gives oblique, one-word answers. I'm starting to feel uncomfortable, like it's time to leave, when suddenly he asks where I'm from.

In a burst of nervous energy, I describe our ranch along the lake, the remoteness of it, explaining how it has a different sort of beauty than what they see here. I tell them about the Icelanders who settled our area, how poor they were, the toil it took, and the debt we owe them for making the ranches what they are today. I ramble on a little too long (as I sometimes do), then realize it and force myself to stop.

"You sound as though you love it there," Doug says.

I'm surprised by his comment and feel my voice catch as I try to answer. I blink hard, hoping he doesn't see how wet my eyes have become.

I can only stare at my notebook so long before I'm forced to make eye contact. The image of him sitting there with the light shining in, brightening one side of his face, is one I'll remember always. The softness in his eyes tells me that Doug Mervyn feels things just as strongly as I do.

"Money isn't why we're in the cattle business; it's only the grease that keeps the wheel going around," he says quietly. He's talking about them and us and all the people who'll be coming to his party that night. "All you have to do is look out the window to see why we're here."

I regain my composure enough to ask how area cattlemen have been managing.

"As far as I know, this situation hasn't forced anyone out of business and there are no ranches around here for sale," he replies. "What it has done, though, especially for some of the older cattlemen, is taken the enjoyment out of ranching—it's just gone."

Doug goes on to say that none of them, especially the old timers, like the idea of accepting help from the government, but during these difficult economic times they've learned to accept it as reality.

In a normal year, he would sell one third of the calves in the fall, usually to an Alberta feedlot. They would keep a third, then sell them as yearlings, and the remainder would be fed to finish and either butchered for local sale or shipped to a packing plant in Washington state.

Thinking the border was set to open in January 2004, they decided to hold the yearlings from 2002 and all their 2003 calves and feed them to finish. This would save them freighting costs to Alberta, and give them a healthy load of calves to ship to the U.S., hopefully to the plant where he was accustomed to doing business.

It was a decision that cost him many sleepless nights and more money than he dares admit. The feed bill was astronomical and when the border didn't open in January as predicted, the price he received for fat steers hovered between 33 and 52 cents a pound. Looking back, he says, they should have just sold all the calves off the cows once weaned in the fall.

"But nothing normal has happened since that border closed," he says, shaking his head. "After a while you just give up trying to guess."

He says it's going to take years for cattlemen to recoup the equity they've lost and some don't have enough years left in them to do it. A lot of ranchers don't even know where they are financially, because the federal income stabilization program, CAIS, has a formula so complex, ranchers can't tell by looking at the numbers if they'll receive a payment. Growing criticism toward the program from politicians in the opposition just adds to the rancher's doubts.

When our visit is over, Bronc and Doug walk me to the car. Outside, the colours in the valley have turned thick and wet under the shadow cast by a disappearing afternoon sun. Two boys around the age of 10 are playing road hockey halfway up the poplar-lined drive that leads to the Mervyn house. It is an elegant, alpine-inspired home that I later discover was built in the 1940s by the von Riedemanns, who were native to Switzerland.

I leave them to finish preparations for the party. As I make my way out of the valley on roads that are still wet but no longer hazardous, I reflect upon the fact that so often the clearest insight comes long after a conversation is done and the most pleasant surprise sometimes awaits at the end of a difficult road.

Cattle along the road leading to Alkali Lake Ranch

Chapter Fourteen

"The short answer as to why people keep farming in the face of poor economic rewards is because to quit farming is to reject a set of commonly held values and beliefs deeply rooted in generations of farm folk that came before."
— journalist and author Peter Schroedter, *Winnipeg Free Press*, 2004

This promises to be a busy week for Mark and Sally Nairn. Tomorrow morning they will start bringing the cattle home, so tonight is our only chance to visit.

Directions take me southwest past Williams Lake to Riske Creek. The scenery along this highway is spectacular and I wonder if the folks who live here ever grow accustomed to this beauty. I also wonder how prospectors navigated these mountains and how many died along the trail north in search of gold.

I arrive just as dusk settles a faint blue haze over everything in the valley. Porch lights illuminate the deck and a golden light casts a warm, inviting glow through the windows of the Nairn's gorgeous log home. I hurry up the steps and Mark greets me before I knock, taking my overnight bag and welcoming me inside. Two dogs, an older border collie and a playful shih tzu, wag happily at my arrival.

I'm introduced to Megan, 17, and Sheila, 14. The girls hover near the stove, stirring the scent of Mediterranean spices into the air, telling me that tonight's meal is pasta with sauce. Their brother, Andrew, is away at the University of British Columbia studying Engineering.

Sally, who I'd met a few days ago in Kamloops, invites me into the living room. She is a petite, pretty woman who laughs easily. Sally offers me

Megan, Sheila, Mark and Sally Nairn

a glass of wine.

"The girls are making supper tonight," she smiles as we sit opposite one another on comfy couches in their spacious living room.

I ask the origins of the room's focal point, an impressive fieldstone fireplace.

Mark tells me he and Sally picked the stones by hand and hired a local craftsman to construct it when they built the house in 1989. The mantle is a gorgeous antique that came with Mark's father's side of the family from Scotland. His great-grandfather Nairn emigrated from Edinburgh.

"That's my great-grandfather," he says, pointing proudly to a portrait above the dining room entrance. "He was the youngest person to graduate from the University of Winnipeg."

Mark was born in Vancouver and became an electrician by trade. He and Sally met and married in 1982, moving to Williams Lake to open an automotive electrical rebuilding business. Their life's dream was to own a ranch, so when Mark's uncle, Marcus Nairn, bought this place in the mid-1980s and took Mark on as a partner, it was like a wish had been granted.

Together, they bought more land, then Mark and Sally sold the business in town. They took over the ranch in 1989 after Uncle Marcus retired.

"We enjoy the family aspect of ranching," Sally says. "Mark was spending more and more hours at the shop; this way, we still work hard but are working together as a family."

Sally opens a large envelope and pulls out an 8x10 black and white photograph of their yard site as it once was. An expansive house, built by the late Fred Beecher sometime in the 1800s, sat almost exactly where their house sits now. Mr. Beecher died in that house in 1936 and was buried up on the hill that overlooks the yard. Just before the Nairns bought the ranch, the owner, Willena Hodgson, had the house ploughed to the ground.

"This is known as the old Beecher place," Mark says, adding the area lost a lot of history when the old house was destroyed. This also was a stopping house along the gold rush trail and, at one time, a lively social centre that kept current with the times. It had a store, liquor licence, dance hall and rooms to rent. Fortunately, Mark was able to salvage some artifacts, including the bar, an old safe and a few ledgers that were stored in the magnificent barn that still stands stoic in the yard. To this day, every time the creek behind the house floods, ancient treasures, including tiny opium bottles, cutlery and hand-pounded iron nails, wash up along the banks.

The loss of the house meant that when the Nairns moved here, there was no place to live. They brought in an 11 foot camper that became home while they framed in the house. Sally says they moved in when it was half built, finishing as they could afford it.

I envy Mark and Sally's decision to build exactly what they wanted. So many times, ranch people move straight from the ranch to the old folks home, having lived a whole life dissatisfied with their house. Every cattleman will tell you it's not the home that sells the ranch, but the outbuildings and the land.

This particular place is approximately 10,000 acres, with about half of that deeded. The place will run 450 cows, but following the drought years, numbers lower than that to avoid overtaxing the pastures. It was a combination of good management and luck that during the dry years just prior to BSE they sold off the bottom end of the herd. They shipped 100 problem cows—animals that were too old, not in calf, those with foot problems and too light in colour. The result was a younger, more uniform herd that has paid off during these tough economic times.

Mark markets his calves the same week every year. In 2003, he sold heifer calves that averaged $1.28 a pound, and tomorrow they'll be bringing the cows home with plans to sell calves this upcoming week. He guesses this year's price will be between 90 and 95 cents.

As President of the BCCA, Mark has contact with many producers, and describes B.C. ranchers as an eclectic group who range from quite simple to very sophisticated. He believes it is most unfortunate that producers have made decisions based on predictions, speculation and fear mongering.

Producers are always looking for ways to maximize profits, so many cattleman were hurt during the crisis because most of the advice they were given, especially during those uncertain first six months, proved wrong in retrospect. As unbelievable as it sounds, this was one of the few times that knowledge did not translate into power. The cattle producer who seems to have weathered BSE the best is the one who didn't deviate from his predictable pattern.

We talk a bit about the psychological effect on cattle men and women, and how when things go wrong, even though logically it makes no sense, producers often blame themselves.

"In some ways I think it's almost harder for the guys operating the third-generation ranches," he says. "There is an expectation there for them to be successful, to keep on, and that adds a lot of pressure."

Mark tells me about a bright spot on the B.C. landscape—the Overwaitea Food Group, a grocery chain that includes Save On and Coopers Foods. They are one of the province's larger independents that decided early in 2004 to move away from imported beef. They no longer carry the U.S.-based Certified Angus brand, switching to all Canadian, with a preference for local beef. This is a huge boost to Canadian beef sales since they will need approximately 13.2 million pounds of meat a year to meet their market demand.

Mark has met with officials at Overwaitea and says he's impressed with their commitment to the industry and the fact they want to work directly with producers. Representatives from Overwaitea say that when a cattle producer is in the store as part of a promotion, beef sales increase. Because of this, B.C. cattlemen are being encouraged to take part in local events, which explains why Sally and the girls are wearing T-shirts with an "eat beef" slogan tonight. They spent the afternoon at the grocery store in Williams Lake talking to shoppers. Like the Haywood-Farmers, the Nairns are a beef poster family.

The girls announce that supper is ready so we move to the dining room. They pass around a huge bowl of spaghetti with meat sauce, a salad and French bread. Sally refills my glass with wine. I'm served a generous piece of cake for dessert, and eventually, we return to the living room to sit by the fire.

Soon afterward, a long day is put to rest and I fall asleep enveloped in the warmth of western hospitality. I won't be the last traveller to find a warm meal and comfortable bed at the old Beecher place.

Morning arrives and I'm up before the sun.

Standing at the kitchen counter, I feel suddenly inspired and begin writing frantically in my notebook. My hand is guided across the page by nothing but a faint natural light coming in through the window.

Mark descends the stairs quietly and turns on the light. I'd been unable to find the switch inlaid into the thick log wall. We laugh at the image of me sitting in the dark as he disappears into the porch, returning a few minutes later with the old border collie on his heels. As part of their morning ritual, the dog sits by Mark's chair and waits while he makes coffee and breakfast.

I finish scribbling a few more notes until the coffee is ready and Mark sits down. As we talk, he stroke's the old dog's head.

"He should be outside, but—" he says quietly, taking a sip from his mug. "He's getting old, you know. Been a really good cattle dog for us, just like one of the family."

We finish breakfast, then leave at daybreak to tour the ranch. Mark takes me first up onto the hill at the highway that overlooks their yard. He waits patiently as I hold back until the sun is positioned just right, with hopes of capturing the beauty here on film. After I've snapped a few shots, we drive west along the highway to where the cows are on pasture. He opens a few gates, then bumps along the grass trail. He slows to a stop each time I lift my camera, enjoying the time spent looking at the cows.

During this drive, I see Mark's pragmatic side as we discuss the business of ranching.

He tells me that as much as he enjoys working with cattle, he likes being at home in his office crunching numbers as well.

"The ranch has to stand on its own," he says, adding that all his ranch decisions are based on solid financial information, not sentimentality.

He also believes that ranchers should be rewarded for their hard work and allowed to make a living raising cattle. He resents the fact that producers are forced to supplement their lifestyle with off-farm work. He understands this is a practical reality, especially for those who are just starting out or on small operations, but blames these circumstances on Canada's weak agriculture policy.

"Agriculture producers shouldn't be the one's subsidizing food production in this country," he says, adding that unlike some European people, Canadians have never starved. Overseas they spend between 20 and 30 percent of their income on food, but here we spend only 10 percent.

Mark has spent enough time working in urban settings to know how skewed the perception can be about rural life. Jokes about tractors having air conditioning or farmers driving new trucks reveal a disturbing belief that agriculture producers are second-class citizens who deserve only the bare necessities of life. Anything more is viewed as extravagance.

Because of uncertainty surrounding the closed border, a year of hard work and a job well done is no longer a guarantee that the bills will get paid. Mark is sincerely worried that today's young men won't be willing to make the same sacrifices as earlier generations. He sympathizes with the young producer just starting out and the fellows close to retirement. He predicts the cash crunch will have the hardest effect on them, each in its own way.

"While the young guy might not have enough equity to weather the losses, the older fellow has lost a portion of his retirement," he says. "And that's a real shame. How are we going to attract young people to agriculture when this happens?"

I wonder out loud how many cattle producers will continue sitting on the provincial boards, especially if criticism toward industry leadership increases.

"If producers value a man enough to elect him to represent them, then they need to stand back and trust him to make the right decisions afterward," he says, adding that he enjoys politics and finds time spent with the Association productive and rewarding. He has spent twenty days this month away from home and says he couldn't do it without the support of his family and the help of a hired man. He doesn't consider time spent representing the industry a sacrifice, because he's doing it by choice. Sometimes though, he grows frustrated.

"If there was an easy way out of this BSE situation, believe me, we would have done it," he says.

Checking his watch, Mark says it's time for us to go, and turns toward the house. As he drives into the yard, he stops by the barn. Sally is outside with one of the four horses they'll use today, all saddled and ready to go.

Mark has promised to show me the barn before I leave. I walk with him and stand back as he swings open the barn door, then we step into old fashioned looking yet immaculate livery. He relays a bit more history of the place, then shows me how the men who boarded their horses here scratched their names and the date of their stay with pencil or charcoal into the door jams and across the plank door of what was once the stable office. The earliest date he has found is 1917.

These permanent marks left behind by long-dead travellers raises the tiny hairs on my neck and arms. Mark smiles at my request to add my name, too. Neither of us needs to say a word about how short life really is—that worthwhile work is never really done and that when we are gone, a stranger will arrive to continue where we left off.

Within the hour, the Nairns are ready to begin the roundup. I leave before they go and watch in the rearview mirror as they lead their horses into the trailer that will take them to the edge of the pasture where Mark's horse waits patiently.

If history can be depended upon to predict the future, it tells us that someday, long after Mark and Sally are gone, this will be known as the Nairn Ranch. And then, who knows what after that.

Mark Nairn is right. Cattlemen shouldn't be subsidizing food production. They also should not be forced to work off the farm or diversify to make a living, especially if they have a large herd that occupies all their time.

Diversify is a buzzword from the 1980s. Staff from the agriculture departments promoted the concept right through the 1990s to farmers who were struggling to make a living. I believe this was introduced to give ideas to crop growers who work intense hours during the spring and fall, but have time on their hands during the winter months. Although grain, dairy and cattle farms are often referred to in collective terms, they are very different operations, and recommendations for one do not necessarily fit the other.

To expand into the purebred business or add value to calves by backgrounding or feeding to finish can make economic sense. But to truly diversify by investing in equipment to custom butcher, grow a niche crop like ginseng or raise exotic livestock is not for everyone. Not only do these ventures take financing, skill, and specialized facilities, but they suck up what's in shortest supply on the cattle farm—time.

A couple can do it when they are young, to generate enough income to build the herd to the point it is self-supporting, especially if dad is half-retired and willing to pick up the slack during busy times.

Many producers agree that time spent in diversification is financially less rewarding than off-farm work. Others say they have done well through farm diversified ventures, but agree it is not necessarily a fix for the cattleman, especially those whose land is not suitable for crops. Off-farm work is viewed as the means to an end for some, equalling one day owning your own ranch. Lines begin to blur though when a ranch that once supported a family no longer meets the cost of production and the cattleman or his wife is forced to take an off-farm job. The closed border has forced many producers over that line, and some predict that rising input costs will keep them there.

A cow and calf on pasture at the Nairn ranch

CHAPTER FIFTEEN

"I know what happiness is, for I have done good work."
- Robert Louis Stevenson

Sometime in the fall, the cows and calves are brought home. By then, the cows are pregnant again and their calves at foot are between six and eight months old, and weighing between 450 and 650 pounds.

On average, male calves are heavier than females, and purebred exotic cattle such as Charolais and Simmental weigh more than the British breeds, Hereford and Angus. Crossbred cattle weigh somewhere in between.

Depending on the size of the herd, at least a full day, usually two, will be spent working the cattle once they are home. All available hands usually help with this chore as there is a lot to do in a short period of time. Cattle become stressed whenever there is a break in their routine. Producers try to minimize the effects by working cattle quickly and efficiently.

Sometimes the fall roundup is the first contact the cattle have had with people since being turned out to pasture in the spring. Once the herd is home, the calves will bawl for their mothers. The one and two-year-old heifers, bred for the first time, are the most skittish because they are not sure what to expect. The cows, especially the older ones, remember routine from year to year and seem to understand that this day marks the beginning of a new season. Cows welcome familiar change.

The procedure varies between ranches, but usually the calves are first separated from the cows and put in different pens. The calves are then run through the chute where they are vaccinated and lost ear tags are replaced.

If the calves have horns, they are removed; horns are like weapons,

Bruce and Lonnie Rolph

dangerous to pen mates and the producers. The methods of dehorning vary between ranches, but however it is done, it's a difficult, unpleasant task for the producer and painful for the calf. Calves that are not dehorned will often bring a lower price at the auction mart. For all these reasons, many cattlemen have switched to hornless or "polled" bulls. Some breeders maintain that horned cattle have better genetics, but the trend in recent years leans toward polled cattle or making a serious effort to stunt horn growth while the calf is still young.

Male calves that won't be used as bulls are castrated shortly after birth to curb their desire to mount pen mates and sterilize them. Some producers do this by stretching a rubber ring over the neck of the scrotum that cuts off the blood supply so the sac will shrivel and fall off. Done when they are newborns, the procedure causes only mild discomfort for a few days. If the ring is not properly placed over both testicles, however, the calf will need to be surgically castrated in the fall.

The steer calves are then usually separated from the female calves. This is a convenient time for producers to choose replacement heifers—calves that the producer feels will make good cows. Records are usually checked and calves from good mothers that have grown well, have sturdy legs and straight backs are chosen as future breeding stock. They will somehow be set apart from the rest, either with a different coloured numbered ear tag or by physical placement in a different pen. Every producer has a system that takes into consideration size, weight, temperament, carcass type and colour.

Sometimes producers will ship their calves within a day of weaning, while others will feed a supplement ration or "background" their calves for a few months. When an animal is sold it must have a national identification ear tag, so at some point, tags are inserted or replaced if they've been lost.

It will take a few days for the calves to settle into their new environment. The quicker they get back on feed and water, the less chance they will become ill from stress.

The cows are also run through the chute. They are vaccinated and given a topical treatment of insecticide that prevents parasite infestations that will otherwise occur over the winter months. Some producers have the vet on hand to do pregnancy checks, will others will simply wait to see which cows begin to cycle again.

This is the time that the cattleman has to make practical, sometimes difficult decisions about his herd. Older cows that are not in calf, are in poor condition, have a bad hip or trouble walking should be shipped. It costs too much to keep an animal over the winter if she isn't going to calve in the spring, and it's just plain cruel to keep a cow that is suffering.

No one dwells on saying goodbye to a miserable old cow, especially if she brings home a calf that didn't gain well—a sign the cow is not milking enough. It is much harder when it's a cow that has given ten healthy calves in as many years. A good mother who is quiet when she calves is worth a lot. All cattlemen have cows like this—the ones that have earned our respect—and this adds burden to the decision to end her life. Some producers cannot bear to watch as the old girls are loaded onto the truck.

The decision is equally difficult but for different reasons when it is a fairly young cow with the same desirable traits. Experts say that if she is not in-calf by fall, it signals reproductive deficiencies, and from an economic standpoint she should be shipped. Ultimately, it is the producer's choice.

The culled cows are held back while the healthy, pregnant cows are either put in the winter feeding area or let back out to pasture where they'll stay until the watering holes freeze over, or the pasture is grazed down or covered with snow.

The fall-out from BSE added an extra consideration for producers because 50 percent of Canada's culled cows—more than 300,000 annually—were sent to the U.S. for processing. An oversupply of cows meant the price dropped dramatically. Many producers elected to keep older cows around that first year or put them down on the farm. A young, "open" cow is viewed in the marketplace the same as a older, barren cow, so producers had to decide whether to ship and receive around $100 for an otherwise healthy five-year-old, or feed her for another year, hoping she'll become pregnant the following summer. Opinions are divided amongst cattlemen over which is more profitable. The cost and availability of feed is usually a deciding factor.

In 1994, the industry developed a set of guidelines for feedlots and cow-calf operators on acceptable herd health practices called *Quality Starts Here*. The intent is to encourage consistent animal husbandry practices that would improve meat quality and give assurance that animals are handled in a way that ensures safe, healthy meat. It is expected that before long animal welfare issues will be integrated into the program.

Not all producers have embraced the idea of keeping on-farm food safety records, arguing on the basis that it takes too much time. Some are suspicious of all programs, especially those tied to government. For years, cow-calf producers have been promised that good on-farm practices will bring them a premium at the auction mart, but some would argue they haven't seen a reward for their diligence.

Because feedlot operators sell direct to the packing plants, they are accountable and docked accordingly if the animals they sell are not of the highest quality. Today's feedlot owner cannot afford sloppy practices and say they will pay more for calves from reputable ranches.

Cow-calf men who participate in these food safety programs do so because they believe it is in the best interest of the industry.

The weather is changeable today as clouds roll in around the time I pull into Williams Lake. I grab a coffee and check my directions. To get to Bruce and Lonnie Rolph's place near Horsefly, I need to take the turnoff at 150 Mile House.

Horsefly. The image of those vicious, biting, grey-green swarming flies causes a frightful assumption about how this place got its name.

The road north is rolling and lined with spruce and pine trees, interrupted by patches of hilly pasture where cows stand quietly grazing. The scenery here is lovely and the time it takes to get to the Rolph's yard goes by surprisingly quickly.

Like the Haywood-Farmer's house, the Rolphs live in a rustic log cabin.

Lonnie invites me into their cozy kitchen where Bruce sits at the end of the table. He has the look of a naturally slim man who has earned his muscles through years of hard work. Lonnie stands at the counter making coffee and sandwiches. She's tiny, blonde, and strikes me as shy.

I ask them to describe themselves, their operation and how they've managed these past 18 months.

Bruce tells me that getting into the cattle business was a lifelong dream, one that he and his father shared. His dad managed a purebred Hereford outfit for many years near Ashcroft, and Bruce worked with his dad there. In the early 1980s Bruce and his dad bought this property together and along with a small purebred herd of Herefords, started a commercial herd. While expanding the herd, Bruce worked at various jobs, including shoeing horses, hoof trimming cattle and sorting cattle at the B.C. Livestock Auction Mart in Williams Lake. In 1996 Bruce took over when his father retired. He still works at the auction mart and does some hoof trimming. Lonnie is the receptionist at the Forestry Department in Williams Lake.

In his mid-40s, Bruce finds there isn't quite enough time in a day anymore to get it all done. Even a hardworking man can't pull the same load he did when 25. Bruce looks forward to the end of the fall cattle run because after that, the auction mart will only need him one day a week instead of three or four.

"I like working there, though," he says. "It helps us keep on top of what's happening in the business."

While most of the producers I've spoken to here run Hereford cows, the Rolphs introduced Simmental blood into the herd a few years back and breed to Red Angus bulls. They used to start calving in February, but moved the dates back to March 1st.

"By fall, I saw no difference in the early born calves to the late," he says. The climate here dictates that they usually begin feeding in early December and continue until early May. They sell their calves at an exotic-cross sale in mid-October and say that, overall, their calf prices have been good.

We talk about the economy of scale, how it takes a certain number of cows to generate enough income to pay the overhead expense of running a ranch. Finding the balance is not always easy—more cows mean more income, but also additional work. Producers who expand too quickly can become mired in debt and a workload too heavy for one man. In order for Bruce to expand enough to afford a full-time hired man, he'd need at least another 100 cows. For now, he prefers a steady approach, saying he's been able to build the herd up to 150.

Thoughts that one of their children might join them on the ranch are still distant. Krista, Kara and Tyler all live and have jobs in the Williams Lake area.

"We wish we could do more for our kids," Lonnie says, adding that all their children are good with cattle and enjoy coming home to help out during busy times. A bright light in Lonnie and Bruce's life is their eight-year-old granddaughter, Chantelle. They look too young to be grandparents and I tell them so. Both smile. There are a lot of advantages to starting your family when you're young, and being youthful grandparents is one of them. Chantelle has made Lonnie's nest seem less empty, and she welcomes that.

I glance at the fridge that is plastered with photos and crayoned art. I recognize Chantelle immediately. She's wearing a thick jacket, bright rubber boots and has her grandmother's wide-eyed innocent smile.

"She just loves the cows and calves," Lonnie says, retrieving the photo and handing it to me for a better look.

I ask Bruce's opinion about how the industry leaders have handled the border crisis.

He tells me that he is president of the local Horsefly Cattlemen's Association, a group of approximately 25 members, and that both Mark

Nairn and Neil Jahnke have come out to their local meeting to address producer concerns.

"A lot of credit goes to guys like them," he says, describing most of the
industry decision makers he has met as down-to-earth cow men. "It's a real
tough time in the industry and it takes a lot of time and commitment to do
what they're doing."

Like many of the producers I've spoken to, the Rolphs would like to
see more markets develop so that Canadian producers aren't so reliant on
the U.S. They are frustrated that cows are bringing only 10 cents a pound,
while hamburger sells for $2 a pound—on sale.

"We can live with the calf prices," Bruce says, "but what we'd normally get for the cull cows and bulls, that was the gravy at the end of the
year."

Although each year is different, most producers with 150 cows will
cull 20 animals a year. The pre-BSE price would amount to around
$16,000. At only $150 a piece now, producers like the Rolphs have lost
more than $1,000 a month in income. Loss of the cull money is making it
harder to pay the bills.

So many producers are committed to the long haul, and Bruce and
Lonnie are no exception. They believe that now is not the time to make
radical changes to an operation. They hold onto the belief that if they can
continue working hard and keep their cow base healthy, they'll be well positioned when the border opens and the industry levels out. The key to staying healthy is to remain consistent.

The Rolphs put on their jackets and boots, then walk me outside.

"One of the toughest things I've seen through all of this is an older fellow who had a dispersal sale," Bruce begins, pressing on a cream-coloured
cowboy hat. "He can't keep up anymore and his son doesn't want the ranch.
He had about 240 cows at the sale and the real good ones were bringing
$500. The rest only $250." Bruce shakes his head. "Everyone was just too
hesitant to bid."

He concludes our visit by saying that all the cattlemen he knows are
waiting for something positive to happen before they start spending money
again. It's hurting the small communities but is a reality that won't change
until income levels return to normal.

There is a popular saying in the west, "If you don't like the weather,
wait five minutes and it'll change for you." Today is a day just like that.
When the sun comes out, it's too warm for a jacket. A few minutes later,

banks of dark clouds roll in, hurling hard snow pellets through the air.

I start driving back toward 150 Mile House and don't realize until much later that I've missed the first immediate turnoff less than two kilometres from the Rolph place. The road I'm on looks the same as all the others—snow-packed, hilly, winding and almost completely surrounded in trees that block out most of the sun.

I notice my car lagging up the hills, which seem steeper than I remember. I try to gather momentum on the way down before starting up again, but have to be cautious because the road is curvy and icy in places. I come around a slight bend and accelerate, but by the time I'm halfway up, I realize that the car isn't going to make it. Each time I accelerate, the back end begins to fishtail. When I let off the gas, I lose speed. Soon I find myself at a virtual standstill, three quarters of the way up a steep hill. There's nothing more I can do. My foot is on the brake, but I'm sliding backwards. The car stops when the right back wheel slips off the road into a narrow ditch along the mountainside. I look back in time to see a three-quarter-ton truck barrel past me. It's an older, rough-looking vehicle with a winch mounted on the front. I make quick eye contact with the young male driver, expecting he'll come back to help.

I open the car door and get out to see I'm not stuck too badly. I wait almost five minutes before realizing that the young man isn't coming back. This rattles me, and suddenly I'm not sure what to do. That truck is the first vehicle I've seen since leaving the Rolph's house. On the way in, I don't remember meeting anyone at all.

I glance at my watch. I've been so preoccupied writing Bruce and Lonnie's story in my head that I've lost track of time. How far have I come? Likely too many miles to make it all the way back to their place on foot, but I remember passing a few driveways between here and there. I can easily walk four miles in an hour, so I lock the car and decide to start out, back in the direction I came.

It's late afternoon and there are places along this mountain that are quite dimly lit. My heart is pounding a bit because I'm afraid of the dark.

If I were on a hike with my husband, all the strange noises I'm hearing would add to the ambiance of being in the woods, but now the call of birds and snapping twigs sound like ominous threats.

Silly, I know, but I'm not what you'd call a wilderness gal.

I sure hope the first place I come to doesn't have a big dog, because if it does, I'll have to keep walking.

If properly motivated, I can run like hell. Not like the women in slasher films who always wear high heels and fall down. No sirree, I've got my flats on.

All this downhill walking means my shins will be sore tomorrow.

That young man who left me here deserves a kick in the ass.

I'm saying all this out loud, and singing, too, hoping the sound of my own voice will make me feel less afraid. I'm not a very good singer.

Forty-five minutes later, a jeep appears around the corner coming toward me. The man slows, and rolls down his window. He stops the car so I can explain my predicament. He's a retired gentleman wearing camouflage clothing. As I climb into the passenger seat, he tells me his name is Bruce Haines and that he's from Williams Lake. My dad's name is Bruce, too. I feel rescued.

Bruce drives back to where the car sits and we retrieve two pair of chains from the trunk of my car. I knew such things existed, but as a flatlander, had never seen a pair until now. Just as Bruce is attaching one to the front passenger tire, I look up to see another vehicle pass by us up the hill. It doesn't even cross my mind that they'll come back, so I'm startled a bit when a man and his teenaged son suddenly appear, walking down the hill, offering help.

I'm sure Bruce is relieved that maybe now I'll stop chattering his ear off.

"You're cattle people, aren't you?" I say to the newcomers. The man, Ernie Fairburn, looks surprised by my proclamation. He introduces his son, Dan. As it turns out, they have a ranch not too far from here.

I say that ranch people would never leave someone stranded. We are better raised than that.

"Imagine your mother standing here," I say to Dan as his father starts working on the back tire. "You'd never leave your mother alone alongside a road like this, would you?" My words have a "you better not" tone to them.

"No, I wouldn't," he says, suppressing a smile.

"Well that's good," I say quickly. "My boy wouldn't either."

I'm embarrassing my son and he isn't even here.

It's not long before Bruce and Ernie have the car back on the road. Bruce explains I missed my turnoff and offers to follow me back. I thank him, but say no, that I'll be all right.

Once I'm back on the road and my nerves have settled down, my thoughts go back to the Rolphs and how much they remind me of other cattle people I know.

Everyone in the industry understands how difficult it is to get into the cattle business. As each decade passes it's becoming virtually impossible, unless a person takes over from a family member or has a huge wad of cash. And while it is the producer with 1,000 cows who is envied, it's operators like the Rolphs who earn the most respect. To build a cattle operation from scratch today means more hard work and sacrifice than most people are willing to give. You can't help but admire that brand of tenacity.

Even the producer running a third generation ranch understands this, because what the Rolphs have done mirrors what their father or grandfather did decades before. Regardless of what circumstance brings cattle men and women to the land, they all identify with that desire.

The more I travel and talk with producers the more I understand that this issue is about the need to eat. It's the cost of feeding cattle that makes or breaks a ranch or feedlot, and it's the ability to feed people that keeps us in business. Both have to be done cheaply, because if we can't do it, somebody else will.

Initially when the export borders closed, an oversupply of meat was created, but retail beef prices remained at pre-BSE levels. This outraged cattlemen who were being paid less for their cattle, but did not see any savings passed on to the consumer.

Early on, there were some savings to be had on the poorer cuts of meat, including hamburger—items that normally would have been shipped to the U.S. That happened because packers and retailers needed a supply of prime cuts, so they were trying to free-up freezer space by offering the poor cuts at a discounted price.

Because there was an oversupply of live cattle, not meat, consumers did not see a reduction in prices at the grocery store. Once the border opened to boxed beef, the high quality cuts were being shipped to the States, so the price was set by that demand. If people stop eating beef because of price, the cost will not reduce. Retailers will simply buy less from the wholesaler, who in turn buys less from the packer, who needs fewer fat cattle. The feedlot operator needs to turn the cattle over in his lot to pay bills—so sometimes he is forced to sell for less. No profits for him means he cannot buy calves at a price that meets the rancher's cost of production.

Boycotting the large retailer will only hurt the feedlot operator and rancher—the very people consumers are trying to support. Buying from grocery stores, restaurants and chains that sell Canadian beef, buying cuts from the local butcher, sides of beef or hamburger directly from producers or a meat shop are ways to keep consumption up and pressure on the links leading back to the grassroots.

CHAPTER SIXTEEN

Ranch improvements always take precedence over
household needs. When Guy and Hilde Rose first took over the
Quilchena Ranch, it seemed to Hilde that whenever she
needed something for the house, like a new stove,
Guy needed something for the ranch.
Gerard Guichon's wife, Ruth, sympathized with Hilde.
"I thought I was marrying Gerard," she told her.
"It took me a while to realize I had married the ranch."
— taken from, *Ranchland: British Columbia's Cattle Country*

The next morning when I wake up, it is snowing hazardly hard. Admitting I am not a good mountain driver, I postpone plans to travel the highway today. As it turns out, rancher Judy Guichon is coming to Kamloops this afternoon, so we make arrangements to meet at a nearby restaurant.

I sit quietly at the kitchen table, watching as my host family clambers out the door to work or school. The door closes and I suddenly find myself alone. And inspired.

Craving a normal day, I decide to make supper. Margaret has one of my favourite spices on hand, a Greek combination from Victorian Epicure. After more than 20 years of preparing the same meals over and over, a friend introduced me to these spices that helped inject flavour into my recipes and variety to meals.

I search Margaret's cupboards, jotting down what I need, then hurry off to the grocery store. We'll have Greek chicken (a treat, since I eat so much beef) with roasted baby potatoes, Caesar salad and asparagus. It will

Judy Guichon

be delicious.

Within a few hours, I have everything prepared and the kitchen tidied. I've set the table using placemats made from the children's laminated artwork. Colourful drawings on construction paper, signed at the corner in awkward child's hand.

With everything ready, I chuckle to myself, remembering how when we were both living in Manitoba and working full-time, Margaret and I would joke how nice it would be to have a wife. How heavenly it would be to come home to a clean house and have supper ready after a long day in the office.

I glance at my watch, humming to myself that it is time to meet Judy. I slide into my shoes and jacket, then slip out the door.

It's a dreary, wet day in a place of traffic noise and cement, but my heart is buoyed as if it were spring. I hurry to the restaurant, smiling, like I've just received a piece of fabulous news.

I sit in a booth near the back where it is quiet and sip a cup of coffee while I wait, giving me time to think. Thoughts of my home and family cause feelings of homesickness to creep up. The longer I'm away, the clearer the realization becomes that in spite of my need to write, I identify strongly with my role as ranch wife.

I've read that the attitude we have when approaching tasks, even the small and mundane, are affected by our feelings that remain long after we're gone. Air is freshest when filled with laughter. Food tastes better if prepared by loving hands; that's what makes grandma's meals so special.

Let me cook for you, means more than just preparing a meal.

The door opens and Judy steps in, shaking the wet snow from her salt and pepper hair. She wears it straight, near shoulder length. The thick woollen sweater pulled over a blue turtleneck looks homemade.

Judy smiles when she sees me and although we've never met we recognize one another immediately.

Judy sits across from me, orders a coffee and we begin talking about the history of the Guichon ranch.

"They came for gold and stayed for the grass," Judy says, describing how her husband's great grandfather, Joseph Guichon, came from France in the 1860s and settled in the Nicola Valley just south of Kamloops. At one point, the Guichons ran the largest ranch in the province with 4,000 head of cattle, 500 horses and 30,000 acres of deeded land. Like many ranching entrepreneurs of the day, the Guichons were food suppliers, hoteliers, machinery dealers and beef processors. Fortunes were won and lost over the next hundred years as they were susceptible, just like everyone else, to the ebb and flow of the North American cattle cycle.

Joseph and his wife had seven children, and like many large families, squabbles and power struggles divided the Guichon partnerships. Siblings went their separate ways. Joseph's oldest son Lawrence was best known for his efforts to restore the valley's native grasslands, which had suffered great-ly from overgrazing, drought and grasshoppers. He also was granted an honorary PhD in Agriculture from the University of British Columbia. Lawrence's son Gerard was a leader in grass management and served on provincial and national cattle organizations. He was named to The Order of Canada and inducted into the Cattleman's Hall of Fame in Billings, Montana.

Judy was raised on a mixed farm not too far from the Montreal Forum in Quebec. In 1969, she went on a cross-Canada tour with friends and ended up travelling the Alaska Highway. With no better place in mind, she took a job in Whitehorse, and that's where she met Laurie Guichon. Laurie was a commercial pilot who made regular trips to Inuvik. They married in 1971, moved home to the ranch where Laurie grew up, and began working with his parents, Gerard and Ruth.

"We moved into the old cookhouse and I had to learn to cook in a big hurry," she laughs, adding that meals needed to be made for a large work crew during haying season.

Laurie inherited a love of cattle and the land from his father and grandfather. In 1979 he and Judy took over the ranch when his parents retired. Then in 1986, they attended a seminar on Holistic Resource Management that changed their way of operating forever.

"It made so much sense," she says, explaining that much of the anxi-ety in ranch life comes from the constant need to make decisions. Holistic management gives producers a process that makes decision-making easy. It starts with developing a three-part written plan that spells out what you hope to achieve. Quality of life, effectively managing your resource base and what you hope to leave behind for future generations become the pri-orities.

Once the Guichons spelled out their holistic goal, the process of deciding how to get there began. One very important aspect of holistic management is understanding that a problem should be viewed in two parts—cause and effect. Producers can often see the effect, but don't always understand the cause. To continue reacting to the effect instead of getting to the root of the problem is both costly and frustrating, and ultimately can cause producers to begin veering away from their goal. This has a negative affect on life quality.

This is a wonderful concept that many producers practise instinctive-ly, but Judy says there is value in writing it down. She says that while cop-ing with the fallout from BSE is hard, it's not the most difficult challenge she's faced.

In 1999, Laurie was killed in a highway motorcycle accident while driving home from Kamloops. He was only 55 years old.

Judy describes him as a careful and proficient driver, guessing he must have swerved to avoid hitting something on the road.

Laurie's death was a terrible blow to the family and it left Judy with four teenagers to raise and a ranch to run. For a while she was angry at his memory for leaving her to deal with it all. At first, living and making impor-tant decisions alone was really rough. She was lonely and didn't think she'd manage.

Although we seldom speak of it, a ranch wife wonders how she would manage if her husband was suddenly taken by illness or accident. Some of us have had this difficult discussion with our spouse, asking him what he'd want us to do, what we'd need to do to keep the ranch going. For Judy, the holistic ranching philosophy took the place of this discussion. Since this was something they developed together, she already understood their com-mon goals and what they were working toward.

Gradually, with the help of a handful of kindly neighbours and long-time ranch hand Jim, Judy found her footing.

"I've always loved cows, so the decision to stay was not difficult," she says. "I needed a base for the kids. Their roots had to stay deep in this soil."

Laurie had planned well, paying off the mortgage during the good years, so Judy was left in decent financial shape. Because they had co-man-aged the ranch, she knew what had to be done, but her day-to-day activi-ties shifted from bookkeeper and cook to a more hands-on, outdoor role. Laurie was organized and an excellent record keeper; everything she need-ed to learn was already down on paper.

Since assuming her new role, Judy has discovered a few things. The first is that not all men can take direction from a woman, so some of their crew left. On a more positive note, she was pleased to learn that their son Michael is a good stockman and became part of the crew.

The most difficult challenge she faced in the years following Laurie's death was trying to take over his commitments on various boards and con-servation groups.

"I tried to fill his shoes, but I don't think I ever really did," she says, smiling softly. "Those were rather large shoes to fill."

In 2001, the Laurie Guichon Memorial Grasslands Interpretive Site was established, 11 kilometres southeast of Merritt. The site was developed by the Nicola Watershed Community Round Table to educate residents and visitors about the significance of the interior grasslands. It is a wonderful tribute to her husband and something that makes Judy proud.

The cattle herd they graze on these lands is a Hereford base cow and they've introduced some of the exotic bloodlines by using Beef Booster bulls. Judy is thinking about reintroducing more of the lineback Hereford cows instead of keeping back her own heifers as replacements. She says the land is pretty tough range, so if they want the cows to bring in a heavy calf in the fall, the herd has to have good feet and be all-around good mothers. The goal is to graze 365 days a year with the exception of drought years. Presently they feed the cow herd only 15 to 20 days.

"Laurie always said, 'We are harvesting sunshine.' It's the most renewable resource there is and the cow is the tool we're using to do it.'"

Judy likes the idea of adding value to her calf crop by backgrounding the heifers and top-end steers. Like many others who finish their cattle, she got caught after the border closed, putting a lot of feed into animals that didn't bring much money in the end. She isn't panicking over the losses, though.

"We had a plan but it didn't work, so we changed it," she says.

I ask how she sees the industry in the future, how it will evolve.

Judy says that a remodelling of Canada's beef industry was long overdue. She believes that increasing the ability to process our own cattle is a positive step. She also thinks that health concerns over the food we eat will continue, and even increase, as agriculture intensifies and people become more mobile. Travel is a huge issue today as more people venture to other parts of the world. There is a very real possibility that travellers could bring back an organism that jeopardizes animal health, and in turn export markets.

But Judy's gravest concern lies not in the marketing of beef. Work on various conservation councils has made her keenly aware of the risk urban sprawl poses to waterways and grasslands in B.C. She worries that the financial stress of the closed border will force teetering producers out of business and some will be forced to sell off land in an effort to survive.

"The loss of agricultural land to urbanization is very real and it is a much tougher hurdle to overcome than the border," she says. Judy believes that where she lives in B.C. is one of the most efficient places to raise beef in the country, but the land base is shrinking and that is driving up the cost of production.

"Consuming is not the reason for being," she says, explaining that people are earning and spending more but feeling less and less satisfied. She says there is no ritual around food anymore, and that people today do not eat roast beef and homemade apple pie like they used to. There is a tremendous hunger for people to reconnect with the land and they are shopping in search of it. The urbanization of rural areas is raising the monetary value of land, but devaluing it at the most basic level. There is no meaning or purpose to it anymore, not once Grandpa's farm is gone.

I'm made lightheaded by her comments. This makes so much sense.

It's the land, I tell her in a fit of inspiration. It's the attachment to the land.

"Exactly," she replies.

The following afternoon I fly back to Calgary. I think about B.C. and all the producers I met, how much I learned. I was surprised that ranchers there are struggling like the rest of us.

As the plane touches down, I decide that given the opportunity to trade places with any of the people I've interviewed, my choice would be to stay right where I am. As David Haywood-Farmer said, "What ties a place to your heart is the fact that it's home."

With this in mind, I decide to leave Alberta earlier than planned. The next morning I get up, pack the car, and am on the road for home by 6:00 a.m. The drive through takes a little more than 11 hours.

November 18, 2004

Two weeks have passed. I find myself once again on a plane, this time bound for Hamilton, Ontario. I'll spend a few days visiting with family, then travel by car northwest into Ontario's most concentrated cattle region.

Christmas will soon be upon us. It makes me think of last year and the Christmas present that never came.

December 23, 2003, was a day that will be remembered by some cattle producers as even more devastating than the day BSE was discovered. Many had changed their marketing plans and a lot of cattle were on hold, expecting the border to open in the new year.

Some were Christmas shopping and others were at home just finishing off the evening chores when the news hit that there was a case of BSE discovered in a six-year-old dairy cow in Washington State. Telephones started ringing as television sets were flipped on, radio volumes adjusted.

The immediate reaction at the grassroots level was—good. Now they know how we feel. The border will open soon because they have BSE, too.

That optimism wasn't felt by industry leaders and politicians. Many were on their way home to spend Christmas with their families. Some immediately turned around, switched back on the office lights, or scheduled flights back to Calgary and Ottawa.

Live cattle prices plummeted. Rumblings began that Canada might somehow be responsible for the outbreak. Over the next few days, it was proven true that the cow had come from Canada. Cattlemen shook their heads in disbelief. All indications were that the border was set to open by early February, but it was soon apparent there was no hope of that now.

Cattlemen had come so incredibly close. Was this a coincidence? The conspiracy theories sprouted legs and began running. One thought was that the animal was in fact American but traced to Canada in a plot to keep the border closed. Another was that rather than take responsibility for their own home-grown case, officials manipulated DNA tests so that Canada would be blamed. These theories were proven untrue as the animal was traced back to a reputable herd in Alberta.

Within hours, many U.S. trading partners, including Japan, closed their borders to American beef. U.S. exports to Japan alone the year before totalled $842 million.

All of this prompted the U.S. to step up its BSE precautionary measures. Specified risk materials were removed from animals over 30 months of age. Meat from cattle tested for BSE was now being held until tests proved negative. Cattle blood and cow brains were no longer legal for use in dietary supplements and all non-ambulatory cattle were banned from the food chain. The case also gave the U.S. reason to take a harder look at the idea of implementing a national identification system. Unlike the case in Canada, meat from the infected U.S. animal did make it into the food chain.

It wasn't a very happy new year in cattle country—on either side of the border.

What the second home-grown Canadian case did was give the group R-CALF time and ammunition to prepare a plausible defence that their border should stay closed to Canadian cattle permanently. Up until then, they'd been struggling for support, but now under the guise of food safety and herd health, they began preparing briefs to support their argument.

On this side of the border, the bargaining began. Bob Speller began consulting with the industry to step up feed and surveillance measures, and enhance identification, tracking and tracing. There would be more testing for BSE on high-risk animals. The federal government promised a total of $92.1 million over the next five years to help cover partial costs of ramping up the current precautions. The government also stepped up efforts to convince Asian countries to open their markets by appointing respected veterinarian Norm Williw to Tokyo to act as a technical expert on BSE.

Surprisingly, the U.S. still allowed cattle brains and spinal material in livestock feed and pet food, so when the Canadians began pushing for harmonized North American protocols regarding feed bans, testing and animal traceback, the American reaction was lukewarm.

Over the past five years, 7.3 million live cattle moved across the border, with 6.3 million exported from Canada and 1 million coming in from the U.S. Up until the border closed there was significant two-way trade in animal feed, so the widespread belief was that if Canada has BSE, so did the U.S.

In their first face-to-face meeting, Prime Minister Martin asked President Bush to re-open the border. While Canadian producers and industry officials were touting the "North American Market," a number of U.S. spokespeople pointed their finger at Canada when backed into a corner over BSE. This left some Canadian officials red-faced and feeling mislead.

Dissension in Alberta resulted in the creation of the Alberta Beef Industry Council, which represents feedlot owners, auctioneers, cattle buyers and ranchers. Tired of waiting for results, the Alberta Cattle Feeders Association met with Shirley McClellan to propose an expansion of the packing and processing industry.

Financial institutions were growing nervous, demanding improved debt-to-equity ratios from the feedlots before extending more credit. Some operators decided not to replace the cattle that would leave their lots in the spring.

The Alberta Treasury Branch forecasted it would lose $29.4 million because of BSE. Minister Speller sat down with lenders to convince them that the government would not bail on the industry.

The large packing companies were pressured by government to supply financial records as part of an investigation into the accusation by MPs that the packers took advantage of taxpayers by reducing cattle prices, knowing the difference would be made up by the government programs. The packers argued that they should not be required to make such information public.

Rumours began circulating that the border could open at the end of

June 2004, following the announcement of a reopening of the U.S. comment period. There was even talk that meat from animals over 30 months would be allowed. Politicians in Alberta were so optimistic this time that there was nothing included in the provincial budget regarding BSE aid for producers.

By now, it appeared that grassroots U.S.A., particularly in Montana, wanted to keep the border closed while industry groups and government favoured open trade. Americans were buying up lightweight Canadian calves and placing them in Canadian feedlots due to low numbers of young cattle in their country, anticipating this could lead to a shortage of fat cattle in early 2005.

On April 18, the U.S. breached protocol and lifted the remaining import restrictions on younger animals, resulting in the import of bone-in meat into the U.S. This caused a huge furor across the line, giving R-CALF legal grounds to launch court action against the USDA, saying their negligence needlessly endangered the U.S. beef and meat industry and consumers by allowing in banned products.

Past President of the CCA, Neil Jahnke, said, "I was ready to bet the ranch that the border was going to open in June. If it hadn't been for that mistake by the USDA, I think it would have."

The glitch meant that it would take another six months to finish writing the final rule. R-CALF won the lawsuit and Canadian packers lost the right to segregated kills. Lakeside Packers stopped processing cattle over 30 months, fearing they'd lose the right to export.

The conspiracy theory? That someone within the USDA made the error intentionally to give R-CALF a leg up.

CHAPTER SEVENTEEN

*"Many of you will remember where you were when JFK was
shot and when the first man landed on the moon. Add to that
the recent crisis because I'll never forget where I was
the moment we learned BSE had been found in Canada."*
— Ron Wooddisse, cow-calf producer, Palmerston, Ontario

By the one-year anniversary of BSE it was believed that the infected
cow cost the industry more than $2 billion. More than half the rural munic-
ipalities in Alberta were facing economic disaster.

The Manitoba Cattle Producers Association broke rank from the
CCA on the issue of specified risk materials, and asked that SRMs be
removed from all animal feed. Producers reacted with surprise that the government still allowed these materials to be fed to pigs and chickens.

A rally in downtown Winnipeg during the World Meat Congress
gathering attracted hundreds of producers. Argentinean agriculture minister Javier Bernardo Usabiaga Arroyo was quoted as saying that all countries,
including Canada, need to begin treating others fairly with respect to disease outbreaks. Argentine beef was banned from Canada after foot-and-
mouth was discovered there.

On a positive note, auctioneer Dan Skeels of Rimby, Alberta, won the
World Livestock Auctioneer Championship. This took place in Billings,
Montana, right in the heart of R-CALF country.

During the media interview portion of the competition, Skeels was
asked how he'd respond to media questions over an issue like BSE. Having
lived the nightmare for nearly a year, Skeels easily outtalked his competitors. The last time a Canadian won was in 1976, when Steve Liptay of

Bowmanville, Ontario, took the title.

On June 28, the Liberals formed a minority government, with the Conservatives and leader Stephen Harper sitting as the official opposition. Cattle producers complained that agriculture was barely mentioned during the election. They shook their heads at the idea of baptizing yet another agriculture minister as Bob Speller loses his seat to Diane Finley.

Two more suspected cases of BSE in the U.S. were confirmed negative once they were submitted to the Gold Standard Test. By then, the cattle herd in Canada had grown to 14.7 million. Producers were thrown into despair following predictions that the border wouldn't open until after the U.S. Presidential election in the fall. June 2004 was described as the lowest emotional point of the entire crisis. Rallies were attracting less people and the issue was no longer making news. With another haying season upon them, producers relate how this felt to playing hockey. It is the end of the first period and the score is already lopsided. You know you're going to lose. How do you find enough heart to finish the game?

Ontario is Canada's largest and most diverse agricultural province.

Everything here is astonishingly close. To be in a shopping mall one minute and then see the conveniences of urban life suddenly drop away, is a marvel for those of us in the west who must travel 50 kilometres for a container of milk.

This is a place with more brick than wood and where the roads leading to many farms are paved. Nestled in the security of North America's Great Lakes, farmland in this region grows lush and producers speak of drainage rather than drought. The climate is moderate, often muggy, but seldom searing hot. The further north you travel, the clearer the skies become. This is where I grew up.

Borrowing my brother's car, I decide to retrace the route I drove to work before I moved to Manitoba. One of my last memories of working at Chipman Inc. was being pulled aside by my supervisor just weeks before my wedding. Because Mark and I worked for the same company, she was acquainted with him. She asked in a very serious voice if I knew what I was doing. She warned that "he was from the country and not materialistic at all." It took me a few days to realize she thought that was a bad thing.

I know the Niagara escarpment well. That approximate five-mile width that stretches from Hamilton to Niagara Falls has some of the best delicate fruit land in the country. Like the Okanagan Valley in B.C., the land is rich in nutrients and the area is sheltered from frost by mountain along one side, lake on the other.

When I was a girl, the worst predators fruit farmers saw were kids like me. We'd hide our bikes in the ditch and climb into the trees closest to the road and eat ourselves sick on what were the juiciest peaches and most luscious cherries in the world. The whole time doing it I knew it was wrong, but couldn't resist. I justify this now by saying tastes acquired in childhood are an investment in the fruit farmer's future. With my tree climbing days long over, I gladly pay whatever the cost for Canadian fruit in season.

Unfortunately, it took less than twenty years for those orchards and vineyards to be covered forever in pavement and housing developments. I'm sure there were people like Judy Guichon who tried to stop it. And you know what they say about history repeating itself.

I'm proud to say that my parents didn't contribute to this debauchery. Turning off the highway onto the winding road that leads up the escarpment, I decide to drive by the old house. We lived just a few miles away, on top of the hill on an acreage lot, land that was mostly rocks and clay. Trees grew to a decent height, but you needed strong arms, a rototiller and loads of topsoil to get anywhere with that dirt. Living up here was like being on the other side of the tracks, so to speak. Urban sprawl still has not sprawled hardly at all, suggesting that things here haven't changed much since I was a girl.

One thing I miss about living here is how beautiful southern Ontario is in the fall. The sights and smells literally do take your breath away—especially the tangy aroma of ketchup being made at the E.D. Smith factory in Fruitland. The smell takes me back to the days of the school bus, paper bag lunches, pastel Hilroy scribblers and new running shoes.

My heart swells a bit at the familiar sights as I follow the meandering highway toward Hagarsville. Stately wide-trunked maple, ash and beech trees line the roads; in places, their limbs marry together like hands, creating an arbour over the narrow road. The sun reflects around the buildings and through the willows that if left to grow, reach elephantine proportions. The occasional autumn-painted leaf is caught in a wind gust and dances to the ground, joining one of the many swirling troups that waltz across the yards and driveways.

This pastoral scene reminds me why my ancestors, Pennsylvania farmers, settled here when they came from the U.S. in the early 1800s. Dad's forebears grew roots on the farms near Waterford; Mom's great-grandparents and their children were tobacco growers at Delhi. The fertile land here sustains all types of edible crops. This is a place of giant pumpkins and twelve-foot-high corn.

This morning's interview is with Bob Speller. He was the MP for Haldimand-Norfolk and named Federal Agriculture Minister soon after Paul Martin became Prime Minister in December 2003. I believe the BSE issue cost Bob his seat in the June 28, 2004, election.

I follow directions to a handsome, brick, Victorian-style home on a country road between Hagarsville and Waterford. Bob is at the door when I arrive. It is Sunday and his wife, Joan, and their two young children are on their way to a community event.

Bob shakes my hand and invites me inside.

We sit across from one another on wingback chairs in a spacious living room in front of a cold fireplace. This is an elegant old house, but not grandiose. The floors are hardwood, the furniture antique. The door frames push up toward high plastered ceilings. Knobs on the solid wood doors are positioned noticeably low.

I ask if the house is haunted and Bob laughs. He tells me that if there is a ghost bumping around in here, they have never met.

I know very little about this former minister. He was my dad's MP and during the election, Dad, who has been following the cattle issue, wanted to know the opinion from the west before casting his vote. Producers I'd spoken to were pleased with Bob, regardless of the way they voted. Expecting that the Liberals would win again, I hoped he'd stay on as Agriculture Minister. Like everything else cattlemen have hoped for since May 20, I didn't get my wish.

BSE seems to have vexed Bob near as much as it bedevilled us. I almost feel like we cursed him and tell him so.

This time he doesn't laugh.

I ask what year Bob was first elected as an MP.

Bob tells me that he's always enjoyed politics and that after receiving a well-rounded education, he began work as an intern in Ottawa. He decided to run as an MP in his home riding and was elected in 1988 during a Tory majority, defeating a Conservative member who'd held the seat for ten years. Because Bob grew up in Hagarsville, he had a solid grasp of agricultural issues and understood farmers. He says he relates much better to small-town western Canada than he does to downtown Toronto.

He says that farmers might be surprised to learn that in many ways, the producers in his riding are similar to those in Saskatchewan. Both places have a primary industry. Here, it's tobacco. He says it's tough being dependent on one product that is being challenged, and sees a lot of similarities between questions asked by producers here and wheat growers in the west.

Bob's time in government was spent mostly on ag issues, where he chaired the rural caucus in the early 1990s and the ag committee in 1993. He learned a great deal from Ralph Ferguson, a man he calls "the best agriculture minister we've ever had."

Bob says he heard rumours after becoming minister that he was an organic farmer.

I tell him we thought he grew fruit.

"I know farmers well enough to know they would rather have a farmer as minister, but not necessarily an organic one," he chuckles, raising his eyebrows.

On December 23, 2003, Bob was the newly appointed agriculture minister. He had just flown back from meeting with the Saskatchewan government about the Agriculture Policy Framework. He was on the highway driving home when he received the call telling him that BSE had been discovered in the U.S. and that the cow might have come from Canada. He turned the car around and boarded a plane to Ottawa. Bob barely made it home by Christmas and spent the rest of the holiday season on the phone with Ann Veneman, the U.S. Agriculture Secretary.

One of his first public appearances in the west came in early January 2004. He was invited to speak at Manitoba's Ag days at Brandon's Keystone Centre. Bob describes how he was led through a throng of cowboy hats and ball caps into the amphitheatre. He was at ground level, looking out into rows of seats that escalated up, nearly surrounding him.

"It seemed like there were a thousand people in there," he jokes. "I didn't know if I'd get out alive."

I laugh, remembering how red his cheeks had been and his serious expression. Mark and I were there, part of the standing-room-only crowd just inside the door. Bob received warm applause after his speech and he spent the next few hours talking with producers.

Being a Liberal from southern Ontario, he's not someone you'd expect would get along well in a western agricultural crowd. And yet the reception toward him was quite good. Part of the reason for this was he seemed more accessible than Vanclief. Also, most producers had set aside their political beliefs, willing to accept help wherever offered.

Some argue that Bob didn't do much for cattlemen, while others say that he didn't have enough time. One thing he did do, though, was thrust himself into the heart of the issue. He made numerous trips into cattle country to meet with producers, even after the election call—a time when he should have been in his home riding working on the campaign. It appeared that Bob made more trips to the prairies in six months than

Vanclief did in the six years he was ag minister.

Conservative Diane Finley was vying for the seat and she ran a solid campaign. Her diligence, combined with the time Bob spent on BSE—a largely western issue—might have cost him votes. Bob said there were a number of serious agriculture issues across the country at the time and that he spent time on those as well, but physically he couldn't be everywhere.

"The BSE crisis was so widespread and ongoing and spirits were really down, especially in June," he says. "I felt it was important to get out there and be visible."

Bob praises the cattle industry, saying he has seen very good leadership throughout the crisis. At the government level, he says that the majority of the politicians approached the issue in a non-partisan way and that there was very little finger pointing. There was a lot of support around the table for financial support to cattlemen, even before the Liberals knew they had a large surplus.

"This issue was very important to the Prime Minister and not just to gain favour in the west," Bob says. "Cattlemen got money at the expense of a lot of other people and I didn't hear the other MPs complain once."

Bob feels bad about the times that he and other government members announced projected dates that the border would open. He says that at the time, all indications were that it would open, but then something would go wrong.

"It never was our intention to give false hope," he says.

I tell him that for the industry as a whole, it was a good thing they did.

He gives me a curious look.

If they hadn't given some hope, especially in that first year, feedlot operators may not have bought calves, or if they did, would have paid prices way below the rancher's cost of production. By giving everyone hope and then continuing to support the majority of feedlots with programs, a healthy percentage of ranchers got prices for their calves that they can live with.

I ask Bob if negotiations with the U.S. suffered because of the turnover we've seen in agriculture ministers.

He says that he hopes not, adding that when he was named to the chair, he was the Parliamentary Secretary of Trade, so he understood the issues going into it. Rather than offering thoughts on his successor, he asks my opinion about the work Andy Mitchell has done.

I tell him the new Minister has not made a strong impression either way.

I ask Bob if he plans to run in the next election.

He says that he is considering it, but now he's busy as President of St. Joseph's Print Solutions, a large Canadian printing company. He wishes he could continue lobbying on agricultural issues, but under regulations governing the conflict of interest act, he can't for two years.

"And that's very frustrating because I've been doing so for 16 years and always had that voice," he says. He really enjoyed his short stint as Ag Minister, but was disappointed at times to hear producers in the west say that people in central Canada don't care what happens in the west.

"That's not true. We do care and did what we could for all groups," he says. "And not because it was Ontario, or Saskatchewan, or P.E.I.—but because it was the right thing to do."

There is no question that Bob Speller is a savvy politician. He is intelligent, articulate, and years spent in the political arena have taught him what to say, the topics to avoid.

But what the desperation surrounding BSE has taught cattle producers is how to read a face. A politician can say whatever he wants, promise whatever sounds right, criticize the government to gain favour or votes. But whether or not he really cares is written all over his face.

Financial compensation offered to producers came in four waves during that first year. The BSE Recovery Program was announced in June 2003, offering $520 million federal and provincial dollars. The majority of these dollars were allocated to the feedlots, and this program is the one that caused controversy with the packers.

That fall, producers who had invested in Net Income Stabilization Accounts withdrew their funds, receiving matching federal dollars. The program was fazed out and was soon replaced by the Canadian Agriculture Income Stabilization program (CAIS).

In November 2003, the federal government committed $120 million to a cull cow program, giving the provincial governments the opportunity to add another 40 percent, which brought the funding total to $200 million. Under full funding, producers who applied were eligible for up to a maximum of $320 a cow for eight percent of their herd for beef cows and 16 percent for dairy. The program was designed to make up some of the difference between what producers once received for cull cows and the dollars they were earning after BSE.

In March 2004, the federal government announced a $1 billion farm aid program that allocated $680 million to the cattle sector. This time, the payment of $80 a head was for all calves inventoried on ranches and feedlots as of December 23, 2003. This was a program with a retroactive feel, helping producers recoup some of the losses they incurred when the border did not open in January 2004 and prices plummeted.

Money for the last program came out of the 2003-04 surplus, and the funding announcement came one day prior to the March 23 federal budget. Overall, cattle producers and industry leaders applauded the program, but Conservative MPs were critical, saying it was a pre-election gimmick to buy ag votes. Supportive industry leaders were dismissed and called "known liberals."

Industry leaders gave thanks on behalf of cattlemen following every aid announcement. Criticism came only twice and that was over how the programs would be implemented. I doubt that industry leaders appreciated the suggestion that they were Liberal voters blinded by personal political beliefs. Some would be downright annoyed.

In July 2004, the government of Canada introduced new animal feed restrictions, requiring the removal of all specified risk materials from animal feed. The cost to the industry to dispose of the materials would be around $27 million a year.

It was estimated there were 80,000 head of American-owned cattle in Canadian feedlots. In mid-July, cattle owned by R-CALF members were slaughtered at the Cargill plant in High River. This generated an uproar from Alberta feedlot owners who were competing with one another for slaughter space. In early August, Cargill's Canadian operation announced it would no longer slaughter cattle owned by R-CALF members. Tyson Foods made the same announcement days later.

In mid-August, the Canadian Cattlemen for Free Trade filed initial claims in Washington, D.C., seeking $150 million in damages under a provision of the North American Free Trade Agreement. The Alberta Beef Producers board decided to support the initiative, going against the earlier thoughts of the government and the CCA.

Mexico announced it would partially re-open its border to Canadian beef. In 2002 they were our second largest export market, buying $282 million worth of beef. Japan was still holding firm on its demands that the spinal cord must be vacuum extracted prior to splitting the carcass and that mandatory testing be done on all animals destined for export to Japan from the U.S.

The CCA passed a resolution calling for a federal government program to coordinate sales of slaughter cattle in order to improve market prices. The delayed marketing strategy would see a certain percentage of cattle held back from market until packing plants could expand their capacity a sufficient amount to handle the volumes. Producers who enrolled in the program agreed not to sell for a set period and were paid to feed the cattle. The plan was designed to set aside cattle ready for immediate slaughter—a percentage of the 2004 calf crop and animals over 30 months of age. Rumblings began soon after the program was announced that this would just worsen the cattle backlog if the packing plants weren't up to speed by the same time next year.

In September, a rally was held trying to stop the construction of the Ranchers Beef plant northeast of Calgary. Concerned residents argued that the facility was not appropriate for the land since there were plans to construct a residential development nearby.

A $14 million dollar, Level Three Biocontainment Laboratory was built in Edmonton to ensure that Alberta had the capacity to increase BSE testing.

Ranchers were starting to ask where the products they normal buy are made. Many no longer want to buy American and Japanese imported products until these countries open their borders to live cattle and meat respectively.

Frustrated prairie farmers and cattlemen were refusing to allow American hunters on their land. Gerry Duckworth, a rancher from Courval, Saskatchewan, printed signs saying that American hunters were not allowed to hunt on his property. More than 3,000 signs were posted across prime duck and goose hunting grounds in Saskatchewan and Alberta. By doing this, producers hoped that the hunters would lobby politicians in the U.S. to get the border reopened.

In October, Italy detected another case of BSE, bringing their total to 123.

Officials from the CCA and the Federal Ag Minister returned from an international trade mission. They reported encouraging signals that Japan and Hong Kong were anxious to resume trade with Canada. China signed an agreement to re-open its border to imports of bovine semen and embryos. Before BSE, Canada was China's number one supplier with around $3 million in sales.

Independent feedlot owners, those who own their own cattle, were feeling pressure from the lending institutions because they didn't have the same stream of income as the other feedlots.

The CCA and Alberta Beef Producers Association came under fire for not putting enough pressure on the Liberal government to improve the programs, and were accused of not representing the feedlot sector adequately.

The Canadian Association of Food Banks reported that an additional 65,000 people were using food banks compared to last year. It made people wonder how many of the folks asking for free food were in the business of producing it.

A French blood donor was identified as France's eighth known victim of vCJD. Recipients of the blood were informed, but no one knows for sure if vCJD can be passed between humans via blood products.

Japan announced that its 15th case of BSE was discovered in a dairy cow.

By November, Canada had exceeded its target for BSE testing at 8,600 animals. That number is expected to rise to 30,000 in 2005.

On November 2, George W. Bush was elected for a second term as President of the United States. South Dakota Senator, Tom Daschle, a vocal opponent of re-opening the border was defeated. Prime Minister Paul Martin called the President to congratulate him on his win and urged Bush to take action on cross border trade problems, especially beef and softwood lumber. In spite of the friendly, hopeful feelings toward the U.S., the Canadian industry is well into its plan to become more independent.

Age verification in cattle became a priority. Canada advanced its national identification program by switching to electronic records and ear tags, with hopes of implementing this in January 2005. Determining an animal's age will be a key step to secure overseas markets.

A patient in a hospital in Dublin was suffering from what is believed to be Ireland's first locally contracted case of vCJD.

U.S. Agriculture Secretary Ann Veneman resigned her post. There was concern in Canada that this will slow talks, but it was reported that the U.S. continued to draft the proposed rule to allow importation of live cattle and additional beef products into their country.

Ontario Liberal MP for Mississauga-Erindale, Carolyn Parrish, is dismissed from the Liberal Caucus for her public remarks regarding the Bush administration. She was quoted as saying, "We are not joining the coalition of idiots," when referring to the U.S. proposed missile defence scheme, and "Damn Americans . . . I hate those bastards." The expulsion came after she stomped on a George Bush doll on the satirical television program, This Hour Has 22 Minutes.

A Leduc, Alberta, area producer offered hunters the chance to come to his farm and shoot a steer for $500. He ran an ad in the newspaper and received dozens of calls. Alberta Agriculture said that while a producer can sell a live animal to a customer, they can't have people killing animals on the property due to food safety and humane slaughter issues. If the producer followed through with the scheme, he would face a maximum fine of $10,000 and a year in jail. The producer said that he didn't care.

Another possible case of BSE was reported in the U.S. The suspect animal, a non-ambulatory Holstein, was given three rapid tests, then the Gold test. Prices on fat cattle dropped three cents a pound. It was announced three weeks later that the test returned negative.

During a brief meeting with the Prime Minister, President Bush promised that he would start the process to lift the ban on cattle, saying that he was committed to resuming trade early in 2005.

PART THREE

ANGER

CHAPTER EIGHTEEN

"There is no one best plan, but it's best to have one plan."
— Sir Winston Churchill

The cow herd in Ontario is the fourth largest in the country at 375,000 cows. A healthy percentage of this province's producers live in the counties of Bruce, Grey and Waterloo, north west of Toronto.

I am on my way to Kincardine, a town situated along the eastern shore of Lake Huron. As I make my way along the narrow, winding highway, I already know how different the operations here are from those I've seen in the west.

There are no range cattle here. The cows that stand grazing in the still-green fields are the larger framed, exotic breeds. Only the die-hard cattleman uses horses and cattle dogs, since working animals are unnecessary in such small spaces. Most everyone here has an all-terrain vehicle.

An earlier glance through the Ontario Beef magazine reminds me how close I am to Walkerton, Ontario. In 2000, an E. coli outbreak in the town water system killed seven people and left 2,500 others ill. Dr. David Biesenthal's cattle operation was identified as the source of the pathogen. Although it was ultimately determined he was not at fault and it was workers at the local water treatment plant who were negligent, a civil suit was filed against Biesenthal for $350 million. His farm was saved by the fact he was able to prove due diligence because he had filed an environmental farm plan. This is something all producers are now being encouraged to do.

Ron Wooddisse, a Simmental breeder and President of the Ontario Cattlemen's Association (OCA), sums up feelings of cattlemen across the country when he wrote in the May 2004 of Ontario Beef:

"It's not surprising that so many of you feel discouraged, disillusioned and fearful about your future in this industry. It's hard to think about how we can make this industry a better place to live and work in on a long-term basis when we're having problems seeing ourselves in business a day or a week from now. Many of you have come to the conclusion that you're not in control of your destiny; that your cattle organizations, like OCA, have no control over your destiny and that even your governments aren't in control. It's hard to figure out what the rules of the game are when someone else sets them, at their time and at their pleasure."

Ron also explained that delegates at the OCA's annual convention clearly stated that they were no longer content with the idea that the industry should return to the way it once was. They want to see change, and have accepted that the industry will never be the same again.

Before I reach Kincardine, I will turn off and follow directions to Stan and Islay Eby's farm. Stan is the President of the CCA, having taken over from Neil Jahnke earlier this year. I was a bit surprised to hear that someone from Ontario was named to this post during this crucial time. I expect that there may be some resentment from Alberta producers who may be feeling that a feedlot operator from the east cannot adequately represent interests in the west.

Islay's directions (pronounced "I-la") are excellent and I find myself at their brick bungalow in the late afternoon. She invites me in, saying that Stan is at the feedlot and will be back soon. We sit and chat as she gets up occasionally to check supper or answer the phone. She tells me they built the house in 1994 on this quiet road with the intention that it would be their retirement home. They are farming in partnership with their son, Steve, and his wife, Janine, who live on the home place four miles down the road.

The phone rings again just as Stan walks in the door. He waves at me then takes the receiver from Islay. We've spoken a few times so he knows who I am and why I'm sitting in his chair. From where I sit, I can hear him talking to a cattleman about recent developments in the border issue. Yesterday there was a positive announcement from the CCA and I'm anxious to hear about it.

Stan chuckles as he hangs up the phone.

"That was a producer from Quebec calling from the Grey Cup game asking about a rumour he heard, but I could barely hear him over the noise," he says. Stan offers me a drink, pours one for himself, then sits in the recliner beside me. He says that it has taken a year, but yesterday the proposed ruling that is needed to get the border open has moved from the U.S. Agriculture office to the office of Management and Budget. It still must make its way through a complicated process, but if things go well, the border will open sometime between February and April.

"This is really good news," he smiles, explaining this hurdle was the most significant in the process.

I ask if I'm interrupting his plans to watch the Grey Cup game. The Toronto Argonauts are playing the B.C. Lions, televised from Montreal. Stan waves it off, saying that with so much going on, he hasn't been following much on television. Being CCA president means not having any spare time. The responsibility demands more than a person's full attention to the point that a man's own operation will suffer unless he has a partner or full-time help.

I ask Stan if he dreaded the thought of taking over as President in the middle of this unresolved issue.

I'm surprised when he shakes his head no, saying that he enjoys the politics of the cattle business almost as much as he enjoys the feedlot.

"Time spent as Vice President prepared me for all of that," he says. "I knew my responsibilities going in and was prepared to step up to the challenge."

On first impression, you'd think that Stan might not be hard enough, that he'd take too much to heart. Not everyone can shut off their thoughts enough to fall asleep after a late evening debate, and there are plenty of those right now.

I'm reminded that he was President of the OCA during the Walkerton tragedy and subsequent inquiry, so Stan has felt the pressure cooker before. Stan remembers that as a very difficult time, but not nearly as difficult as the challenges presented by the closed border.

Stan says he agreed with the direction in which Neil Jahnke was taking the Association, so the transition was relatively smooth when he stepped in. He is careful to not get caught up in the east-west rivalry that exists within the industry, a reality that permeates most every other aspect of the country.

He says the one thing that has been most difficult to deal with is the lack of understanding between the distinct segments of the industry. He has been trying to break down the barriers between the cow-calf and feedlot sectors; and the packing industry, in an effort to get cooperation between all three, but it hasn't been easy.

This would be a difficult undertaking during prosperous times, near impossible during a crisis.

Stan explains that the short-term goals of the CCA in 2004 was to get as many cattle processed for the highest price possible, provide financial assistance where there were shortfalls, and get the border open. This meant creating programs that restricted when fat cattle and, later, calves could go to market. Not all producers were in favour of establishing an orderly marketing plan, but after more than a year of volatility, the CCA directors felt there was no other choice.

"Saskatchewan has the most free-enterprising group of producers you'll ever find," he says. "They didn't like it and said so."

I ask him about the people involved. Time spent talking to producers from different provinces has shown me how needs vary, so proposed solutions brought to the boardroom must vary, too.

Stan agrees, saying that whenever a large group of individuals come together, there is bound to be some conflict. Discussions around the table were at times quite spirited, but he can see that everyone there is trying to do what is best for the sector they represent. Sometimes concessions had to be made to protect the industry as a whole.

I mention that producers have complained that the CCA hasn't effectively communicated its plans to the grassroots.

Stan is a bit disappointed to hear this, adding that communicating to 90,000 people across the country is not an easy task, especially since the Association's resources have been stretched to the limit. He gives credit to the staff who he says works incredibly hard.

I ask about Lyle Vanclief, wondering out loud why a man who appears to dislike farmers was chosen Agriculture Minister.

Stan surprises me by saying that he knows Vanclief fairly well. They went to the University of Guelph at the same time, and, of course, had many dealings regarding the Walkerton and BSE issues.

"Lyle is dedicated to agriculture, and is a good policy person," he says, stopping short of adding that he is not much of a people person. The radical, in-your-face, uninformed producer is not going to get anywhere with Vanclief. "Lyle does not suffer fools gladly."

Echoing Neil Jahnke's opinion of Vanclief, Stan found him quite easy to work with.

There is an optimism, exuberance and honesty to Stan that gives me hope. I fall asleep that night in the Eby's guest room, looking forward to George Bush's upcoming visit to Ottawa. I allow myself to hope that a firm announcement about the border opening may come then. Maybe this time it might actually happen, and we will be given a firm time frame to plan around.

The next morning we have a quick, early breakfast, then drive to the feedlot where Steve is already out doing chores. The place is immaculate, which doesn't surprise me since Stan appears to be the sort of man who runs a pretty efficient operation.

Cattle here are not kept outdoors during the winter, but in large, well-ventilated barns. Stan opens the barn door and I follow him inside. He explains that the cattle are brought in by late fall and fed this way until April. An average of forty inches of precipitation in a winter means cattle become too wet if left outside. This stresses the calves and increases the likelihood they will develop pneumonia.

The Eby's barn resembles a large quonset with a high, open ceiling. The cattle are divided into two large pens with a lane down the centre. A three-foot-tall opening runs the length of the barn, leaving enough space for the cattle to poke their heads through to the outdoor feed bunk. The walls are mostly solid except near the roof where there are wide openings that let the breeze blow through.

"Historically fed cattle prices were $5 to $7 a hundred weight stronger in Ontario," Stan says, explaining that the competitive factor changed dramatically when the Crow Rate—a subsidy to cover grain transportation costs—was introduced in the early 1980s. The packing industry in Ontario and Manitoba had become antiquated, and cheaper grain in the west meant producers in the east were finding it hard to compete. The pendulum suddenly swung west when Cargill built a packing plant in Calgary and Iowa Beef Processors bought Lakeside Packers in Brooks, positioning Alberta to take over Canada's cattle feeding and packing industries.

"At one time we saw 600,000 calves from the west come into Ontario," he adds. "Now that number is down closer to 100,000."

Ontario produces half as much beef as it consumes. There is tremendous frustration felt by producers here as they suffer the same price collapse and unwanted herd growth as in the west, but can do nothing except watch as trade deals allow imported beef to continue to pour into the province.

Unable to go south with fat cattle, feedlot operators in Ontario find themselves at a competitive disadvantage. They aren't being paid enough for their fats so they can't compete with the Alberta lots for calves this fall. Stan says it costs him an extra 10 cents a pound to cover the cost of transportation and feeding enroute to bring animals from the west.

"The two major packers here like bigger cattle and work in tons," he says. "That's why you'll see the herd here resemble those in Manitoba. It's the reason those exotic cross calves from the Interlake come to feedlots here."

Stan says that the largest packer in the province, Better Beef at Guelph, has the ability to process 2,000 fat cattle a day. The second largest plant is Gencor Foods in Kitchener, a facility that can process 800 cows a week. Expansion of the facilities will see those numbers rise to 1,500 by the spring of 2005.

Since BSE, typical profit margins the feedlot operator sees on fat cattle here have dropped to only 43 cents a hundred weight, or $5.16 for a 1,200 pound steer. With a turnover of only a few thousand animals a year, feedlot operators can't afford to make any mistakes. This past June, the Ebys lost more than $53,000 on the fat cattle they sold.

Stan says that as long as the border remains closed, there needs to be enough competition in the packing industry to kill an additional 1,000 animals a day in order to keep the feeding industry alive in Canada.

"Tyson and Cargill are expanding, so we see they are in this for the long haul," he says.

I thank Stan for his insights. This afternoon he will board a plane for Calgary, and make stops in Saskatchewan and Manitoba before arriving home later this week.

With more interviews arranged, I ask directions to the next farm. We shake hands goodbye, with a tentative plan to meet again at the Alberta Beef Producers Annual General meeting in Calgary in two weeks time.

Chapter Nineteen

Any rancher will admit that cattle are not really tame. They continue to behave as cattle naturally do. Some have better temperaments than others, but even a bottle-fed calf can grow into a bull that is deadly. They do not become pets, nor do they show affection for humans as horses or dogs do. More like cats, they have stuck with us because we feed them. Shaping their envronment with technology and government, and changing our lives to fit theirs, makes it possible to enjoy their benefits. Obtaining hay and feed, building pens and barns, and learning how to preserve milk and its products has changed us far more than it has changed the bovines.
One could argue that they domesticated us.
— Cattle: An Informal Social History, page 285

The cattle business is full of contradictions.

Nothing happens fast on the ranch.

There is no clock to punch, nobody there telling the rancher when to get up in the morning or what he needs to do. He can spend days or weeks away at a time, arriving home to find that things didn't change at all while he was gone.

The nature of the business dictates that if a producer wants to make changes he is forced to move slow.

It takes a heifer calf a year and a half to grow to breeding size. Once pregnant, the rancher waits nine months for the calf. Six months after that, the calf is ready to sell. A year after that, the feedlot operator has grown it to butcher weight. There is no way to speed up this process. If calf prices

Clarence Ackert

skyrocket, the rancher cannot increase production to capitalize on good times. All he can do is sell what he has, and hope the good fortune will last for another year.

Once a herd has been bred to calve during a certain month, it is difficult to change because the cows cycle accordingly. Switching breeds is also done slowly. Unless a cattleman sells off all his cows and buys the breed he wants, it takes many years to introduce the characteristics of a breed into the herd. Since good cattle live and produce calves for 12 years or longer, it is conceivable that a rancher near retirement who took over from his father can still have the great-great-granddaughters of a cow he remembers as a child.

The contradiction in all of this is that the producer still must be prepared to react quickly, to capitalize on whatever opportunity presents itself, or minimize his losses.

Mostly everything is out of the cattleman's control, adding stress and uncertainty. And while there may be no clock to punch and the cattleman can leave whenever he wants, there are times he absolutely cannot go anywhere without tempting disaster.

The cattleman cannot influence what he depends upon the most—the weather. He has no control over how fast the grass grows, how much rain there will be or if the sun will shine tomorrow. Frost, hail, flood and drought sit as ominous threats in the back of his mind.

The cattleman will tell you that he can be home every day for six weeks straight and it's the day he goes to town that the steers break through the fence and take off running down the road.

The watering bowl will freeze over on Christmas Eve.

He'll tell you about the summer he could barely make hay because it rained so much, that the only sunny period was over the weekend of his brother's wedding. It started raining the day after, ruining three hundred bales of prime alfalfa.

Cows always calve during a storm.

Plan a trip to the city and a cow will start birthing a set of twins—coming backwards, of course.

If he has just enough bulls for the season, one will surely turn up lame two weeks after being let into pasture. It won't be the scruffy six-year-old he planned to ship that fall, but the high-priced two-year-old bought that spring. The calf that is found dead for no apparent reason is seldom the sickly, potbellied, late-born heifer, but the nicest, heaviest steer.

The more he treats a calf, the greater the chances it will live long enough to die a week before going to market.

And regardless of how big the yard is, if the cows get into it, they always stomp through the garden.

The most successful cattlemen are those who plan well, work hard and sell out when times are good. An inordinate amount of good luck is a tremendous help.

If the feedlot operator is the financier of the industry and the auction-eer the peacemaker, then the cow-calf producer is the workhorse. What he gives the industry is the raw product. While running a ranch doesn't involve making high-pressure, daily financial decisions of a feedlot operation, it does require a strong back. The ability to work long, physical days is the trademark of the cow-calf producer. Some will complain that being at the industry's grassroots means being price takers, having no one to pass losses onto, but others will smile with the satisfaction of knowing their place in the industry is secure. You can't pay a man to calve out cows. You have to love doing it to do it well, so there is little fear that big business will ever want to take over the ranch.

Clarence and Shirley Ackert's home couldn't be situated in a lovelier spot, perched halfway up an escarpment that looks out over Lake Huron. The couple will have a little more time to sit and enjoy the beautiful view, now that their purebred Limousin herd is gone.

This past Saturday afternoon, the Ackerts had a dispersal sale in near-by Listowel, and say that the end to their days as cow-calf producers tastes bittersweet. At nearly 73 years of age, Clarence doesn't have the muster to go through another calving season. His wife, Shirley, has been looking for-ward to the day that she and Clarence could enjoy retirement without con-stant thoughts of the cattle and the farm. Despite the fact this was an unset-tled time to sell, the Ackerts felt they had little choice.

"We just couldn't wait any longer," Clarence says, shaking his head. He's a bit sad, somewhat relieved, not quite wound down from cattleman mode. He's been in the business forever, so it's going to take a bit of time for his thoughts to switch from cattle to the quiet ponderings of retired life.

Shirley makes coffee and sets down a plate in front of us filled with cheese, crackers and homemade cake. She leaves us to talk, disappearing into her sewing room to work on a project.

I ask Clarence if they received enough money for the cows.

"We were disappointed, but not surprised," he says, adding that prices averaged $900 for purebred, pregnant cows. Before the border closed, purebreds with a solid pedigree like his would have brought double that amount.

Clarence says they decided to keep back the heifer calves with plans to feed them over the winter and sell them in the spring. Talk of the border opening early in the new year makes him hopeful.

"We had pretty good cattle," Clarence says quietly, adding that they sold April-born steer calves in late October that weighed an average of 640 lbs. and brought $1.36 a pound.

"Maybe we'll get a decent price for those heifers; that would be nice," he says. "It's all going into the retirement package and every little bit helps."

Clarence is a third-generation cattleman whose grandfather, Ernie Ackert, settled in the area during the early 1900s. Ernie was a bit of an innovator who fattened cattle that were shipped back to Scotland by boat during the 1920s. Clarence inherited a love of cows from his grandfather who liked to show cattle at the Royal Winter Fair, which in the early days was called the Toronto Feeder Cattle Show & Sale. One year, Ernie brought home the Grand Championship Hartford trophy.

Clarence grew up on a mixed farm, had a dairy herd and that meant milking cows every day. For a while they had purebred Holsteins, then in 1965 they dispersed that herd and specialized in the beef business.

"Dad saw a Limousin bull in High River, Alberta and said, 'That's the best looking bull I've ever seen.'" The Ackerts decided these were the type of cattle they wanted to raise, and bought 20 purebred cows on a handshake in partnership with a man named Doug Fletcher. The partnership lasted 25 years and gave Clarence and Shirley some of the most interesting years of their lives.

Clarence says that in the early days, making a living raising cattle was pretty straightforward. In recent years, though, he has found times tougher and the room for error far more narrow. A poor decision or a bit of bad luck can leave an operator in a precarious position.

Clarence has always been an innovator, a fellow willing to diversify and try new things. He's grown different crops and Christmas trees, but as much as he's enjoyed these ventures, they have never resulted in much profit. He took a position as field manager at an alfalfa plant about fifteen years ago to supplement their income when times got tight, but the workload was too much for one man. Feeding every night in the dark began to take its toll.

"The Lord helped me calve the cows those years," he chuckles. "He was my right-hand man."

Clarence sat as President of the Canadian Limousin Association and the connects there helped him and Shirley make friends across Canada.

While they never made a fortune raising cattle, their life was spent doing what they loved. Like many other producers nearing retirement age, the stress, uncertainty and loss of equity has taken the enjoyment out of owning cattle. There is no bitterness in his voice, at least not yet, just a hint of sadness.

We go for a drive across his land so he can show me the heifers. As we stand there chatting and watching the animals watch us back, I ask if either of their four children want to take over the operation. He says not right now, but that they will keep the land for a while, maybe put in a crop or lease it out. His expression tells me it will be a sad day when he decides to let it go.

"A young guy still has lots of years to make up the losses we've seen, but I don't have that kinda time," he says as we get back into the car and he turns around to go back to the house. "I thought we'd better just get out now. Who knows what's going to happen next?"

Along the way, he offers a bit of advice to young men just starting out. He says they should be sure to pay Canada Pension Plan contributions for their wives. He didn't realize this until Shirley started receiving her pension and it is much lower than it could have been. He doesn't want other farmers to make the same mistake.

There is one more thing he wants to show me before I leave. He takes me downstairs to see his family tree. It takes a few moments for me to understand what he's talking about, as he runs his big hand over a thick tabletop. It is a varnished tree trunk sliced horizontally so it shows the tree's growth rings. It is from a beech tree that came from a farm that his dad owned and the block was cut from a stump after the bush was logged. Clarence estimated the tree sprouted in 1850. He decided to make this their family tree and started by printing his name and birthdate on the fifteenth ring, then continued outward with every family's birthday after that.

Satisfied that we have seen and talked about the most important things in his life, Clarence walks me to the door. We promise to stay in touch and I tell him I'll visit again when in the area. I sincerely hope he does well when he sells the heifers and tell him so. He nods, then shrugs as we say goodbye.

All he can do is hope, too.

A privilege of doing work you love is looking forward to each day. Most cattlemen dread retirement because selling the herd often means moving away from the land they have lived on their whole lives. Selling to a son or daughter often means they can stay. Knowing the land will remain in the family and that their long-established traditions will continue offers some comfort.

It is difficult to generalize the worth of a ranch at retirement because there are so many factors that must be considered. It is easy, however, to estimate how much must be banked so that a producer can live a modest lifestyle. If a full-time producer who has no other income sells the farm and moves to a house in town at the age of 65, and lives for 20 more years, he will need a minimum of $500,000 to support himself—$100,000 to buy a house and $20,000 a year to cover living expenses. Banking $1 million after the ranch is sold frees the rancher of worry about how he will manage if he or his wife needs specialized health care or if the cost of living continues to rise.

The most lucrative way to sell the ranch is to dispose of it piece by piece. Producers usually begin by selling the cattle over a span of a few years, preferably at the top end of the cycle. The land is then sold off in chunks to the highest bidder. Equipment is best sold privately or by auction. If the house can be picked up and moved to a lot in town, all the better. The end result is that the farm is gone, swallowed up by the neighbours, its history lost forever.

Some producers will sacrifice financial gain to see their life's work stay intact. These are the ranchers who choose to sell the place in its entirety to someone looking to get into the cattle business. Often times they sell to someone who has earned enough equity after working in another profession for a few years, producers from another province, or an immigrant farmer who has sold out overseas with plans to start fresh here. Most often the ranch is sold outright, but sometimes the retired rancher will finance the new owner's purchase by holding title to some of the land and receiving annual payments.

The least lucrative way to sell the farm is to pass it on to a son or daughter. If the land is situated in an area near a sprawling city, the appraised value may have skyrocketed. If the rancher wants to pass it onto his son or daughter, he must sell it far below market value, because pasture and hayland can't generate enough income for the son or daughter to make the payments.

Problems arise when agreements are not clear-cut or the parent dies suddenly, leaving behind nothing but a verbal agreement. Many ranchers have found themselves at midlife forced into buying out their sibling's share of an estate, often times at appraised market value. Divorce is another nightmare that often means mortgaging a livelihood.

Despite knowing all that can go wrong, those who love the lifestyle will forge ahead and buy the ranch anyway. Any reasoning human being will ask themselves why producers continue on in spite of unpredictable weather and uncertain prices. If luck is against them, they'll spend their retirement years watching every dollar.

Manitoba journalist and freelance writer Peter Schroedter was challenged to explain why producers keep on in spite of mounting difficulties. Peter has written extensively about the BSE issue for the *Winnipeg Free Press* and *Farmers Independent Weekly* newspapers. A former sheep farmer, he grew up on a ranch north of Winnipeg.

Peter's answer to this time-worn question was intelligent, thorough and succinct. He describes agricultural producers as a separate sector of society who have a unique value system, " . . . especially the traditional cattle producers whose attachment to the land, livestock and nature is as strong as you'll find in any aboriginal culture." Peter believes that "farmers share a common culture that makes them resemble an ethnic group more than a business or professional caste. The farming community has its own traditions, myths, music and status symbols. There is even a prescribed dress code that distinguishes farm people from the rest of society."

One thing that farm people are very good at is being able to differentiate between wants and needs. They care about the land and have a stubborn attachment that means they will do whatever it takes to get the job done. The farm takes priority over everything else in life and children raised in agriculture learn this at an early age. Not many urbanites who were not raised on a farm make a successful transition to full-time farming.

Peter says that "there are no established traditions for a farm family to leave the life. The only acceptable way out of farming was through old age or death. Any other reason was much like rejecting the rest of the community's basic beliefs. In a community where the future is always uncertain, often the only thing that makes any sense is a fixed belief that next year will be better."

He explains that leaving the farming life is more complicated than selling a business. Peter had built and sold a handful of off-farm businesses over the years, but it took him three years to decide to sell the livestock and quit ranching. "The process was long and complicated on a deeply emotional level. I had to square it with my father's memory, because we shared the immigrants' dream of owning our own land, and he helped me get started. I had to convince myself that I wasn't any less of a person in the eyes of my peers because I was giving up on something in which they all steadfastly believe."[14]

CHAPTER TWENTY

"No tree becomes rooted and sturdy unless many a wind assails
it. For by its very tossing it tightens its grip
and plants its roots more securely;
the fragile trees are those that have grown in a sunny valley."
—Seneca the Younger, Roman philosopher

If the climate for raising cattle doesn't improve in this country, we are going to start losing our young producers to frustration and the promise of better paying work elsewhere.

At least that's the impression I'm getting while sitting here talking with Craig Trelford. Craig farms with his father, Murray near the town of Paisley.

Craig is pretty easy to understand. There are hundreds of young men just like him, struggling for a foothold on the farms and ranches between here and B.C.

You know the kinda guy I mean.

He is the kid who learned to drive a tractor at 11 years old and has owned livestock for as long as he can remember. While other kids his age were playing video games or watching television, he was showing cattle at 4-H shows. By the time he graduated from high school, he could run every piece of equipment on his dad's farm. He spent most weekends feeding cattle, making hay, calving cows or harvesting crops.

He's a farm kid.

Strong, capable, and wise beyond his years. Farm kids are taught from a young age how to be resourceful and know to keep working until the job is done. He is the kid everyone wants to hire. Given a choice, he'd rather

Craig Trelford

work for himself on the land where he grew up with a bit of help from dad. He's always believed that if he works hard and plans well, he will be rewarded fairly for his efforts.

The problem is 27-year-old Craig Trelford isn't sure anymore.

He is annoyed and has every right to be. After all, he's done everything right. Following high school he earned his Agri Business Diploma from the University of Guelph, bringing home cutting-edge knowledge in farm management. He's been careful with his money, investing in his future livelihood by purchasing cattle while still in school. In 2002, Craig had an excellent debt-equity ratio so he bought the farm he'd been renting. Unimproved land here sells for around $1,500 an acre. He began clearing bush and improving drainage, knowing that land is an asset worthy of labour and investment.

Craig has a herd of Hereford-Angus-Limousin cows that he crosses with Limousin bulls. He feeds his own calves and buys in calves from Alberta to fill their backgrounding lot, feeding the cattle up to 1,000 lbs.

In 2003, he married girlfriend Amy Isber. They were thinking about expanding the feedlot, but that plan was put on hold when the border closed. Craig didn't feel the full effect of BSE until the spring of 2004.

"Like everyone else we thought the border was going to open that winter, but it didn't," he says. "The spread between what we paid for calves and what we sold them for as backgrounders was $100."

Normally Craig tries to keep the spread closer to $400 to be sure all his costs are covered. With only a $100 difference, he lost money and in order to try to make up the losses, he needs to have cattle ready to sell when the border does open. The problem is, that it's hard to compete with the Alberta feedlots right now for the calves. Further complicating matters is the fact that the value of the Canadian dollar is rising, so even if the border does open, the value of exported cattle will be less.

Craig's operation is diversified enough that cash from custom work and his corn and soybean crops is helping pay the bills. He calculated the number of hours he spent last year against the amount of money he made, and says it doesn't make good sense to keep farming this way.

"It is ridiculous to have to work this hard, seven days a week, to make a living," he says. "I don't mind work, it has never bothered me before, but now when you work all year long and there's no money at the end of the year, well, it's just crazy."

So many producers say the best way to describe this to a salaried person is to say it's like going to work every day but not getting paid. At the end of the year, all your living expenses become another loan that has to be paid off eventually, but will the bank continue to lend you the money if your job doesn't generate income?

Craig says this is the first time he has seen his debt grow without having an asset to show for it.

"It was much easier making a living when dad started out," he says, explaining that his father was able to support the family by feeding cattle. Murray turned 60 this year and is beginning to think about when he'll retire.

"I haven't lost all hope, though," Craig says. "I guess you could say I can't afford to quit. I definitely need to make changes around here because I'm just not willing to work this hard for what I did last year."

Craig is also very concerned about the number of private feedlots that have turned to custom feeding for the multinationals in order to stay in business. In a way he appreciates that the big packers are pumping money back into the industry by buying and paying producers to feed from them, but he calls it a double-edged sword. He fears too much control by those at the top of the chain will force prices down at the grassroots.

I ask if he has applied for assistance through any of the government programs.

He says that he applied for CAIS and set-aside cattle. Money from the set-aside cattle really helped but he isn't sure if he'll receive anything from CAIS. His main focus right now is trying to decide if he should risk more equity to buy calves and if other options exist to position himself properly for next spring.

Craig suggests that he might expand his cow herd so that he doesn't have to buy in as many calves. If he's going to do that, now would be an opportune time, but it would be done at the expense of someone else. He shakes his head at the irony of that.

"So I'll pay some guy who has worked his whole life rock-bottom prices, because that's the market, plus I can't afford to pay him more?"

It's a rhetorical question with the answer buried in the conscious of every man who will make this decision.

It is refreshing to see a young producer who isn't afraid to say that the industry has been wronged and that it makes him angry. Craig should be teaching a course somewhere in agriculture pride. Unfortunately, we don't see the same reaction from earlier generations, not because the anger isn't there, but because the subliminal message agriculture producers have learned to accept is that failure, regardless of circumstances, is their fault.

It's the price they seem willing to pay for doing what they love.

As I pull into Paisley, looking for a place to have lunch, I am reminded that small-town Ontario isn't much different than small-town anywhere else.

I enjoy a bowl of homemade soup and scone at the local teahouse, while watching out the window as cars move slowly along the street and people stop to chat with one another.

My next interview is with trucking company owner Greg Hutton. I get back in the car and follow directions to the outskirts of town, where Lloyd Hutton Transport is impossible to miss. Sitting atop a ridge, a long steel building stretches the width of a neat, gravelled yard. Lines of tractor-trailers and Peterbilt trucks sit in two neat rows. Out front there is a small corral and loading chute, a wash bay and fuel tank. Two men are on the roof installing metal sheeting in place of shingles.

I pull open the door to find a female dispatcher on the phone. She looks up from her desk, smiles, then covering the mouthpiece, calls for Greg. He waves that he will be with me in a moment, then finishes his conversation with a trucker. Another man holding a coffee mug lingers by the door. As the truckers leave, Greg invites me into his office.

I want to call him Lloyd, probably because the name is everywhere. It is part of the company logo printed on pens, the door, signs, calendars and even his T-shirt. I write Greg in big letters across the top of my notebook.

He shakes my hand, then sits down behind a heavy desk. While he takes a call, I use the opportunity to glance around the office. Framed photos of his family sit on the bookshelves and there are a few certificates tacked on the walls. His office is neat, inviting, and looks like a nice place to spend the day.

Greg hangs up the phone. I ask about the company's history and he gladly shares it, saying that Hutton Transport will celebrate its 60th anniversary in May 2005.

The company began in 1945 with a single truck and a few panels. His grandfather, Lloyd, was a farmer who hauled his own livestock to market. It wasn't long before he made a business hauling for neighbours and friends. By 1987, the business had grown to 25 trucks. Greg's father, Jim, took over the business when Lloyd passed on, but then in 1993, Jim died suddenly of a heart attack leaving 20-year-old Greg in charge. With the help of many loyal and long-time employees, Greg made the transition from the teenager who would hang around and help out, to owner.

When BSE hit, the fleet was 50 trucks in total; small compared to some trucking companies, but the largest in the immediate area. Greg has 10 trucks that service the local cattle industry, moving animals between barns, pastures, auction marts, packing plants and to different farms.

He says that immediately after the border closed, business became erratic. He'd go days without a call and then following an announcement or rumour, cattle would begin moving in such quantities that his trucks couldn't keep up. Business has been dwindling since, and the unpredictable workload over the past 18 months has cost him some good drivers. Not everyone can haul cattle. It takes a different set of skills, and these are the employees who will be difficult to replace once business returns to normal.

"Producers lost so much money, most of the barns are empty," he says, adding that in September 2003 he took 70 loads of local fat cattle to the packing plants. This year only 18.

The largest portion of the business is 35 trucks that haul freight to Western Canada and then bring cattle back to Ontario. The type of trailers Hutton uses are very unique. They can be converted from hauling general freight to livestock by removing panels to expose vented walls, put in decks, then bring a load of calves back to the east. The trucks are washed out and another trip is made.

With the decreased cattle numbers coming back from the west, Greg finds himself in a bind. Trucking is such a competitive business that he can't afford to haul a load of furniture west without having something to bring back. As a result, he's lost business, customers and income.

"People who know I haul freight think I have that to fall back, on but that's not the case," he says, adding that or every load of freight to the west, he needs a load of cattle east to complete the cycle. "This has hurt all sides of the business."

Greg is trying to make good business decisions, but like so many others affected, his business management has turned into a guessing game and the last 18 months has been a real roller coaster ride. For the first five weeks in 2004, he moved almost no cattle at all.

He has talked with other trucking companies and most say that business is down by a third. Greg now finds himself competing with companies who are doing everything they can to keep loads full. It has increased competition in an already aggressive business.

Through all of this, costs continue to rise. Greg says that over the last few years the price to insure his vehicles has doubled, quadrupled with some trucks. Fuel is one of his larger expenses and it has nearly doubled as well. He can't let himself be undercut by the bigger companies, but knows that the producers he hauls for can't afford to pay more.

"We're all in a real tight bind," he says, adding that he never would have thought that a year and a half later this border would still be closed.

With the exception of the packing plants having less competition, we can't think of another business that has benefitted from the closed border.

There is a coalition of truckers lobbying the federal government for financial help to see them through the crisis, but so far they've had no luck.

To stay competitive and keep current, Greg needs to update his fleet by about 10 percent each year. By doing this his equipment doesn't get too old, there's value left in his trade-ins, equity in the business, and enough cash flow to allow for unexpected expenses or expansion opportunities. With the favourable U.S. exchange rate right now, it is an opportune time to buy a new trailer. He would save $24,000 more than what it would have cost last year, but just doesn't have the cash flow to do it. Greg admits this sounds much like farming. He may own a trucking company, but he's got a cattleman's heart. He grew up around his grandfather's herd so he understands first-hand what cattlemen are facing; he also owns 60 cows.

The toughest days are those that include having to placate annoyed customers he simply cannot accommodate. Greg says that's when he would rather be with the cows.

"I really enjoy what I'm doing here, but I like calving season, too, especially watching the young ones run around," he says.

He understands that companies and farms must weather bad cycles in order to profit from good ones. Fortunately, he has seen tremendous support from his family and his staff, who are emotionally tied to the business and its success.

"We have a staff turnover rate of eight to nine years, and we have one driver who has been here for 27 years," he says. "We're family run and take pride in treating our drivers like family."

If there is one thing he has learned from this current crisis it is that everyone affected is growing weary from the constant battle.

"Even though there have always been hardships in farming, this cycle we're in has to be the rock bottom," he says. "Fathers have always encouraged their sons to take over, but now I'm hearing guys trying to push their kids away."

And while an open border will help the cattle producer, it will create immediate challenges for Greg. He's lost some infrastructure, so if the demand to move cattle is strong, at first he'll have a difficult time keeping up. If he hasn't lost too many customers because of the crisis, he'll eventually get the business back to where it was—unless Ontario's cattle feeding industry never recovers.

Times are as uncertain for him as for the cattleman, but regardless of what happens, Greg is committed to keeping the doors open.

"My business is like the farm—both have been in the family forever," he says. "I'll fight to the bitter end."

It's not until I leave and ask to take Greg's picture with one of his trucks that I notice they are painted the most passionate colour there is.

The colour of blood.

Greg Hutton

CHAPTER TWENTY ONE

"The rule to be observed in this stable at all times, toward the
cattle, young and old, is that of patience and kindness. A man's
usefulness in a herd ceases at once when he loses his temper and
bestows rough usage. Men must be patient. Cattle are not
reasoning beings. Remember that this is the Home of Mothers.
Treat each cow as a Mother should be treated. The giving of
milk is a function of Motherhood; rough treatment lessens that
flow. That injures me as well as the cow.
Always keep these ideas in mind when dealing with my cattle."
— Posted in William Dempster Hoard's Wisconsin dairy, 1800s

I've never had a firm understanding of the dairy industry. Hopefully
an interview with Brian Hastie, a dairy producer from Durham, will answer
a few of my questions and clarify how dairy producers have been affected
this last year and a half.

I follow the well-worn path from Brian's house to the barn that sits
only a few hundred feet away. There is a dangerous looking sign tacked on
the door warning that non-farm personnel are not allowed. I knock, hesitate, assuming that the sign is there for me, too. A voice hollers for me to
come in.

I step into the milk room where it is collected into a covered, giant
stainless steel, covered, tank. The air is thick with the richness of cream,
alfalfa and cows.

Brian is cleaning up after the morning milking. I introduce myself,
then ask about the sign. His expression tells me he isn't sure what I mean.
He's looked at it so often, he doesn't even see it anymore. The realization

Brian Hastie

suddenly strikes and he waves it off. I guess it is a deterrent, a warning to keep strangers from barging in. A "No Trespassing" sign for the animal rights activist, perhaps?

Brian finishes rinsing out a container—three times by my count—before wiping his hands on a cloth. He invites me to go back to the house, joking that he spends enough time in the barn. I follow him back down the path, then wait in the kitchen while he takes off his boots and coveralls. The house is simple, tasteful, tidy and looks new.

We sit facing one another on chairs pulled up to a breakfast nook. His wife, Linda, is at work and their two children are away at university.

We discuss the daily grind of the dairy business and I ask what makes a man decide to tie himself to home in such a way. Brian tells me that for him, it was a logical fit.

He grew up on a mixed farm not too far from here where his parents milked cows and raised cattle, chickens and pigs. Brian attended the University of Guelph and graduated with a Bachelor of Science Degree with a major in crop science. Soon afterward he began working for Nutrite Fertilizer as their Soils and Crops Specialist.

After he and Linda married, they decided that they wanted to raise their family in the rural area. When Nutrite began a phase of downsizing, he accepted a position as a territory salesman in the Durham area. They bought this small farm in 1981, began milking four cows for cream, and expanded as they could afford it. Eventually Brian cut the amount of time he spent on the road selling fertilizer in half, and by the time he resigned from Nutrite, he had bought enough quota that they were milking 25 cows. By then, they had switched from cream and were selling strictly milk.

I ask him to explain the milk quota.

Brian says that while this wasn't always the case, producers today who want to milk cows must purchase the right to do so, in the form of buying quota. One quota is based on the kilograms of butter fat produced per day. One kilogram of quota equals approximately one cow per year, depending on how well the cow milks. He milks 30 to 35 cows at a time, averaging 10,000 kilograms of milk in a year.

Searching a drawer, he hands me a newsletter from the Dairy Producers of Ontario. Turning it over, he shows me the bid for one kilogram of quota that week: $27,601.

Holy cow. I ask how long it would take to pay that off.

Brian tells me it takes 6 to 8 years of milking to pay back each quota he buys. Quota is purchased and sold in what looks like a rather complicated system. He explains that producers wanting to sell quota offer it for sale by putting a price on what they hope to receive. Producers wanting to buy, put in a bid stating how much they are willing to pay. The highest and lowest bids are disregarded, so that quota that week sells in the middle or average range. Sale of quota is the dairy producer's retirement funding.

I ask if the closed border has affected his income.

Brian tells me that he has lost around 18 percent total income—what he would normally get for cull cows, bull calves and the sale of replacement heifers.

He tells me that the demand for Canadian genetics is high, so most replacements were sold into the U.S. and Mexico prior to BSE. Half of Mexico's replacement heifers come from Canada, so the closed border is also hurting their milk industry because their borders are closed and animals cannot travel through the U.S.

Brian says the dairy producer who has been hit hardest is the guy who feeds cull cows and dairy calves or the one who raises replacements, because their market is almost completely gone. Young producers, those just starting out, or producers who just bought quota prior to the closure will also be feeling the pinch.

"That 18 percent might not sound like much, but it makes a big difference to them," he says.

Like the cattleman, dairy producers are always balancing how much they need to make a living against the amount of work that must be done. To increase his income, Brian would have to buy more quota, expand the barn and invest in more cows. His place is less automated than some because technology comes at a hefty price. He says his set-up is about right for how much he's willing to take on. As it is, Brian works seven days a week, year round.

His day starts before 5:00 a.m. Milking takes two hours. He comes in for breakfast, then cleans up the barn, has lunch, and does chores for most of the day. He milks again at 5:00 p.m., arriving in for supper around 7:00 p.m. During the summer months, his work days are even longer as he must fit in time to make hay. He says that milking cows is physical work that is hard on the shoulders, wrists and knees.

Brian says that he is well paid for his efforts but that he won't see the reward until he sells his quota. Dairy producers want to keep a protected system, because it keeps their income stable.

He says that some consumer groups are against supply marketing because they believe it elevates the cost of milk at the retail level. In fact, with every 250 ml glass of milk purchased in a restaurant, the dairy man gets 16 cents. The processor receives 10 cents. Milk sells for $1.50 to $2.00

a glass.

"BSE is a perfect example of how the consumer continues to pay the same price no matter what," Brian says. "You wouldn't see the price in the restaurant go down if there was an oversupply of milk; the producer would just receive less money for his product."

We discuss the food producer's message and how difficult it is to get it to the consumer.

Brian believes that a lot of people are so far removed from the farm that they don't understand where food comes from. Many people also don't understand what it is like to work physically every day. He believes ignorance of another man's lifestyle is what causes the lack of understanding for one another that we see so often today.

Brian believes that every person at some point in their lives should have to sell something to someone. This is a curious statement that makes more sense the longer I think about it. If people were forced into believing in a product enough that their livelihoods depended on it, they would discover and appreciate how hard some people must work.

And he also believes that the farm kid should be forced to go out into the world; everyone else should have to spend some time on a farm.

"You can always tell the guy who has never been off the farm and the city person who has never been on one," he says.

Brian thinks that if Canadians continue their passive attitude toward the U.S. then the closed border will remain an issue for a long time. He hopes that when the border does open, support toward Canada's packing industry will continue.

"Surely we've seen enough from all of this to know that we have to look beyond our own gate," he says. "We have to start protecting our meat industry a bit better than we have."

Islay Eby has invited me to stay another night. She answers the door looking a little flustered, saying she has made supper for us both. As I slip off my boots, she tells me that she just received a call and needs to get in touch with Stan right away. Someone from the government's privy office just extended an invitation to Stan and a guest to attend the State dinner in President Bush's honour. He is one of five invited from the cattle industry.

I'm not sure if she said "state" or "steak."

She's not sure if the guest means her or someone else from the cattle industry.

Apparently, the list is kept rather confidential.

I wonder who is picking up the tab for the airplane tickets.

Islay tells me once they land in Ottawa, they will be taken to a confidential location, undergo strict security screening and then be bused to wherever the dinner is being held.

I assume that means the Parliament Building. Do they have a caterer for events like this?

The phone rings. It is Stan. I listen as Islay relays the information again. The tickets will arrive by Purolator Courier tomorrow. Husbands and wives. Islay hangs up the phone and we try to decide who else might be there.

Neil and Marilyn Jahnke?

Dennis Laycraft?

Shirley McClellan? Ralph Kline? Who else?

I guess that the CCA will pay for Stan's plane ticket and he will pay Islay's way.

We speculate for a few minutes about what this will mean for the industry. Then we spend the rest of the night talking about the most pressing issue.

What in the world is she going to wear?

I can hardly wait to talk to Mark. News that the cattlemen have been invited to the State dinner sounds like a good omen to me. I board the plane for home anticipating what will happen November 30. I feel as though I am privy to a great secret and it gives me a heady, important feeling. I suddenly understand how after feeling this, why a person might want to pursue a position of importance, how much those accustomed to being on the inside must miss it after losing power. I suppose it's the same feeling that makes people want to arrive in a limousine, spend exorbitant amounts of money on trivial things. It's this feeling of importance that causes a person to believe their own press.

This time, I am certain that the border will open.

All signs are pointing in that direction. Fences appear to be mending between our governments. The rule is nearly approved. We've been lead to believe that the President of the United States is the most influential, powerful person in the world and he's coming here to have dinner with us.

How can the border remain closed after that?

CHAPTER TWENTY THREE

"A just war is in the long run far better for a nation's soul
than the most prosperous peace obtained
by acquiescence in wrong or injustice."
— Theodore Roosevelt

December 1, 2004. It is a heavy news day.

One of Canada's best known authors, Pierre Berton, died yesterday afternoon at the age of 84.

Ken Jennings' Jeopardy! winning streak is over. He lost last night, ending a $2.5 million, 74-game domination of the popular television trivia show.

The brothers charged for their role in Walkerton's tainted water tragedy appeared in court yesterday. Stan and Frank Koebel plead guilty to charges of endangering the public after they admitted at a judicial inquiry into the disaster that they faked well records and allowed untreated water to flow to town residents.

And finally, a report on President Bush's visit. Bush thanked Canada for its hospitality at last night's State dinner, but offered no promise when the border will open to cattle. He was quoted as saying, "Look, the Prime Minister has expressed a great deal of frustration that the issue hadn't been resolved yet, and I understand his level of frustration. I fully understand the cattle business. I understand the pressures placed upon Canadian ranchers. I believe that as quickly as possible, your cows ought to be allowed to go across our border."[15]

Saskatchewan Premier Lorne Calvert, who was at the dinner, reportedly spoke one-on-one with President Bush.

Art Jonasson, Mark Emilson, Thor Jonsson, Susie and Vince Wilkinson

"I was left as a result of our conversation with the impression of some real genuine concern on the President's part about this issue," Calvert said. "It's my impression that this is a President who appreciates the eyeball-to-eyeball conversation."

General thoughts from industry leaders at the dinner were that Bush went as far as he dared go when he said, "I've sent word over that they need to expedite that request as quickly as possible. As quickly as possible, young cows ought to be allowed to go across the border."

Good news, but cattlemen were hoping for so much more. The CCA issued a press release reminding producers that the rule to re-open the border still has a number of steps to go through. The U.S. Office of Management and budget has until February 17, 2005, to complete its legal review of the rule, but may complete it earlier. Once this is done, it will be published in the Federal Register and at that point we'll learn whether the rule is deemed major or minor. If major, the earliest the rule can come into effect is 60 days after it is published, allowing for potential Congressional review.

Thoughts are that the border will open sometime in April 2005.

Now I feel a bit foolish. I'd let optimism and hope cloud normally clear thinking. It hadn't occurred to me that the invitation to cattlemen was simply a gesture of goodwill—I'd thought it meant there would be an announcement we wouldn't want to miss. In retrospect, I could argue that this was nothing but a big waste of time and money. But that's because we don't live a life of privilege where someone else pays the bills. There is no expense account, no money spent that isn't hard earned. We don't fly places on a whim, nor do most of us indulge in expensive dinners.

This was an elaborate goodwill trip that had to be done. It is all a part of playing a game with people who have unlimited resources. If the Prime Minister's office invites you to dinner, you go. It looks pretty hick town to refuse. Doing so could be considered an affront to everyone involved, including the President. This far into the negotiating process we don't want any misunderstandings.

But does President Bush feel the same way?

Today he is in Halifax, offering thanks to residents there who reacted so kindly to U.S. citizens stranded in Nova Scotia during the September 11, 2001, terrorist attacks that grounded flights across North America.

News reports and editorials suggest that Bush was thanking Canada one moment, but also scolding our country for not taking a more active role on the U.S. "war against terrorism." He used the reaction of former prime minister William Lyon Mackenzie King to make his point. Bush said that

King did not wait for Hitler's Nazis to attack Canada before sending troops to fight in World War II.

Bush quoted King's words directly: "We cannot defend our country and save our homes and families by waiting for our enemies to attack us. To remain on the defensive is the surest way to bring the war to Canada."[16]

The suggestion was also made that Canada should sign onto the controversial ballistic missile defence program. The timing left cynics wondering if there would be no further delays getting the border open if the Prime Minister agreed to participate in missile defence. Both governments deny this pressure exists, but political observers and editorialists were not convinced.

Prime Minister Martin was quoted as saying, "Whatever decision we make will be in Canada's interest. We are a sovereign nation."

Although there is a near desperation to get the border open, the grassroots cattleman does not hope Canada's decision makers will give in to this type of pressure. The suggestion that Bush might be bullying us tempts us to point out a few observances as well.

Like the fact that while Bush may fully understand the cattle business, whoever wrote his speech doesn't. Cattlemen don't call everything a cow.

And if my knowledge of history is correct, Canada did indeed join World War II, only seven days after it was declared. The United States didn't enter the conflict until two years later, not until Japan bombed Pearl Harbor. Hmmm.

Thoughts that President Bush would come to the Canadian cattleman's rescue by using his position to influence an outcome is quickly dissolving. Some believe he is playing both sides of this issue to his advantage. Others take his words at face value, adding that the President cannot subvert the judicial process.

The most sensible and likely best assessment came from Garry Smith, president of Alta Exports International Ltd. Smith predicted early in the crisis that the U.S. will resume trade only when major American packers find themselves strapped for slaughter cattle, forcing them to lobby hard for a resumption of that trade. He doubted much change could be brought about by Canadian negotiators that he viewed as "understaffed, outleagued and overpowered."[17]

Mark and I have decided to return to our regular marketing plan. Usually we sell our heaviest steer calves in early December; we feed the smaller steers and heifers, then sell them in February, while continuing to background the late born calves until April.

We held over our entire 1993 calf crop with plans to sell them after the border opened. When it didn't, we held them through the lowest point in January, finally selling for an average of 83 cents a pound in February. In retrospect, the decision cost us 20 to 30 cents a pound, plus the cost of keeping them over. The calves ate thousands of dollars worth of feed and left behind a lot of manure that had to be moved out in the spring.

Our barnyard was designed in the 1960s around a massive, hip roof barn, in the days when people milked cows for a living. The barn became unsafe and was demolished in the late 1970s, replaced by a smaller, more modern-looking unit. The corrals were expanded to accommodate 75 cows.

Since then, the herd has grown to 200 cows and Mark has re-done the corrals again. Many cow-calf producers will say they have a limited amount of space to work in, that backgrounding poses penning and watering challenges. The solution is to rip everything down and rebuild, but there isn't enough money or manpower to invest in a better set-up so cattlemen learn to make do with what they have.

That's one reason why producers enjoy tours to other ranches and feedlots. Sometimes seeing another cattleman's barnyard, fencing and watering systems helps producers see their own operation from a different perspective. Most are interested in the way other producers operate, but will ignore condescending advice from so-called experts.

When BSE hit, a myriad of suggestions were made to help producers plan in order to minimize losses. Producers are pretty adept at sifting through, deciding what will work for them. There is nothing they think about more than their cattle and how they plan to make money.

So it is disheartening when comments are made about cattlemen that only represent a small percentage of the industry. Early in the crisis, an article in the *Western Producer* called cattle producers the worst business managers in all of farming. The journalist was quoting Alberta Agriculture Beef Specialist Christoph Weder who said that 97 percent of cow-calf producers have "absolutely no clue" what their cost of production is when they go to market their weaned calves in the fall.[18] Weder admitted he was making the bold statement to get producers' attention, but statements like that perpetuate a stereotype that agriculture producers are just a bunch of dummies who bring misfortune on themselves.

Weder was trying to make the point that producers need to understand how much it costs them to raise a pound of beef. But his assumption that producers don't know this is based on the fact that most haven't sat down at a computer or filled out the formula provided by the Department of Agriculture. My question is this: What exactly classifies as knowing your cost of production?

Ask any cattleman how much he needs per pound for his calves this fall and he'll tell you off the top of his head. He'll base the estimate on his needs last year, then calculate in the fact he's got more debt and that fuel has increased. Cattlemen are pretty much bottom-line people. The bottom line right now is that knowing his cost of production does nothing to help him earn enough at the auction mart, and that can be downright depressing during times like these.

Weder said that producers have to stop focusing on the price they get and start looking at the costs. Producers talk about costs all the time and don't spend more money than they need.

Weder also recommended that producers hold back their calves and background them, adding that he believed 70 percent of producers wouldn't even entertain the idea. "They're going to do the same thing they've done for the last 10 years—take the market price the day they sell their calves and go home, go to the coffee shop and bitch about the price."[19] The article ended with Weder saying he was frustrated, and that if producers won't make changes to their operation, then he won't feel sorry for them anymore. What he doesn't talk about is how difficult it is sometimes to apply new ideas to an old set-up.

Weder's crystal ball was no better than any other, so he can't be faulted for giving bad advice about holding back calves. Cattlemen spent the fall of 2003 discussing at length whether to keep their calves. We sat around the table with good friends and neighbours, Keith and Dorothy Halldorson and Art and Jackie Jonasson. The Jonassons decided to sell the majority of their calves in the fall as they always had, and it turned out to be the right decision.

Like us, the Halldorsons chose to winter their calves. Keith and Dorothy ranch in partnership with their son Clive and wife Wanda. They fed 450 steers and heifers from October until mid-January. They had some on self-feed but also carried, by hand, 140 five gallon pails of grain a day—for fourteen weeks—in addition to their regular chores. They could have bought a feed wagon, but since the objective was to make money instead of spend it, they put their heads down and did the work instead. When the border didn't open, calf prices plummeted. Everyone who gambled lost. If everyone who gave advice had their paycheques docked every time they were wrong, they'd learn to be as cautious about giving advice as cattlemen are about taking it.

Cowboy math says that for every cattleman who sits around complaining, there are 100 out there getting the job done. Cattlemen where I'm from don't have time to sit in the coffee shop.

This year we have decided to sell our calves on the internet through the local TEAM agent. Thor Jonsson is a cattle buyer who has been in the business for 25 years. He has a feedlot and is an order buyer for clients in both the east and west. He recently became a dealer with TEAM.

Thor has invited us to his house today to watch the internet auction take place. He has a handful of local producers who have consigned cattle in today's sale, including our neighbours Art and Jackie Jonasson. Vince and Susie Wilkinson are also here. They are young, progressive producers who make their living raising cattle near Eddystone, Manitoba.

By the time we arrive, Thor's office is crammed with people. The sale has already started. There are 4,175 feeder cattle on today from ranches all across western Canada. We watch, making note of the prices, and chatting quietly. It will be at least 15 minutes until Art and Jackie's cattle come up for bid.

We ask Thor what would happen if the power went out and the computer shut down in the middle of the sale. Thor explains that if something went wrong with the technology, he would phone the office in Calgary and continue the sale over the phone. Because he is the consignor, he has to give final confirmation from the seller that they agree to accept the final bid. Nothing sells accidentally.

We watch as Thor studies the screen, getting a sense of this week's price. Top quality steer calves are selling for around 97 cents a pound and the heifers are at 87 cents. I'm handed the sheet from this week's sale at the Ashern Auction Mart and it shows prices there about the same.

We watch as Thor bids on a few lots. We can't tell whether he plans to put them in his own feedlot or ship them out of province. We tease him a bit, suggesting he should be paying more, but are careful not to go too far. We need as much as we can get for our calves, but understand the feedlot operator can only go so high. The calves Thor is buying today will be ready for the packing plant by late next summer.

Everyone grows quiet as the Jonasson calves come on the screen. They have on offer nearly one third of their calf crop—ninety five 650 pound steers or a full tri-axle load. Thor has described them as: One iron (one owner), high performing three-way-cross steer calves. These calves come off a high indexing cow herd with top gaining bulls purchased every year. The calves spent the summer on native pasture and the fall on alfalfa and grass. These calves have not been implanted but have been vaccinated under the Pfizer Gold program. The mother cows have had the nine-way vaccine.

The bidding speeds through the low 80s but begins to slow by the mid 90s. Buyers have 15 seconds after the last bid in which to bid again. The last bidders seem reluctant, then it times out at 98 cents a pound. Art and Jackie look at one another. They have already discussed at length the price they are willing to accept.

"Sell them," Art says. Thor pushes the sold button and the name of the buyer comes up. These calves are going east.

"The guys in Ontario and Quebec like to get them straight from the farm into the feedlot," Thor says, adding that this is what attracts so many buyers to TEAM.

Susie Wilkinson is fidgeting on her chair and Vince is watching the screen intently. These are two of the nicest, easy-going people you'd ever want to meet. Today, though, they are a bit tense. One more lot will sell and then it will be their turn.

"We want a dollar, right?" Susie says. Their young son climbs onto her lap.

Vince hems and haws. "We want a dollar, but are we going to get it?" he asks. Their first lot of sixty 565 pound steer calves comes on the screen. Bidding is aggressive and we watch as it inches toward the dollar mark. Everyone cheers as it passes $1 a pound, settling at $1.02. They tell Thor to sell, then watch eagerly as the next lot comes up. This time, they are selling bigger calves—ninety five 650 pound steers. The bidding stops at 96 cents a pound. Thor asks if they want to sell or pass. Vince and Susie look at one another and shrug. Vince squints a bit and that look a cattleman gets when he's doing math in his head comes over his face. We all turn away and whisper quietly about something else, trying to give them as much privacy as we can.

"Okay, sell them," Vince says.

We assure him it's a good price, 650 weights are selling for between 94 and 98 cents a pound today.

Vince and Susie agree. Prices could be worse. They say they can live with it, then shrug that they have little choice. Next week, prices could go down. Or they could go up. How long does a person wait?

Thor explains that the buyer will send a truck to pick up the calves within a week. The calves will be unloaded at Thor's lot, weighed, and then taken east. Thor will give them a cheque before the stock leaves his yard.

We continue to watch the sale and soon see a lot of 640 weight steer calves comes on the screen. The seller is Regan Wilkinson, Vince's brother who is selling through Myles Masson, the TEAM agent at Ste. Rose du

Lac, Manitoba. The bidding is aggressive and they sell for 98 cents. Next, a group of one hundred and five 610 pound heifer calves comes on the screen. We watch as the bids move slowly, stopping at 85 cents. There is a long pause and then the word "pass" flashes on the screen.

"Way to go," Vince chuckles. "Somebody's got to show them we mean business." We all laugh. The cow-calf man's only recourse against low prices is to refuse to sell. With approximately half the calf crop heifers, their bringing only 85 cents lowers the overall average to only 91 cents.

I ask Vince and Art what made them decide to sell through TEAM.

"There's less stress on my calves if they don't go through the auction mart and I like that this way they sell in one lot," Vince says. "And if the price isn't right today, well, the calves are still content on the cows."

We talk about erratic prices, especially seen on days that announcements are made. Prices will drop 10 cents a pound on a day with negative news surrounding the border issue. The TEAM method of selling makes it easier to pass if an announcement drives prices down halfway through a sale.

Art agrees. He's watched a few TEAM sales earlier this fall and says there is a lot less pressure to sell. If he doesn't like the price, he can pass, but if the calves are taken to the auction mart, the producer pretty much has to sell them.

"This way of selling isn't for everyone, though," his wife Jackie says. "Your cattle aren't anonymous, and that can come back to haunt you."

"That's right," Art adds, saying that they would rather know than keep their heads buried in the sand. "If your cattle don't perform well in the feedlots, then you'd better find out why."

There is some concern within the industry that the electronic way of selling cattle will hurt the profitability of auction markets, possibly forcing them out of business in the future. There is no doubt if an auction mart loses a lot of big herds to TEAM that business will suffer, but Jason Danard, TEAM product manager, says this way of selling will never replace the traditional auction mart. It only works for medium to large uniform herds that can supply at least a half-load of cattle.

According to Larry Jordan of the Kamloops Auction Mart, becoming a TEAM agent was a positive move for their cooperative, especially when considering how lengthy their sales were during the busy fall run. By selling a few thousand head a week via the internet, it cut back on their stockyard expenses. The cooperative still earns a commission on every animal it sells and the live sales are now shorter, so buyers are less fatigued and the cattle that do come through the ring sell quicker.

"Any time you sell a man's cattle at midnight, you're never going to see him again," Larry said, adding that for them, selling electronically is a "win, win" situation.

Cattle selling the traditional way at Maple Creek, Saskatchewan

Chapter Twenty Four

*"Never put your money into anything that eats
or needs repainting."*
— Billy Rose

December 2004

One more week and I will be done interviewing. This motivates me to get back in the car and begin driving, once again to Alberta, where I have at least a dozen interviews left to finish.

It surprises me to learn that I've grown to enjoy this drive. It is familiar now, the highway between home and Lethbridge, and these hours spent sitting in the car gives me plenty of time to think. Today I am ruminating over things I've heard, to try and find meaning in life's rituals. The saying "It is not the destination but the journey that is important" is a cliché that I've grown to understand the more I travel this road, the more comfortable it becomes. Small, mostly irrelevant memories add to the experience, filling up the blank space between wherever it is I am on the road and my destination.

Life on the ranch is much like this. As I was preparing to move from southern Ontario, my city friends could not understand why I would choose to do such a thing. More than 20 years later, I can honestly say I've never faced a boring moment. The days along the road I've travelled have been rewarding and full of promise of what might come. Ranchers really don't have their sights on a destination when they go out each day into the elements to tend the land and their livestock. They just have that day's journey in mind, and for most, are content that it is all they really need.

Mark Canart

If feedlot operators are the financiers of the industry and cow-calf producers the workhorses, then cattle buyers are the industry's middlemen. Like stockbrokers, they buy and sell every day, hoping that the market doesn't crash in between.

These businessmen work in dollar amounts that most of us cannot fathom. It is not unusual for a buyer to roll over millions of dollars worth of cattle a week. He'll keep back a small percentage for himself while waiting to get paid so he can invest in another load of cattle.

To be a successful buyer, a man needs to have a keen eye and a quick mind for figures. A good cattle buyer can spot a stag (uncastrated calf) in the sale ring in seconds. He can estimate the weight of a calf within a few pounds. If a cattle buyer is not on the phone, then he is writing figures on a piece of paper. He can withstand the rigors of travelling between auction marts day after day, and is able to sit through twelve-hour sales. He is motivated by the knowledge that each day there is a bargain out there, and he wants to be the one to find it.

The cattle buyer is the front man for the feedlot operator and the one who takes the flack from both the buyer and seller over prices. Everyone knows that in order for him to make a living, he has to buy as low as he can, then re-sell at a profit. He is constantly being asked for market predictions and to estimate what a group of calves might bring. It takes decades for the cattle buyer to build a reputation of trust, but only one shady deal to exile him from the industry forever.

His best friend is a low Canadian dollar.

His worst enemy? The closed border.

While out in B.C., I met Mark Canart. Originally from Elkhorn, Manitoba, Mark moved to B.C. in 1979 and worked for the Kamloops Livestock Co-op for five years. He started buying cattle to feed, then began order buying for others. Now he does all that and owns his own trucking business. Up until the border closed, Mark was buying cattle for a handful of large feedlots in Washington state, Idaho and Kansas. Losing these customers has bitten a huge piece out of his bottom line.

I followed him into the stands during a sale. He chose a spot high enough that he could see, but not too far from the auctioneer.

"This has really affected me," he said, watching the auctioneer pull bids from other buyers.

I waited, carefully timing my questions so they didn't interfere with his bidding.

"Fifty percent of the business I do, or shall I say did, goes south," he said, explaining that usually he buys close to 2,000 calves each spring to put on grass for the summer. The year the border closed, he had all that summer's calves bought and turned them out to pasture as usual. He held onto them over the fall hoping that the border would open. When it didn't, he was forced to sell at a loss.

"This has been an eye-opening experience for a lot of cow-calf guys who held onto their calves," he said. "Now they know first-hand how hard it is to make money feeding cattle."

What saved Mark's hide was the fact he had 1,000 cattle on feed in the U.S. He bought only 200 calves to put on grass this past spring and once again is anticipating that the border might open this coming winter. Right now, he is order buying for others and running his trucks, but says business is down 40 percent, and the profitability in hauling just isn't there because the trucks are running empty a quarter of the time.

"I'm hurt bad enough that I can't afford to make another mistake," he says.

I waited while he bid aggressively on a pen of calves, successfully outbidding the other buyer.

It is always interesting hearing predictions from cattle buyers, so I asked Mark what he thinks is going to happen in the future.

He predicts that the industry is going to evolve so much that producers won't recognize it as the same business 10 years from now. He believes that a lot of the small producers will sell out because they won't be profitable and ranch size will continue to grow. Technology will overpower some of the older producers who won't want to comply, as well as the smaller producers who can't be bothered to keep up with the times because it doesn't pay for them to do so.

Electronic identification of cattle and sound record-keeping will become mandatory. Mark says that Canada is five years ahead of the Americans regarding national identification. Electronic traceback and the compact nature of Canada's industry compared to the sprawling numbers in the U.S. will help open up foreign markets to Canadian beef once the borders do start to re-open. In his estimation, the future looks bright for the progressive cattle producer.

Mark wants to see the U.S. border open, but he also would like to see our industry prepare itself to meet the demands of countries like Japan.

"If they want BSE testing, then we have to give it to them," he said, adding that no other industry dictates to the consumer what they should and shouldn't have.

I asked if the Alberta feeding industry is going to be able to survive pressure from U.S. buyers once the border opens.

Although he thinks that not all of the players will still be around to compete once everything shakes out, he did seem confident that overall Alberta will still be in the game.

"Southern Alberta has the infrastructure, the grain, good weather and easy access to large number of calves. None of that is going to change," he said. "It's a perfect place to feed cattle."

Twelve hours of driving and I'm back in the heart of feedlot alley.

I awake the following morning to find the weather hasn't changed much since I was here in late October. It is sunny and a bit cooler, but to a Manitoban, this feels positively balmy for December.

This morning I will meet with Lethbridge M, Rick Casson at a nearby restaurant. The federal and provincial governments played an important role in keeping the industry afloat, and I am curious what Rick might have to say.

The relationship between the agriculture producer and the politician is one of ambivalence. Mostly the cattleman ignores the politician until disaster strikes, then he goes to him for help, expecting immediate results. The politician is paid regardless of measurable results. He can be the worst representative imaginable, but if elected for two terms, will receive a government pension. The cattleman can work hard all year and end up with little financial reward. This is a real sore spot with producers who feel their own retirement is in jeopardy.

Those producers who have spent some time in the corporate world understand that there are challenges to every type of work.

There is more attached to being an MP than sitting on a plane, attending ribbon-cutting ceremonies, talking on the phone or thinking up clever ways to get re-elected. The astute politician knows his constituents well enough to differentiate between the opinions of the vocal radical and the concerns of the average man. Such a politician can forgive a producer who is venting out of frustration because he has nowhere else to turn.

It is a demanding job and the satisfaction taken home at the end of the day is no different for the politician than for the cattleman. The closed border has put pressure on everyone connected to the cattle industry.

I spot Rick Casson as soon as I enter the restaurant. Lethbridge is a small enough place that everyone knows Rick when they see him. He is standing in the aisle right now, bent toward and listening to the people sitting in the booth across from ours. He waves for me to sit down, finishes his conversation, then joins me at the table. He glances at his watch. He'll fly back to Ottawa this afternoon so we don't have a lot of time.

I warn him that I'm really not interested in hearing a rant from the opposition, but want to know how he's been affected by all of this.

"I had brown hair on May 20," he chuckles, running a hand across his mostly grey head. "It's been a real pressure cooker, let me tell you."

We order coffee and breakfast.

When BSE was announced there were 950,000 head of cattle on feed in Canada, and 700,000 of those animals were in Rick's riding. He tells me it was pretty obvious from day one where the hurt would be. His phone started ringing immediately.

I ask Rick where he is from and how he got started in politics.

He says that he was raised in Diamond City, Alberta, a small town just north of Lethbridge. Although he didn't grow up on a farm, he has always considered himself rural, and says that Diamond City serviced a large farming community back when towns were smaller, in the days before Alberta's boom. Rick became involved in municipal politics, serving on council for 18 years. His education in the feedlot industry came when he was Mayor of Picture Butte. He has been the MP here since 1997.

Rick says that the first bit of advice he gave producers who came to him was that they needed to approach the government with a single, solid voice and clear objectives.

"It was apparent almost immediately that the border closure is completely unnecessary," he says, taking a sip of coffee. "Knowing this has layered frustration on top of hardship for a lot of these folks." Their worry has caused him sleepless nights and he says not many Albertans will escape unscathed from this economic crisis. He says that this issue is a personal one since he has numerous family members and friends involved in the industry. Right now they are looking to him for help, and some, for hope.

Rick describes the average feedlot owner as an aggressive, type A businessman who deals in millions of dollars daily. They are critical of government because the bureaucratic wheel turns much too slowly for their liking and their needs.

There is a measurable amount of worry on Rick's face as he talks about the future of his riding, describing how disquieting it is to see these feedlot operators knocked down. He describes how the emotional climate along the countryside has switched from initial feelings of shock to desperation and then hope—only to have that shattered when the border didn't open as expected. He says that now, an eerie quiet has settled over the region.

"This has really hurt the pride in this area," he says, adding that he has had calls from some pretty desperate people. "It's very hard for these guys to come to the government with hat in hand. It's heartbreaking."

Rick says that although getting through the next year is everybody's focus right now, there is trouble brewing behind the scenes. He believes the next biggest issue the industry will face is packer ownership of cattle. Packers have admitted to owning 20 percent of cattle numbers before BSE, but now, nobody will say how much they own. He explains that packers are slowly gaining control of the industry by buying up cattle and making attractive feeding agreements with feedlot operators. The packers are removing competition from the marketplace by custom feeding 2,000 head in a 10,000 head lot, but only if the feedlot operator will agree to sell what he owns through their plant. It's a tempting option for the feedlot man during these times—gives him steady income and ensures no standing in line when the cattle are ready to go. The benefit to the packer is obvious—they don't have to bid against one another for the animals.

But Rick says that competition fuels this industry and the engine will soon begin to stall. If the packers gain too much control, the benefit producers see now could suddenly flip and begin working to their disadvantage. If the feedlot operator becomes dependent on packer cattle, then the packer can offer to pay less for feeding. If this feedlot won't take the deal, someone more desperate will. This will shrink the profit margin of the feedlots, giving them less equity and buying power, which means that before long they won't be able to compete with the packers for young calves in the fall.

Rick is frustrated that the Competition Bureau won't even address the issue because they say it is not against the law to make excessive profits.

"How can we get these free enterprisers back on their feet when the deepest pockets now are the packers who own or control the largest supply of cattle?" he asks.

Rick blames the government, saying they let this get out of hand and that if the problem existed with Bombardier or Chevrolet instead of the cattle industry, the Liberal government would take it more seriously. He laments that nobody from the government is leading the charge to sell Canadian beef and that any bit of optimism felt in the industry right now is coming from the U.S.

We talk about that fading optimism and he shakes his head.

"It's gotten to the point that we don't dare speculate," he says, adding that he hears a rumour almost every day. "Even the tiniest rumour can travel like wildfire and affect the market dramatically."

I tell him people want to know what the Conservative Party of Canada would do if they were in power.

Rick says that the Conservatives have a plan that would channel $10 million into developing new world markets, provide loan guarantees for cow-calf producers, develop a herd rationalization program that would take care of mature animals (as a last resort), and instigate BSE testing that would satisfy the OIE.

He is also worried that the packing industry has not expanded enough to accommodate the potential backlog of cattle on the set-aside program. If the border doesn't open in 2005, the industry could still be in trouble.

"Yes, I am critical of the current government," he says. "I wouldn't be doing my job properly if I weren't."

I tell him that when it comes to politics I don't know what to believe. Criticism for the sake of making the government look bad does nothing to help the cattleman. We need our politicians to be fair, to do the right thing and not criticize for the sake of making the other party's policies look bad to finagle votes. I use the newly introduced CAIS program as an example. The Liberals say it is the answer, the Conservatives criticize it and the rancher is mystified by it. What should we believe?

Rick seems to agree there is no place for political maneuvering when livelihoods are threatened.

I ask what is the best-case scenario for the future.

Rick says he'd like to see private cattle ownership return to pre-BSE levels.

The Canadian industry has to stop hanging its head and begin taking advantage of the fact that we have a better food safety system than the U.S.

We must begin exploiting the fact that we are world leaders in beef quality and our reputation is respected worldwide.

Canada must begin slaughtering and marketing a huge percentage of its own cattle so that live cattle exports become a smaller percentage of the business.

We must change the climate so that young producers will run toward the industry instead of away from it.

Best-case scenario is that Canada, not Nebraska, sets the basis price for beef in North America.

I ask how much of this can be achieved.

Rick finishes his coffee and pays the bill.

"I hope all of it," he says.

We both know that scoring this goal is going to take a lot more than hope.

CHAPTER TWENTY FIVE

"A good ol' boy in the Panhandle told me the other day
you can still make a small fortune in agriculture.
Problem is, you got to start with a large one."
— Jim Hightower, 1986

Cochrane is in the heart of Alberta's ranch country. I've been told it is a wonderful town and believe it after speaking with Alex Baum, owner of Cochrane Dodge.

During the drought 2001, Alex became involved with Ranch Aid Alberta, a group that helped distressed cattlemen by bringing in hay from other provinces, paying for it through corporate and personal donations. Two years later, BSE hit.

Early on in the crisis, Alex believed that BSE was not being taken seriously by the country's leaders, so he decided to try and do something about it.

Alex got together with former professional wrestler Dan Kroffat and they came up with a few ideas. They decided a petition might help so they had a webmaster design a site for them called opentheborder.com. Visitors to the site were asked to sign an online petition that would be forwarded to the government once 10,000 signatures were received.

"The response was tremendous," Alex says, adding that when the number hit 114,000 this past fall, they took the petition to Ottawa. They presented it to Myron Thompson, MP for Wild Rose and to Nova Scotia Senator Terry Mercer.

They also delivered more than 2,000 e-mails, mostly from cattle producers, who wrote in their own words how they were affected by the crisis.

Cor Van Raay

KAREN EMILSON

"Reading those e-mails was pretty tough," Alex says, adding that judging by what he's read, there have been a number of producers who have gone bankrupt, had mental breakdowns or were considering suicide.

"Ranchers are anything but whiners and complainers; if anything they internalize how they are feeling," he says. "We wanted to do something positive, to make a difference for our ranching community."

Alex says that shortly after visiting Ottawa, they received a call from Washington, asking them to bring the petition there. He says there is a strong movement in the U.S. to get the border open, and he says they will go to the U.S. if it is determined the invitation is a serious one.

Alex says that people need to understand how this economic crisis has affected not only the cattleman, but all the small towns in western Canada. He cites his own business as an example. Usually he would sell between 10 and 15 pick-up trucks to the ranching community, but he hasn't sold one in more than a year.

"The ripple effect here is unbelievable," he says, adding that he can't think of anyone in the province who is not affected by agriculture. "This was once a thriving, vibrant area, but now things are pretty quiet."

I ask how long the web site will be up and running.

"Until we achieve our goal," Alex says. "We have to get that border open."

I am starting to worry. I need to leave for Calgary soon but I still haven't interviewed Cor Van Raay. We've been playing a game of phone tag that began during my last visit.

Just as I pull in the driveway, the cell phone rings. It's him. Cor asks me to refresh his memory about who I am and what exactly it is I want.

I've heard he doesn't agree to this sort of thing very often.

"How long will it take?" he asks, sounding pressed.

I explain that interviews vary from a half hour to an hour—some take two, it all depends on how long the person I'm meeting with wants to talk. He doesn't need to know about the ten-hour marathons that also involve huge amounts of food and a bottle of wine.

"I'll give you 15 minutes," he says. "What I have to say won't take very long."

Fifteen minutes. Better than nothing. Within a short time I am on my way to Iron Springs. My stomach starts to churn.

I'm not sure what it is about this man that makes me nervous. Maybe it's the fact that he is the largest independent cattle feeder in the country.

Or maybe it is his gruff telephone manner. I think I'm rattled because when I was working for the Manitoba Cattle Producers Association, a group of Manitoba producers took a bus tour here to feedlot alley. When they returned, one man said to me, "Cor Van Raay is to Canada's cattle industry what Garth Brooks is to country music." He has made more, done more, sold more and taken more risks than any contemporary to date. So I, and everyone else, wants to know what he thinks. Rumours abound over how Cor is managing through this crisis.

I turn toward Iron Springs and am distracted for a few minutes by a plume of smoke to my left. As I get closer, I see that a section of feedlot pens have been bulldozed into a pile and lit on fire. I turn at the Van Raay Farms sign and drive past a modest home. The lot is spacious, neat and the air is fresh and clean.

I have no idea what Cor looks like, so when I pull up to the feedlot office, I'm left wondering if that is him standing outside on the sidewalk by the office door. If so, then he is taller, thinner and older than I expect. I introduce myself, then follow Cor into his bright, tidy office and we sit across the desk from one another.

I ask if the pile burning at the end of the feedlot is a sign of what's to come.

He laughs, and I'm relieved he gets my joke.

He says that this lot is one of the older ones and that it needs renovating. He has ripped down the east side and plans to build new. This is a good time to do it since the lot isn't full.

I remember reading somewhere that the average cost of building a 25,000 head feedlot in Lethbridge county is near $12 million. Cor owns seven feedlots of his own, plus two more in partnership with a man named Rick Paskal. Cor is part-owner of a few other businesses in the area, and is a major shareholder in Ranchers Beef, the new 850-head a day packing plant initiative that will break ground near Calgary early in the new year. To say he has a lot of money tied up in this industry is a gross understatement.

I ask what we need for the industry to return to normal.

"Get the border open," Cor says.

That didn't take long. Now I need to think of something else to ask. While I'm thinking, this unassuming man begins to speak in a voice so quiet, I have to lean forward to hear him.

"Fat steers are like a box of ripe apples," he says. "The longer they sit, the riper they get, the lower their value."

Cor explains that when the border closed, his inventory was immediately worth half of what it was the day before. He says that for every dollar he puts up, the bank will loan him two. When an inventory is suddenly worth half its value, not only does that put the borrower in a deficit position with the bank, but it reduces his cash down to zero.

"I lost millions," he says, adding that if it wasn't for government help, he wouldn't still be in business. "People heard I got $28 million from the programs and they said, 'Oh, that's so much,' but not if they knew how much I lost."

Cor says that when you are in this business you grow accustomed to the regular ups and downs, but that this is the toughest financial struggle he's ever faced. He doesn't blame the packing plants for trying to buy cattle as cheap as they can, saying he has been in business long enough to know better than to take it personally—everybody is just trying to make money.

I wonder out loud how much bounce back is left in the industry.

"You can only lose like we did for one year," he says, adding that it will take at least three years of healthy profits before he'll be able to make up those losses, to be where he was when this began.

Right now, his lot is only 50% full. He bought approximately 60,000 head of cattle this fall, but, of course, wants to be full when the border opens.

"Although I've given up trying to guess when that might be," he says, adding that his lot was full in December and it cost him a bundle. Fearing the industry could "drop like a rock," he is only betting what he can afford to lose. Cor wants to stay in a good financial position with the bank so that when this turns around—he seems confident that it will—he'll be ready to dive back in.

"I have a big appetite for risk," he says. "But my kids are telling me to play it safe right now."

The phone rings and he answers. His tone immediately changes as he picks up a pencil. He asks the person on the other end how much the cattle weigh, jotting down the figures on a pad. How many are there? He does a few manual calculations, then tells the fellow how high he can go. The phone rings at least three more times and he buys cattle with each call. Now I understand his gruffness. A phone call means business and business usually translates into money spent. He buys more than a half million dollars worth of cattle in 45 minutes.

"Last year we would have had the best year ever, we were set to go," he says as he hangs up the phone. "But instead, we had the worst." Cor explains that the industry was at the low end of the cycle and the trend toward high-protein diets had raised consumption in both countries, so demand was there. If BSE hadn't happened, the low cattle numbers would have meant cow-calf and feedlot operators would have made money at the expense of the packer. Instead, it was the packer who won out, at least here in Canada. He visited a few feedlots in the U.S. last year and says that some of them had the best year ever. Because of demand and cheap feed, there were operators there who made up to $600 a steer at times.

The worry for many feedlot operators now is how the closed border will affect the regular cattle cycle. With record low numbers of cattle in the U.S. and record high numbers here, it could be disastrous for both countries if the border doesn't open soon. The U.S. packing industry is suffering, and U.S. feedlots are importing cattle from Mexico in record numbers.

Cor was part of a delegation that paid a visit to Washington last year, before the animal with BSE was discovered in the U.S. At that time, it appeared that the Americans were receptive to opening the border, but the bureaucrats were setting the timetable. This visit helped him put into perspective how irrelevant we are to the huge U.S. bureaucracy. Since then, R-CALF has mounted a defence that is definitely complicating matters.

Cor believes that R-CALF supporters are not free traders and the BSE discovery gave them the mechanism to keep the border closed.

With 18 months of hindsight available, I ask what the industry should have done differently.

"We should have focused on getting our packing industry going, especially after that case was discovered in the U.S. in December," he says, nodding in the direction of his empty pens. "The way I see it, this is far from over."

I ask how badly all of this has hurt the local economy. Cor believes that other businesses must be feeling the affect because he alone has been forced to lay off 20 employees.

Cor is one of the producers who are suing the U.S. government under Chapter 11 of the North American Free Trade Agreement (NAFTA). When the U.S. signed the agreement it gave us access to their market. According to NAFTA, members must provide other NAFTA parties with treatment no less favourable than they give their own investors. It was determined a year ago that the closed border is no longer about health and food safety. The Canadian Cattlemen for Free Trade have decided to go ahead despite the fact that the CCA and Canadian government do not agree with the move. Initially their claim was filed for $150 million in damages but that amount continues to rise as more cattlemen add their names to the suit.

I want to know more about Cor, but he is a private man so I'm given only a few details. I've heard rumours that he came to Canada from Holland as a young man, landing in Vancouver with $5 in his pocket. He worked as a lumberjack in B.C., which gave him enough money to begin renting land. He started growing sugar beets, gradually increasing his farm's size. The demand for sugar beets evaporated around the same time the feedlot industry started to expand, so Cor made the switch, coming in to the industry on the ground floor.

"I never planned to start feeding this many cattle, it just happened," he says. "It just became a very natural thing to do." Cor says that he still has a large farming operation that consists of 15,000 irrigated acres—land he needs to spread manure from his lots.

Cor strikes me as an honest man who is also very modest. People who are jealous of his success have taken pleasure in the damage the closed border has done to his business. A rumour is circulating that he doesn't own the cattle in his lot, that he has been forced to custom feed as well.

I ask him if this is true and he tells me no. He custom fed around 2,000 head early in the crisis for an individual, but owns everything now.

I am glad to hear this. Partly because I like Cor but also because ranchers need these big operators to stay independent and regain a financial footing. Cor is one of only a few whose numbers rival the feeding companies owned by the multi-nationals.

I point to the TEAM auction hat he's wearing and ask if he buys cattle via the Internet. He says he does but didn't buy anything this week. I mention that we sold for the first time this way on Friday and got 99.75 cents a pound.

He asks what made us decide to sell through TEAM.

I give him the reasons, including that we like that our calves are less stressed by the process.

"What difference does that make to you?" he asks. There's a glint in his eye and I can tell he's ready for some lighthearted banter. "You don't get any more money for them."

Maybe not, I agree, but we hope that whoever buys them might like them well enough to bid on them again next year—maybe pay a bit more per pound if the calves perform well.

I ask Cor for his final thoughts.

He thinks for a moment then says, "I think when they do decide to open the border, they should make the announcement one day, open it the next. It would have less of an effect on the market that way."

I ask if he minds if I take his picture. He laughs at the idea, saying how

I don't need a picture of him, that my book will be just fine without it. It takes a bit of convincing, but finally he agrees.

As I'm preparing to leave, Cor points to a certificate on the wall. It was awarded to him recently for completing a full marathon. He tells me that he jogs regularly and runs a nine-minute mile. The last full marathon he ran, he completed in four hours and 15 minutes.

I tell him that the skills and mindset it must take to go that kind of distance should come in handy right about now, since the cattle industry seems to have hit the wall.

I glance at my watch. An hour and a half.

Not a marathon, but a better time than I expected.

CHAPTER TWENTY SIX

*"So live that you can look any man in the eye
and tell him to go to hell."*
— John D. Rockefeller, Jr., June 1930

Pride is a difficult thing to explain. Either a person has it or they don't, and as the BSE crisis has proven, it can be taken away in an instant. Once it's gone, there is no way of knowing how to get it back.

Just ask Robert Vander Heyden. He is a typical Alberta cattle feeder—young, energetic and optimistic. Robert has got a tolerance for risk that is long, and a memory that is short. In spite of this, he says that he's never going to forget what the closed border did to the industry.

"If it weren't for the programs, I'd be out of business, plain and simple," he says from his feedlot office in Picture Butte. He is sitting behind a small desk in a sparsely furnished room that has nothing more to it than what he needs to get the job done. A table, desk, computer, filing cabinet and a few chairs.

"People talk about how much money we got from the government, but we're one link in a chain and the government had to keep this link going," he says. "Because of that help we put more in the pocket of the cow-calf producer than people realize."

I ask how he got started in the business.

Robert grins. He tells me that he grew up on a nearby feedlot, married his high school sweetheart, Cindy, then set to work shortly afterward with the goal of owning his own feedlot. He bought land and an old homestead from a neighbour in 1988. He built everything from scratch—levelling the land, hauling gravel, building bunks, corrals, holding facilities and

Robert Vander Heyden

then later on, a new house. He's proud of the fact he built the place with profits from feeding cattle. If anyone ever told him he'd never make it, he had proven them wrong.

The lot is built for a capacity of 5,000 head and he was eyeing expansion before BSE hit. He was three quarters full anticipating the cattle would be ready to go to the packing house in the early fall.

"That's when it hit me hard," he says. "The most frustrating part with this issue is that we can do everything right and the packers still get away with paying us 35 cents a pound for fat cattle. It's disheartening."

Like most everyone else in the business, Robert bought more cattle that fall and began doing some custom feeding to help pay the bills. He believes the industry is being held at gunpoint, and worries that the door is wide open for the U.S. to come in and take over.

"They already own the packing plants and now they are buying up feeder cattle like you wouldn't believe," he says.

Up until 18 months ago, this hardworking businessman was being rewarded for his efforts. Now, he feels like he's chasing a carrot at the end of a string, like on the Bugs Bunny cartoons he watched as a kid. Like everyone else, he wants to have cattle when the border opens, but he's given up trying to guess when that might be. He's grown immune to both the good and the bad news reports and has adopted an "I'll believe it when I see it" attitude.

In order to save his business, Robert had to rely on government programs. He says that while the money helped him regain a financial footing, the sense of pride he once felt of having done it all himself has faded.

"In this business when it's good, it's good, and when it turns sour—" he whistles through his teeth and aims his thumb at the floor. "A guy has to be prepared to weather those bitter times, too, and most of us are. Everybody makes mistakes, but when they are your mistakes you learn from it and move on. This feels different somehow."

Robert is convinced that with increased testing another animal with BSE will be discovered. He just hopes that Canada is declared a minimal risk country before that happens, otherwise, it could give the American protectionist group R-CALF more ammunition in their fight to keep the border closed.

He was glad to hear that George W. Bush won the election, especially since Democrat John Kerry came right out and said he wanted to keep the border closed. Robert also believes the closed border has become a political issue and that the President isn't doing enough to resolve it.

Robert says the whole issue has made him stop and reflect on his choices. He says that life is too short to work all the time and the realization hit one day that his kids are growing fast and that he hasn't had a Christmas off in 14 years. He has made a lot of sacrifice to get to the point he was at before BSE brought everything tumbling down. Now he resents that time he has invested, and says that after nearly 20 years of hard work, he's left teetering on the edge, powerless to do much about it.

A lot of people he knows are feeling the same way. Enthusiasm throughout the whole region is down. People are not feeling like they want to go out, partially because the emotional roller coaster is exhausting, but also because cattlemen feel like they under a microscope. If they buy a restaurant meal, a bottle of whiskey, or something new, they hear the whispers: "It can't be that bad."

I've heard that Lethbridge County is a competitive place where neighbours aren't always friendly with one another. Despite the prosperity the feedlots have brought to the area, there is a strong anti-feedlot sentiment here and the reasons are varied. Some are concerned for the environment while others resent the fact that expansion of the industry in the 1980s drove up land prices. Today, a section of irrigated land in this country sells for $1.3 million. This creates a lot of wealth for those selling out, but makes it hard for the cow-calf producer and grain farmer to expand.

Robert says he has heard numerous snide comments since May 20, 2003, and his skin has grown thicker as a result. Some people are jealous of the feedlot man's success up to that point and believe they have finally received their comeuppance.

"The buzzards are circling," he chuckles.

Robert is not imagining the barbs—I have heard them, too.

He wheels his chair back, then starts digging through the filing cabinet behind his desk. He pulls out a sheet of paper, then wheels forward.

"My daughter wrote this in February and it was published in the local paper," he says, passing me a handwritten letter.

He sits quietly watching as I read the first half that explains where she is from, the BSE issue, and worries about bankruptcy. The last half of the letter reads:

> *"I am only 13 and it is really hard for me to deal with all the pressure and stress that is going through our community. It is also hard for me to see families that I know struggling to keep their families strong. I am one of the kids who are affected most because I am the daughter of a feedlot owner. When people are being laid off or quitting and when I see businesses shutting down, that not only makes me*

worry but it makes me upset.

Thank you for taking the time to read my letter. I hope that now you realize how hard this is hitting our country, our province, our community and most importantly, our families."

Sincerely, *Amanda Vander Heyden*

I hand the letter back to him and he skims over it.

"My kids are feeling it more than I realized," he says, face softening as if he's just read it for the first time. "Thirteen-year-old kids shouldn't feel stress like this." He quietly tells me he doesn't want this lifestyle for his son.

There is nothing much left to say. No more questions to ask. Robert and Amanda pretty much said it all.

He walks me outside and waits while I snap a picture of him by his truck. Robert says that he's never been anti-American, but this situation has made him understand the sentiments felt in other parts of the world. He hands me a brown package with a sticker taped to the outside.

"Give these to your husband," he smiles.

The words R-CALF USA are printed in bold letters followed by a raised middle finger.

I must admit, it's how most cattlemen are feeling right about now.

Chapter Twenty Seven

"You can see what man made from the seat of an automobile,
but the best way to see what God made
is from the back of a horse."
— Charles M. Russell

It is very difficult to fight a war if soldiers believe their enemies have lives that include a family, job and a host of dreams. So when preparing troops during basic training, one of the first thing the army commander will do is dehumanize the enemy. Create the vision of a common adversary, a nameless, faceless opponent who will kill you unless you murder him first.

Today I'll venture into enemy territory, so to speak, to meet with U.S. cattle producers. My guess is they aren't much different from us.

Laura Hutchinson, an acquaintance and producer-writer for farm.tv here in Lethbridge has decided to come along. I'm glad for the company and she is anxious to hear the American point of view.

We are on our way to see Edith and Jay Clark, ranchers living 20 miles southeast of Sweetgrass, Montana. If things go well, tomorrow we will travel further south to Valier to meet R-CALF members Pam and Darrell Swanson. I contacted them last time I was here, but they didn't have time so we agreed to try again. Talking with them should give me insight into why producers support R-CALF.

At Milk River, I pull into Jan Spencer's gas station and fill up. Before leaving, I decide to call the Swansons.

Pam answers the phone. I introduce myself again and explain why I would like to meet with them. She hesitates, telling me today they are moving cattle 40 miles from home and will stay overnight at their son's house.

Jay and Edith Clark

She isn't sure what time they will be back tomorrow. There is a weariness behind her words and I can't tell if it is the result of another busy day, or if she is searching for an excuse.

I tell her that I am prepared to meet at any time convenient for them. She sighs, and I can feel the opportunity slipping away. I tell her that I think I know how they feel because we are cow-calf producers, too. I want to understand their position and promise to treat them fairly in the book. I am not the enemy. Persuasion gets me nowhere.

Pam's tone is matter-of-fact.

"I really have only one thing to say to you," she says. "These are the best prices we've ever seen. As far as I'm concerned, that border can stay shut forever."

A market report from Western Livestock Auction in Great Falls, Montana, confirms that U.S. ranchers are receiving excellent prices for their calves. At the end of October, 2004, 500 to 600 pound steer calves were averaging $1.10 a pound and selling as high as $1.23 U.S. Before the border closed, prices averaged closer to 85 cents a pound.

The border crossing at Coutts is quiet today. Both Laura and I are nervous. She doesn't have a passport and worries that if she is turned back, it will spoil my plans.

Pam Swanson's refusal to meet with us makes me feel like a spy, as if my objective is to infiltrate the enemy camp and bring back secrets to share with my comrades. I am disguised as a middle-aged farm wife. My weapon? A pen.

The border guard asks the purpose of our visit, so I give him the simplest answer—we are going to visit friends near Sweetgrass. He nods us through.

Edith has offered to meet us at the turn around. We smile at one another through our vehicle windows, then follow her white SUV across the highway and onto the gravel road that curves toward the Sweet Grass Hills.

I've read that these hills are made up of three buttes, named West, Gold and East. They are surrounded by a sloping prairie of undulating grass spread out as far as we can see. There are a few theories concerning what created this landscape. People believe the Hills were a result of a volcanic eruption that blistered the earth, causing the buttes to rise up like permanent boils. It is generally believed that the rolling landscape between here and southwest Saskatchewan were the consequence of a meteorite hit about 65 million years ago. It altered the landscape and changed the environment, which accelerated the extinction of the dinosaurs that once inhabited this part of North America. The result is a rugged terrain that is dauntingly vast—filled with sky and wind that is beautifully austere.

We follow Edith to her ranch-style house that is nestled in the hills. She invites us in to sit in the kitchen. The southwestern style is welcoming and in keeping with the landscape outdoors.

Edith immediately says "Don't mind the wall" when I ask directions to the washroom. Down the hallway leading to the bedrooms, in view of the kitchen, is a wall covered in handwriting. I pause to read some of it, then call out for an explanation. She explains that it began as a joke back in 1996 when they were redecorating and her son left his signature on the wall. It struck Edith as a wonderful, unique idea, so she decorated around it and after that, every person who visits is expected to leave their signature behind. I scan the wall, calling out a few names.

". . . he designed the animal kingdom at Disney World," Edith replies.

I ask about Gunnar Asgeirsson from Iceland. She tells me he was an exchange student. The wall is plastered with family, friends, one-time acquaintances—and a few old cowboys who are gone now.

Edith introduces us to her husband, Jay, who is waiting in a big chair near a large living room window that looks out over the prairie. There is a measured politeness to our words, a tension, as we all begin talking about the closed border. None of us wants to be insensitive, to say something that could be misinterpreted. My questions are carefully worded. I want to hear their truth, but I don't want to learn that the cow-calf producers here are struggling because of us.

"There was a time when a guy could pay for the land and make it work, but I'm not so sure anymore," Jay says. "We've experienced five years of drought, so it hasn't been easy. For a while we were having to use equity to operate. Our cattle prices are at record levels now, but the price of everything else has gotten so high." Jay worries about what will happen if prices go down, saying that most producers share his concerns.

These hills have been Jay's home his whole life. He grew up on a nearby ranch, then bought this place in partnership with his father in 1965. Edith grew up in Sweetgrass. In 1964 she and Jay married. They have three children—Matt, Nate and Connie. Nate is a veterinarian practising in New Jersey. Connie lives in Seattle. Matt and wife Lynda and their two children live in the yard nearby.

Over the years the Clarks have bought all the land they could, in some cases amalgamating a small neighbouring place into theirs. Their ranch has grown to a size that should support two families. They run a herd of black, white face Angus cows and use black Limousin and Angus bulls.

Edith has always worked off the ranch. She was a nurse for many years, serving the latter part of her career as the Director of Nursing at the local hospital. She was instrumental in setting up a medical program at a private prison in Shelby. In 1999, Edith ran and was elected as a Member of the State Legislature and served three two-year terms. She decided not to run in the recent election so she's feeling at loose ends right now.

She is a member of the Montana-Alberta Coalition that helps bring understanding of issues in respective countries to both sides of the table. They work together to find common ground and compromise on issues involving transportation and water, then offer recommendations to the governments.

Edith predicts that water is going to become the biggest issue in the coming years, since there is a shortage of it in these dry hills. Right now the agreements over who owns the rights to its use are ambiguous. The flow that feeds the Milk River passes through the Clark land, so historically they own the water rights. The potential for conflict exists, especially if someone along the river decides to build a dam or reservoir. For this reason, Edith believes it is important to firm up agreements between all parties involved, including Canada and the U.S.

Edith has been asked to give the American perspective at an conference on Agriculture Issues in Alberta in January 2005. She says that with both countries touting free trade and a global economy, it's disheartening to see such division in the cattle industries.

"Why are we fighting among ourselves?" she asks. She believes we should be working together to market North American beef as the best in the world and be less concerned by where the meat originated.

I quiz her on the economic realities of being a cow-calf producer in Montana.

Edith tells me that the biggest threat to their ranches are the wealthy hobbyists who are buying up rural Montana and turning it into a rich man's playground. She says these people are coming from all over the country and don't know much about country life. Many are environmentalists who want to escape the city, so they don't want to see any development, including mining of natural resources like gas and oil. Edith explains that Montana is a large state with a low population base. The hobbyists are forcing up land prices and taking land out of production, increasing the burden for everybody else. They do not necessarily pay their fair share of tax, especially if they apply for conservation easements.

"Montana could take a few lessons from Alberta on how to utilize its natural resources," she says, adding that this would help keep taxes within a reasonable range for everyone.

Edith and I agree that it is impossible to compare a ranch in Canada and the U.S. to decide which country is a more advantageous place to do business, because there are many factors, including a very different tax structure.

One factor easily understood by Canadians is the fact that U.S. producers must pay capital gains tax on land when they sell out. In 1988, land in Montana sold for $70 to $120 an acre. Now the same land is assessed at $480 an acre and taxed accordingly. Ranchers are having a hard time making a living because the annual tax bill is eating up the profits. When producers finally do sell out, they have to pay 40 percent in capital gains tax.

Edith says that they understand all too well the angst Canadian ranchers are feeling, because they've struggled to make a living raising cattle their whole lives.

"The R-CALF producers are hurting more than Canadian producers were before the border closed," Edith says. "Their backs are up against a wall."

She attended an R-CALF organizational meeting in Shelby and says that while she understands producer's reasons for joining, she does not agree with the organization's methods. She says that producers at the meeting became overly focused on the number of trucks carrying fat cattle and feeders into the U.S. There also was a lot of resentment expressed over how much more difficult it was for them to send feeder cattle north.

Transportation costs are a huge expense for Montana producers because virtually all the cattle here are fed in Iowa, Nebraska, Minnesota and North Dakota. It is 1,600 miles from the Clark ranch to Iowa, but only 100 to 150 miles to feedlot alley. Earlier import restrictions and the traditionally low Canadian dollar means feedlot operators in Canada aren't likely to buy in U.S. calves. Since the import restrictions have relaxed, some Americans have placed calves in Canadian feedlots for custom feeding. The problem is, once they've crossed the border now, they can't cross back, so producers can't take advantage of lower slaughter numbers in the U.S. and subsequent demand for cattle at the plants.

Edith says the resentment felt toward Canadians is not just about beef, but lumber as well. She believes that the anger people are feeling is real, but misplaced, and that much of the problem lies in the fact that U.S. manufacturing is being out sourced to other countries, while raw products still come in from Canada. She says closing the border just complicates matters.

"There is no doubt the closed border has hurt our economy," she says. "The packing industry, Montana truckers, gas stations, convenience stores—the whole state has felt this to some degree." She says that fuel consumption was down so much in 2003 that the Montana government anticipated a state deficit.

I have spoken to enough Americans over the years to know that our health care system is one that the average citizen in the U.S. envies. I guess this is a sore spot with ranchers, and Edith agrees. She tells me that they have a health care insurance bill of $12,000 a year. I say that we pay for health care through our taxes, but I don't know what it costs in a year. I tell them our system isn't perfect, that it is constantly being criticized. I don't pretend to have the answers, but admit that given the choice, I would stick with our flawed system rather than switch to the American model. At least Canadians are secure in the knowledge that they won't be wiped out financially by critical illness or an ongoing medical treatment.

Edith tell us that just as in Canada, people in the west feel they are dictated to by the high population numbers in the East. The Clarks wish the border ran north and south because they have more in common with Alberta than they do with New York. Over the years they have done a lot of business in Alberta, saying the favourable exchange rate meant they could buy feed and machinery over the line and transport it home easily. During the three-year drought that began in 2000, they made hay in Canada and hauled it home.

Before the bombing of the twin towers on September 11, 2001, the border between Alberta and Montana was pretty loose. There were never any problems sorting cattle that got mixed between countries and moving animals to another pasture was easy. It used to be that the Clarks could go cross-country to visit their Canadian neighbours, but now they have to go the long way around through the border crossing because of the new Homeland Security rules. They fear that if they don't comply and get caught, they could be in serious trouble.

"That's the border right over there," she says, pointing out the window to a fence line only a few miles away. "The cows don't seem to know the difference." She looks a bit sad, like she wants to say that it's too bad people don't know the difference.

The Clarks say that one of the hardest things they have had to deal with since the border closed is that they sense resentment from some Canadian cattlemen. No longer can they joke with friends like they once did. This whole situation has put strain on a few friendships, including those with R-CALF supporters.

"We just avoid discussing it, that's all," she says.

In keeping with the hospitality I've experienced the last few months, Edith serves a lovely lunch of roast beef, vegetables, buns, salad and dessert.

Afterward, we take a tour of the ranch.

Jay explains that their place is located on the north side of the West Butte. They call the Hills "islands in the middle of the prairie," and say that on a clear day they can see the Rocky Mountains. The grass on their pasture is all native—fescue and June grasses. Deer and elk roam the place and they see the occasional cougar.

They show us a bit of history—the spot where the Gold Butte Stage Coach would switch horses, where the old school once sat. Jay tells us that his grandmother was the teacher, that his dad went there, that he did, too, and that their sons were some of the last kids to go. The school closed down as so many small schools have, and now the children are bussed to nearby Sunburst.

Jay and Edith are at the age when they have started to think about retiring. If their only consideration was money, they could get by for the next decade, then sell out to the highest bidder. But they love the lifestyle and want it preserved. They plan to sell their share of the place to Matt.

"We're never going to get rich doing this or leave a lot to our kids, but it's been a good way of life. I just wish we knew for sure what the future holds, for our son's sake," Edith says.

The setting sun casts the hills in a gorgeous golden glow. We stop the truck and get out to stand on the land. They tell us that farmers here have given into subsidization as a way to stay in business, but the ranchers have resisted help, and that resistance, born from independence and a desire to avoid regulation and control, could prove disastrous in the end.

I turn my back to the sun, but Jay stands facing it head-on, raising his hand like a visor. He tells us that in the mid-1990s, there were 15,000 head of cattle in Toole County. That number has since dropped to less than 5,000. He says this is happening across Montana and they know a number of producers who have just up and quit.

"It's a real shame when worry and frustration can take away the beauty of a place," Jay says, lowering his hand, then looking over his shoulder at the hills. I can't help but think how right they look here. There is a straightness to these folks and a forthright way of speaking that is the trademark of ranch people.

I pull out my camera to get a shot of the Clarks basking in this golden light. We stand for awhile longer, then return somewhat reluctantly to the truck.

Back at the house, I take a few more pictures as Laura and I prepare to leave. Edith gives me the names of a few R-CALF supporters who might be willing to meet with us. I phone and leave messages, but have no luck tonight. We decide to drive back to Lethbridge and try again tomorrow.

We are invited to sign the signature wall, then I ask for a few final thoughts as we step back into the brisk, late afternoon air.

Edith thinks for a moment, then smiles. "I guess you could say we are more alike than different. All we're trying to do is make a living—just like you."

PART FOUR

ACCEPTANCE

CHAPTER TWENTY EIGHT

"Calling Canadian beef unsafe is like
calling your twin sister ugly."
—American Meat Institute, May 2004

R-CALF USA.

It is a clever acronym that, spelled out, means Ranchers-Cattlemen Action Legal Fund, United Stockgrowers of America.

The organization's mission is to represent the U.S. cattle industry in national and international trade and marketing issues to ensure the continued profitability and viability of U.S. cattle producers.[20]

Canada's first dealings with R-CALF came in 1998 when R-CALF filed a live cattle anti-dumping (selling below the cost of production) case against Canada and Mexico and a countervailing (subsidy) case against Canada. Early in the dispute the International Trade Commission (ITC) dismissed the Mexico case, but the claim against Canada dragged on for a year. Tariffs were imposed at the border on live cattle exports, and it cost the Canadian industry close to $5.5 million in legal costs to fight the claims. In the end, the ITC ruled in Canada's favour and the tariff money, which was held in trust, was returned to the cattle exporters.

R-CALF members still believe that they were ruled against unfairly and that Canadian ranchers are government subsidized and continue to dump cattle into the U.S. market below the cost of production.

Back in 1998, R-CALF was labelled a protectionist organization by Canadian industry leaders who carefully distinguished between them and others in the U.S. industry. They were quick to squash anti-American sentiments that filtered up from the grassroots.

The "RancHers" Patti Scott, Lenore McLean and Erin Butters

These same leaders who were involved in the anti-dumping and subsidy suits were not surprised when R-CALF surfaced shortly after the border closed in 2003. In the back of everyone's mind was the expectation that
regardless of what science might prove, R-CALF would be working behind
the scenes to try and keep the border closed.

That opportunity presented itself in April 2004 when the USDA made
an error and began allowing unauthorized beef products into the U.S. This
gave R-CALF grounds to file a lawsuit against the USDA, saying the government department was negligent in protecting the U.S. beef industry and
American consumers from potentially BSE-infected meat. United States
District Judge Richard F. Cebull granted the cattle association's motion for
a Temporary Restraining Order. As a result, the U.S. rule to open the border became stuck in the American legal system.

Canadian producers can almost understand R-CALF's desperation to
keep the border closed, but are left disgusted by their jingoistic, fear-mongering tactics. R-CALF is trying to scare the American public into believing that the BSE problem in Canada is widespread and that Canadian meat
is unsafe. These tactics will work as long as there are no home-grown cases
of BSE discovered in the U.S., and could backfire if BSE is discovered
there.

On November 24, R-CALF lashed out against the USDA for
announcing inconclusive test results, claiming that whenever BSE is mentioned, it leads to unnecessary concerns on the part of the public and the
commodities markets.

"U.S. cattle producers are experiencing financial losses measured in
the tens of millions of dollars due to USDA's test announcement policies,"
said R-CALF USA President Leo McDonnell. "While R-CALF is thankful this latest announcement resulted in a negative test for BSE, and while
we want to continue to emphasize to U.S. consumers that USA beef is safe,
we cannot comprehend USDA's logic in the way the agency chooses to dis-
rupt the U.S. cattle markets."

McDonnell said the USDA is sending contradictory messages to the
cattle industry and to consumers.[21] He goes on to say that the USDA's policy of releasing unconfirmed cases suggests that even the prospect of
detecting a case of BSE has huge safety implications, and that there is no
human health risk associated with these test announcements.

The USDA defends the announcements, saying that it is better to be
up front with the public about unconfirmed cases than to have the information leak out and appear that the industry has something to hide.

But McDonnell is resolute in his message. "USDA also should target its tests to the highest-risk animals—those from Canada—so that we are testing those cattle most likely to have BSE."[22]

R-CALF's tactics play well with the American public who are living in a climate of fear over international terrorism and possible sabotage of their food supply. The ban on Canadian meat is a popular thing to do and gives R-CALF the appearance of being industry caretakers regarding food safety. They supposedly have the inside track and are on the side of the people, opposing the government that so often is accused of having something to hide.

Canadian producers are blatantly told, "If you were in our shoes, you'd do the same thing."

Americans know that their money earns between 25 to 40 percent more on the Canadian side of the border. And yet, I have on a few occasions discussed how for us the same item in the U.S. costs us 25 to 40 percent more because our money is worth less. It's amazing the blank looks I've received. One man asked why I would want to buy anything in the U.S. with everything being so cheap in Canada!

I have heard that R-CALF producers complain that we get paid so much more for our cattle than they get for theirs. It seems almost ridiculous to suggest, but is it possible that R-CALF producers who listen to a Canadian market report on the radio think it is in American dollars?

The year before the border closed, 600 pound steer calves were bringing $1.30 a pound. With the dollar exchange at 37 percent, that equals out to around 90 cents American. So if a U.S. producer ships his calves and gets 88 cents, then hears that the same weight calves brought $1.32 just over the border . . .

"If it ain't Alberta, it ain't Beef" reads the bumper sticker on the truck in front of me. It's a well-known slogan that has been known to raise the hackles of beef producers in the other provinces. After all, Alberta may be the cattle feeding capital of Canada, but the genetics of those calves come from all across the country.

I'm on my way to the Alberta Beef Producers' (ABP) Annual General Meeting in Calgary. There will be directors, delegates and producers from across the province there, as well as representation from the CCA and some of the other provincial organizations. Fallout from BSE and the closed border will top the agenda.

But before I turn onto the highway that will take me north, I must make a detour first through Iron Springs. Do I call first or don't I?

I want to avoid appearing stupid and unprofessional, so I try to think of a grand excuse—a lie actually—that will explain why I've returned. What I've come up with sounds too much like "the dog ate my homework," so I try to think of something else.

I turn on the flash and have the camera ready to go. I park the car, hop out and hurry in.

"You're back," Cor says as he hangs up the phone.

Yes, I tell him as I lift the camera and focus. He worries a bit that he isn't wearing a better shirt. I wait while he straightens his hat.

I tell him I had trouble with the camera.

"What kind of trouble?" he asks.

"Trouble is," I say, "this camera needs film."

I'd forgotten to load one before I left home, so now I have to return to my earlier interviews and re-take the pictures.

Cor chuckles. I get a few shots, then hurry away, taking less than a minute of his time.

With my backtracking done, I leave for Calgary. I pull into the hotel at dusk. People say that any given day the weather in Calgary can be very different from what it is in Lethbridge. I discover this is true when I step out of the car to find the temperature has plummeted. I wrestle a stiff cord out of the trunk and plug in the car.

I am reminded of one of the first annual meetings I attended when Mark was a director with the Manitoba Cattle Producers Association. The meeting was in a town called Melita, at the beginning of December. On the morning of the second day, Mark and I found ourselves in the company of director Doug De'Athe and his wife, Claire. The De'Athes ranch in south-central Manitoba.

Near the end of the meeting, resolutions from the membership were brought forward. Resolutions are motions from the membership that give direction to the board for the upcoming year. These resolutions are voted on and either passed or defeated.

Doug stood up and brought forward a motion for discussion. Holding up a slip of paper, he read from it a few reasons why the particular suggestion should be pursued by the board. The audience sat quietly until he was done, then shifted uncomfortably in their chairs. Some stood up and spoke in agreement, there were others who opposed it.

Greenhorn that I was, I didn't understand the implication of the suggestion, which in all honesty, sounded pretty good to me. I started feeling a bit sorry for Doug and his idea especially after his wife, Claire, stood up and proceeded to lambaste the suggestion in a 10-minute oration that nearly caused a standing ovation when she was done.

I almost fell off my chair. I thought this was terribly funny and wondered what discussions must be like around the De'Athe dinner table. It wasn't until much later that I understood Doug wasn't in favour of the idea at all, but as a Director, it was his responsibility to bring forward all motions passed at his local meeting. It's one of the least favourite things that Directors have to do—speak in favour of something they don't believe in.

I later came to understood the motion Doug brought forward was that the MCPA support the NISA program, which Claire (and others) argued could be considered a subsidy by the U.S. and result in trade tariffs. Producers have worried about losing access to the U.S. market long before BSE.

I quickly check into my room before returning to the hotel lobby. Within minutes I find myself met by a throng of cattle producers, all wearing name badges, leaving the last meeting of the day. Some of the men and women who pass by smile politely, while others are immersed in tense conversation with the person beside them. Checking the meeting agenda, I read that they just finished the first round of resolutions.

I am looking for a man named Cam Ostercamp. He is the President of the Beef Initiative Group (BIG), a grassroots organization that is trying to find the support to build at least one, maybe two, producer-owned plants.

I recognize Cam immediately from the photos that have run in the farm papers taken during his tour across the western provinces. Cam is slim and dressed like a cow man in denim and a western shirt. He's distracted, looks annoyed. He introduces himself and we sit at the edge of the lobby lounge.

Cam has just come from seeing the majority of the resolutions supporting BIG's idea defeated by the ABP board.

Cam has been working tirelessly trying to get this project off the ground and he's mad as hell.

"They just soundly defeated half of the common-sense resolutions brought forward," he says, face red with frustration. "They are in there applauding the expansion of the packing plants that have taken advantage of us for the past 18 months."

A few minutes with Cam and I figure out he's a cow-calf producer who hates the idea of giving away his culled cows. He estimates that Cargill and Iowa Beef Processors (IBP) control 80 percent of the fed cattle slaughter in Canada and that once their expansions are complete, that figure will increase to 90 percent. He says the arguments he heard include that the Alberta Beef Producers Association does not want to dictate to the packers how they do business.

"Packer ownership completely dictates the price of fat cattle," he says. "They (industry leaders) have no backbone whatsoever. They are pandering to the American packing industry and are just too damned scared to piss them off."

He says the industry leaders are blinded by the desire to get back to the old way of doing business, and that while he's getting a lot of support from producers for his idea, it isn't being brought forward by the industry groups that have the ear of the government.

"They simply do not relate to the guy whose place is mortgaged," he says.

I ask him to explain his group's plan.

Cam says the industry needs to reduce its reliance on the U.S. by cultivating other markets, develop producer-owned infrastructure, and develop a plan to process, export and create value for beef over and under 30 months of age. BIG wants to build a producer-owned, 1,500 a day slaughter facility for both culled cows and fat cattle. They would like to see it bridge financed by government with a producer levy applied to all producer-owned cattle sold across the country. Once the debt is paid, the levy would be discontinued. Cam explained that all producers who had paid the proposed $3 a head levy would then become owners on a share basis. The advantage would be that the plant could compete with the multinationals because it wouldn't have to worry about servicing a huge debt right from the start.

Opponents to the idea of building new plants argue that the large plants have earned high enough profits over the last year that they could undercut and sustain losses for a very long time if they wanted to put a new competitor out of business. Why encourage producers to invest in something that will go broke after the border opens?

But Cam believes there is enough room for everyone, that by giving the customer what they want, their plant will cultivate new markets rather than competing for the same customers. Besides, there is no guarantee that the border will stay open. Another disease outbreak or suit by R-CALF could shut it down again.

"Our goal is to put producers in the position to control what happens from umbilical cord to cryovac," Cam says, adding that if foreign markets want BSE testing then we should give it to them. "They (Japan, Taiwan) blatantly told us, 'Meet our protocol requirements and our market is open to you.'"

Cam says ranchers cannot rely on the profit-driven packers to be "nice," and that producers need to own a part of that industry to protect themselves in the future. If producers own a share of a plant they would be encouraged to retain ownership of their livestock longer and would finish a greater number of cattle themselves.

He is also annoyed by the fact that the Canadian taxpayer paid the tab for the bail out and then was forced to pay full U.S. retail prices for meat.

I completely agree with Cam's logic and understand his frustration. The Rancher's Choice group in Manitoba has faced a ridiculous number of roadblocks in their quest to build a cow plant there. Producers who have invested in this plant are waiting patiently, watching as loss of income from the culled cow means the profit margin on the ranch has gone from $175-$200 a cow down to $50-$125. That gives a 200-head operation $25,000 take home—at the most, before income tax. Pay the tax bill and the average rancher isn't making enough to support his family.

There are those within the industry who dismiss the cow-calf man's concerns because the dollars he works in seem insignificant to the money that turns over everyday in a large feedlot or packing plant. But they should know it is all relative—that it is just as devastating to lose the ranch as it is to lose a $100 million feedlot. Either way, a family has lost its livelihood.

Some have even made the unpopular suggestion that the rancher should consider income from the cow as secondary—that she is a by-prod-uct of calf production. About the quickest way to get a beef producer's blood boiling, is to compare him to the dairyman—minus the milk cheque.

Cows eat, too. Since profitability on these operations is all about how much it costs to keep animals fed, how long can ranchers be expected to feed cull animals with no expectation of a fair return?

We shipped a load of cull cows that brought an average of $800 a piece in the winter of 2003. Now, the same animal is bringing $125—a reduction of 80 percent. We will accept that cull cows are a by-product of calf pro-duction when consumers are paying 80 percent less for hamburger in the stores.

It sounds as if Cam thoroughly investigated this idea and has a good business plan. It's obvious this isn't something he thought up overnight; it's been in the works for more than a year. There are well-known, reputable ranchers on the BIG board backing the idea. And while this might look like a solution to the cattleman's problem, nothing in this industry is ever simple.

If BIG was the only group proposing to build a plant, the main obstacle it would have to overcome is trying to get the majority of cattlemen in the five beef producing provinces working together. That in itself would be a challenge, since a mandatory levy means cattlemen don't have a choice, and they are sure to buck against it for that reason alone.

But since there are similar groups trying to get plants up and going in each province, a mandatory national levy paid to BIG will give them a huge advantage over all the other plants. Is it fair to force a man who has invested in one plant to pay a levy to another?

Others will say that they don't mind paying $3 a head to have another plant brought into the mix, but they don't think it should be producer owned or government subsidized. As it is, there is grumbling from the small, privately owned abattoirs, that government initiatives to expand the packing industry are unfair competition to them.

A number of committed individuals have come forward with business plans to increase cow and bull slaughter capacity in their respective provinces. Eighteen months after the border closed, Blue Mountain Packers at Salmon Arm, B.C., and Natural Valley Farms at Neudorf/Wolseley, Saskatchewan, were the only two new initiatives up and running.

Last fall I interviewed Jim Quintaine, a cattle buyer from Brandon, Manitoba. Jim grew up in the business and has been buying cattle for 35 years. The day BSE was announced, he stood out by the corrals and offered producers who came in 45 cents a pound for their cull cows. Like many people, Jim thought the border would open within a few weeks. Only one producer took his offer—everyone else took their cows home.

"Luckily for me they did," he says. Two weeks later, cows were selling for 10 cents a pound.

I had asked him if building cow plants in Western Canada would solve the problem, and he said the business could be successful if the border doesn't open to culls for a few years. Jim offered words of caution against cattlemen investing in and building the plants.

"Packers and cattlemen are like wolves and sheep," he said. "One feeds the other." He went on to explain that the natural competitiveness between the packer and the rancher means that each lives at far ends of the spectrum from one another. When one makes money, the other doesn't.

"Who is going to make the money, the rancher or the plant?" he asked. "If the objective is for ranchers to get better prices for their culls, this may not be the way to do it."

When the owners are the same people, it poses a new set of problems, especially in a cooperative where the management must be accountable to a large membership; like everyone else in the business, ranchers will go wherever they get the best price.

Jim remembers the demise of Canada Packers in Winnipeg. He says that a lot of people blame high union wages and inefficient facilities for the shut down. While those certainly were factors, he says a major reason why a new fat cattle plant was never re-built in Manitoba is that it's not a favourable location.

I tell him that being in the middle of the country is perfect.

He disagrees.

"Plants need to be either where the fed cattle are, which is west, or where the people are, which is east," he said, explaining that in a business that operates on small margins, transportation is a huge factor. A fat cattle plant won't be profitable if it has to truck in the cattle and then ship out the meat. "If Manitoba was the place to build, Cargill or IBP would be here already," he said.

CHAPTER TWENTY NINE

I assess the power of a will by how much
resistance, pain and torture it endures
and knows how to turn to its advantage.
— Friedrich Wilhelm Nietzche

Each beef-producing province has an association like the Alberta Beef Producers Association. These are non-profit lobby organizations that represent the interests of the grassroots producer. Although the structure and funding mechanism for each organization varies between provinces, in general terms the organization is run by a manager who is given direction from a delegation of members elected from provincial zones or districts.

Direction to the board is made in the form of resolutions brought forward from the grassroots at annual district meetings. Those resolutions are voted on at the Association's Annual Meeting.

The Association's annual budget is based on the amount collected from producers through a levy or check-off, which is collected on a per head basis when cattle are sold. Dollars are allocated to the national organizations that promote beef consumption (Beef Information Centre), cultivate foreign markets (Canada Beef Export Federation) and fund research projects (Beef Cattle Research Council).

Each provincial organization helps fund the Canadian Cattlemen's Association (CCA) and either appoints or elects members to sit on that board. The structure is democratic, and in theory, a small cow-calf producer from P.E.I. can aspire toward the CCA Presidency. More commonly, however, the top position on the CCA board is filled by someone from the top five beef-producing provinces. Interestingly, Quebec declines membership in the CCA.

The higher the aspirations, the more politically astute the person must be. Respect within the industry, popularity, political acumen, an ability to maneuver and a promise to give plenty of time, elevates these men to the Presidency. These are highly committed individuals who have a strong vision of the industry's future. To date, no woman has made it to the top spot.

These organizations attract individuals who, at first, are surprised to discover the depth of the industry and overwhelmed by the information suddenly at their fingertips.

Each provincial organization is like a microcosm of society. After a board is together for a while, personalities of those involved are revealed. Each board has its leaders, followers, fence sitters, procrastinators, bullies, agitators and workhorses. They all serve a useful purpose in directing the board. A strong chairman knows how to capitalize on the board's strengths and minimize its weaknesses. Most producers agree that time spent on the provincial or national board is reflected back on with pride and a sense of accomplishment.

It takes a great deal of commitment to contribute to these organizations, especially during challenging times like these. Passion toward the industry doesn't dissolve when directors leave the board. Tightly woven kinships often develop between these folks who have so much in common, and some of the friendships cultivated will last a lifetime.

Past directors will sit in the periphery, questioning decisions made by the new leaders. Nothing is more intimidating for a new President than to look out into the audience at the annual meeting and see some of the most respected men and women in the industry, many of them past directors, listening quietly to what he is about to say.

For the most part, the work of provincial organizations is mostly ignored by its membership, until crisis strikes. When livelihoods are suddenly threatened the leadership must prepare itself for challenge, which inevitably comes, as factions within the grassroots rise up to question leadership decisions.

The biggest fear at the grassroots is that their provincial organization will stop fairly representing their interests. This fear is strongest when the balance between industry sectors begins leaning in favour of one side over the other. Simply put, if there are too many cow-calf operators on the board, the feedlot man starts to get nervous, and vice versa. The worry is that decisions will be made with no foresight or consideration for the other sector.

These are high-profile organizations that wield a lot of power. Sometimes they attract people who just want to further their own agenda and may not even understand the industry. In the sports world, people who give advice but can't back it up with action are called "armchair quarterbacks." In the cattle industry they are referred to as having a, "big hat, but no cows." The grassroots dislikes this type of director, but they are also to blame for electing them in the first place.

Producers know that the directors representing them are not necessarily more intelligent, but in most cases are better informed. They struggle as anyone would to make the correct decision, as issues are debated around the board table and recommendations are then brought forward to the government.

Cattlemen elect contemporaries to represent them, but the fear exists that once in power, these people will become part of the machine, spending more time with politicians and bureaucrats, caught up in the daily machinations that make it easy to lose touch with the grassroots. Turnover on a board is a good thing because the long-time members are forced back to their own beginnings as they acquaint new directors with the purpose and mandate of the organization, reminding themselves why they are there.

Directors with the CCA work hard to consider the peculiarities of each region when making decisions that affect the industry as a whole. With the highest concentration of cattle in Alberta, it is assumed by other provinces that Alberta's concerns will come first. This is not necessarily the case, since only seven of the 27 members elected to the CCA board are from Alberta.

The politics and complexities of the multi-billion-dollar cattle industry and its forever-changing dynamics are fully understood only by a select few. Throughout the closed border crisis, politicians and governments have taken direction from the provincial associations and the CCA. Producers will never know for sure how much provincial prejudice, bullheaded stubbornness, wrangling for power, self interest and political partisianism has come into play during these discussions. The grassroots has no choice but to trust these elected cattlemen.

There have been some unfortunate casualties during this crisis, but considering the industry was on the brink of total collapse during the summer of 2003, credit definitely should be extended to the men and women who made the decisions that kept the industry propped up for the last 18 months.

Someone said it is harder to get elected to the Alberta Beef Producers (ABP) Board than it is to run for government. Listening to the nomination speeches and glancing through the selection of candidates listed in the annual meeting brochure indicates this could very well be true.

My cell phone rings, pulling me out of the meeting. It is the communications director with R-CALF. She tells me that my name and number was forwarded to her by an R-CALF member. I'd left numerous messages days ago trying to set up an interview with someone. Until now, no one has called me back.

The woman asks for clarification about why I need to speak to an R-CALF director. I explain for what seems like the thousandth time what I am doing. She hesitates, then asks me who will be publishing the book. I tell her it's too early in the process to say for sure, but that I expect it will be out in the fall of 2005.

"Our resources are spread very thin right now as we plan our next move against Canada," she says. Yes, that is exactly what she said. "We can't waste our time talking to someone with no credentials, especially without a guarantee it will be published."

I'm left speechless for a moment. Kudos to her. My cheeks grow hot and I start stammering.

"Oh, this will be published," I say, regretting I'm not better prepared for this sort of reply. Most of all, I wish I didn't sound so childish, so polite, so . . . Canadian.

"Then you call us back once you have a publisher's name," she replies in a tone I haven't heard since kindergarten.

I want to run out and paste one of Robert Vander Heyden's R-CALF stickers on my car bumper this very instant!

Too annoyed to go back into the meeting, I console myself in conversation with Cindy McCreath.

Cindy is the CCA's Communications Manager. She began working for the Association in 1998, around the same time I started with the Manitoba association.

I vent for a few minutes about the frustration I feel over not being able to talk with anyone from R-CALF. Cindy listens and smiles and I can tell my woes are faint compared to what the folks in her office have dealt with. I ask how she has been, how she is holding up under all the stress.

Cindy tells me that the atmosphere is calmer now, but in the first few weeks the demand for information and the media onslaught was more than she could have ever imagined.

"Basically I was pinned to my desk and staff brought me food and water," she says, adding that work was starting to return to normal when the case was discovered in the U.S. and traced back here. Cindy knew immediately what that meant when she read the USDA webcast and went back to the office on Boxing Day. She remembers little except that she had Christmas day off. The fallout from BSE has preoccupied her thoughts almost every waking moment since.

"I don't think for anybody in our office this is just a job," she says. "These people are so dedicated to the industry, it's remarkable, really."

She says that she doesn't know how she would have managed without the help of family and neighbours. Many mornings she had to leave early and appreciated that neighbours were able to take her children to school.

I ask if she has had any time off at all.

She says that she was able to find some uninterrupted time in February 2004 so she took her children to Disneyland.

I ask what aspect of all of this has been most difficult for her.

Cindy says the hardest thing to deal with is criticism coming from the grassroots, especially since she believes the grassroots is who everyone is working so hard to represent. She remembers receiving an e-mail in that first few weeks from a producer who asked why the CCA was remaining so silent on the issue. Cindy says staff were fielding hundreds of media calls every day and sending out press releases daily. Meetings with everyone from the producer to trade ministers of foreign countries were ongoing. She isn't sure what else they were expected to do.

Cindy believes that in some ways, as hard as it was, the industry has undergone a cleansing, a sort of seismic shift that has seen a change in mindset that normally would take a decade to achieve.

"It really has been something to witness," she says, "but honestly, while I think it has made us all stronger, I wouldn't want to do it again."

Dennis Laycraft is standing near the doorway of a meeting room as producers flood into the hallway for a coffee break. He's talking with a handful of Alberta delegates.

As the Executive Vice President of the CCA, I expect he probably has the most stressful job in the industry right now. He is the man in charge, reporting back to the national board, which is under tremendous pressure from the provincial organizations who are being hammered by the grassroots.

Dennis is the industry's front man and I can't think of a better person for the job. I hardly know him, but have heard nothing but good things. It sounds as though he possesses the three key qualifications a person needs to work for an organization such as this—an amazing recall for details, a cool head and an ability to flex with the leadership and enhance whoever is in charge.

Dennis glances in my direction and I catch his eye. He nods, acknowledging that he has promised me a few minutes of his time, so I sit in a comfy chair in the hotel lobby to wait. Within a few minutes he hurries over, glancing at his watch as he sits across from me.

"I'm on my way to my daughter's ballet recital," he says.

I promise that this won't take too long. I ask what it's like having the toughest job in the industry.

Dennis chuckles. "A person doesn't realize how busy they can become overnight."

He tells me that the weekend BSE was discovered, he and his wife Elizabeth (Libby) and their two small children, Callie, age four, and Blaine, age two, had just driven to Chilliwack, B.C., for a short holiday. The phone call came that the test result was positive, so he flew back to Calgary. He has little memory of that first week except that it began with a Canada AM television interview and ended with the phone company calling to ask if he wanted to upgrade his cell phone plan.

"That pretty much sums up the last 18 months," he says, adding that for the first while, he carried a packed suitcase to work, so that he was prepared to fly out on a moment's notice. The ticket was always one way because he never knew where he'd have to fly next, or when he was coming home. Dennis spent more than 50 percent of his time on the road.

I ask what in all of this he's found most challenging.

He says that throughout this crisis he hasn't been able to detach himself and that he has had to work at thinking about anything else.

"And that's the hardest part because when you have a young family, it doesn't take long to realize that they are purely interested in you," he says. "I have had to make a concerted effort to take my mind off of work."

Dennis grew up in southern Alberta on a ranch nestled in the Porcupine Hills near Nanton. He graduated from Olds Agriculture College in 1981 with an Agri Business degree, specializing in livestock production. He applied for, and got, the top job at the CCA in 1990.

He says the cattle industry runs deep through his family, with two brothers and a lot of friends whose incomes are reliant on cattle.

I ask how prepared the CCA was to handle the onslaught that followed the BSE announcement.

"We were as prepared as anyone could be," he says, explaining that he and Ben Thorlakson were on the front lines in 1993 when the very first BSE case was discovered. It turned out to be from a British-born animal, so the media settled down pretty quickly once this was established, but it served as a lesson in preparation for him. A communications plan was developed that included fact sheets and key experts willing to discuss the issue with the media should the need ever arise.

I ask what was the most encouraging moment to date.

"Bar none, the partial opening to boxed beef was the most gratifying thing we've seen," he says, adding that credit is due, in part, to the bureaucrats and politicians in Ottawa who have done all they could to address the needs of the industry. He says that while ranchers are often critical of government, they should know that these politicians and civil service employees have a rather thankless job. He said that many of them worked overtime and weekends to accomplish what we've seen so far.

Dennis says that the most encouraging comments of support came from U.S. Agriculture Secretary Ann Veneman, although he is past the point of guessing when the border might open. He says the CCA is formulating a sustainable plan that will position the industry regardless of whether the border opens.

We talk for awhile about perception and reality and he says that even though everything tied to the industry appears simple on the surface, the underlying issues are incredibly complex. Because of his background, he relates to the simple, homespun values of the ranch, knowing that they don't intertwine easily with the bottom line of big business. Finding the balance between the two is difficult.

I ask what we need in terms of a packing industry.

He says that as of December 2004, the fat cattle slaughter numbers in Canada were up to 88,000 and by the summer of 2005, should be at 95,000.

"It is an incredibly difficult and competitive business to be in," he says, explaining why the industry cautiously supports the building of new plants. The reality is that producer-owned plants have closed in the past, so the industry is continually trying to evaluate past occurrences against present needs and future possibilities. We agree decisions would be much easier if we knew the future. This causes him to think about the implementation of the National Identification Tagging system, the most controversial producer program ever tackled.

"It's hard to find a producer who disagrees with it now," he says.

I ask what will happen to our industry when BSE is discovered in the U.S.

He hesitates and I can tell this is one of those questions he'd rather not answer.

I help him out a bit by telling him my prediction.

I believe that BSE exists in the U.S., but their industry is in a state of denial. With an industry ten times the size of ours, the scope of dealing with the possibility is too difficult, so they just hope it never happens. Maybe they have had positive cases and are covering them up. I make reference to U.S. Olympic athletes who never test positive for steroids despite strong suspicions to the contrary. I still haven't cooled down from my chat with the woman from R-CALF.

Dennis smiles. I can't tell if he agrees or thinks I'm crazy.

Because, I continue, if BSE is confirmed in the U.S., and it will be, consumption there will drop by at least 25 percent. The American public will not react as Canadians have and God help them if a celebrity speaks out against the beef industry. Think back, I say, to how consumption dropped in the mid-1990s, when Oprah Winfrey had Howard Lyman on her show and she made the statement, "That just stopped me cold from eating another hamburger."[23] What will happen to our beef exports when the U.S. government is unable to convince consumers that their beef is safe? Look how R-CALF reacts when times are good; imagine how protectionist they will become when things turn sour.

I don't really expect Dennis to reply. If I were in his position, I'd be more careful about commenting on predictions, too.

So I ask him what words come to mind when he reflects back on the last few months.

Frustration is the first word he mentions.

Disappointment over the fact the Association's quiet actions are being interpreted by some as doing nothing at all.

Baffled in knowing what to say, when to say it, or whether to say it at all.

Irritation that even though Canada held the most thorough, honest investigation into BSE to ever take place, the border remains closed.

Thwarted by the fact that in spite of the vocal support from the USDA and other organizations across the border, R-CALF is gaining momentum.

And time. This is taking much longer than anyone anticipated.

Dennis says that sometimes when he stops and lets himself think about it, he becomes overwhelmed by all that has happened. And with it still not over, he continues to focus each day on what needs to be done. He has tried to not take criticisms personally and is confident that the industry has seen great leadership from the national board.

"This is a highly charged situation, so I've seen the best and the worst in people and sometimes from the same person, on the same day," he says as he stands, apologizing that he has to go.

Callie's recital beings in an hour. He has promised her he won't be late.

The afternoon slate of meetings is finished so I return to my room and freshen up for the banquet. I'm a bit concerned that I have no one to sit with at dinner. On my way back down to the lobby, I step onto the elevator and strike up conversation with a fellow wearing a beef producer's name tag. We walk to the banquet hall and stand in line talking. He introduces me to acquaintances of his, and I tell everyone that he made the mistake of talking to me on the elevator, so now he has to put up with me through dinner. Everyone laughs. Once again I'm relieved to experience gracious western hospitality.

It is much different seeing a photograph of someone and then actually seeing them in person. Shirley McClellan is sitting up front at the head table. She has been invited to tonight's event as the guest speaker. Shirley was successful in her re-election bid just weeks ago. She is now Alberta's Treasury Minister.

The reasons for her popularity and success are immediately apparent.

Shirley is commanding, charismatic and sincere as she addresses the crowd from the podium. She would make a wonderful Premier. She begins tonight's address by thanking the Association for inviting her to the dinner and for giving her the opportunity to speak. She looks comfortably pleased to be back among the cattlemen who demanded so much of her time this past year and a half.

"I'm here to keep an eye on our investment," she smiles, looking out over her glasses at the audience, eliciting a ripple of warm laughter. "Because that's how I consider the help we gave beef producers. It wasn't an expense to our government, but an investment in the industry and in the province's future."

As she speaks about the friendships and working relationships developed between herself and industry leaders during the crisis, Shirley tells us how she always knew, but came to learn first hand, the resiliency and sincerity of cattlemen. She calls them honest, straightforward and a pleasure to work with—even during these most difficult times.

As the room sits listening in absolute silence, I get the strong sense that this is a woman who has earned the respect of not only the people here, but an entire province. Shirley played a crucial role in keeping the beef industry alive in Canada, and did so with tremendous grace. In July 2004, Forbes Magazine named her one of Alberta's 50 Most Influential People.

Earlier today, the new Minister of Agriculture, Doug Horner, spoke at the luncheon. He described Shirley as "the right person in the right place at the right time." Cattlemen agree. And tonight, emotions are running high.

I suspect part of the reason for this is the strain these people have been under to make the correct decisions and say the right thing while under constant scrutiny. And of course, the crisis isn't yet over.

Like survivors of a catastrophe, Shirley and members of the ABP executive share first-hand knowledge of what went on behind the scenes. It has bonded them in a way the rest of us will never fully understand or appreciate. But we see shades of it tonight through the inside jokes, presentations, bone-crushing hugs and a few tears. Before she finishes her speech, the crowd of 400 rises in ovation. If admiration could carry a person around the room, Shirley's feet wouldn't have touched the floor all night.

Regretfully, I never do meet Shirley in person. Stan Eby had offered to introduce us, but by the time I'd finished talking with producers, I turned around and she was gone.

I slip the key into my hotel room lock and push open the door. My mind is tired from the last few days' events. Kicking off my shoes and turning on my laptop, I carry it to the bed where I sit for awhile making notes.

This feels familiar and I miss my former job with the Manitoba association. I am reminded of the time I attended the CCA semi-annual meeting in Penticton, B.C. Time spent with the MCPA taught me one of the most valuable yet intimidating lessons of my life—that there is a lot I don't know. This is a rather sobering realization for a writer who is expected to write with confidence and conviction about many given topics.

What I remember most about the industry folks I met is everyone's patience. Greenhorn that I was, nobody ever made me feel foolish for asking a question, the answer to which I am sure they'd given many times before.

The hot topic at that time was the proposed implementation of a national cattle identification system. The provincial managers and communications professionals were all brought together to discuss how the program would work.

Rob McNabb, the Association's Assistant Manager, answered our many questions.

I was in favour of the tagging system, but I knew a lot of producers who were not. They complained about the cost, time needed to insert the tags and retainability. Some were paranoid that this was one way for the government to get a hold of their cattle numbers. Others worried that this was a step toward stricter regulations. Many felt it could give packers and feedlot operators the data needed to hold primary producers liable if there was something wrong with an animal or the carcass.

Many producers embraced the program, hoping that they could follow their animals via the tags through to slaughter and be given performance data from the packing plant. This could be valuable information to the cow-calf man anxious to improve the genetics of his herd.

The issue was debated at length and it was decided that in order to appease the naysayers, the program had to offer strict confidentiality. The numbers would only be used if there was a herd health risk like BSE, Foot and Mouth or TB. Unfortunately, this didn't change the minds of the conspiracy theorists, nor did it offer a marketing benefit to supporters. Acceptance of the program was lukewarm.

Now we are left wondering how the U.S. can get away with not having a similar system. Apparently, opposition to tagging is even stronger in the U.S. where cowboys are far more owly than the ones we have up here.

I can still remember the serious look on Rob McNabb's face when he told us that someday Canada would need to trace back to the herd of origin.

He told us that it was just a matter of time.

Chapter Thirty

*"No one would have ever crossed the ocean
if he could have gotten off the ship in the storm."*
— Charles F. Kettering

Arno Doerksen is still basking in the glow from last night.

I arrive at his house early in the morning. His wife, Wanda, and two of their three sons, Lorin, 17, and Barry, 14, are sitting at the kitchen table. They invite me to sit down and fill my cup with coffee.

Yesterday was Arno's last day in a two-year stint as Chairman of the Alberta Beef Producers. Last night, he took centre stage as fellow board members thanked and honoured him with speeches and gifts in appreciation for the time he's given to the industry. A video presentation prepared by the ABP assisted by his sons, melded together the public Arno and the husband, father and cattleman. It was a wonderful tribute that showed him with his kids, on the tractor, working cattle and humorous shots of him, mostly on the phone.

I ask the boys what the last year and a half was like for them.

They say that before their dad decided to take on the responsibility of Chairman, they talked about what it would mean. He would be away a lot more, would miss some of their hockey games, and it would mean more responsibility for each of them around home. They encouraged him to do it and nobody in the family regrets it for a moment.

"It definitely was not a negative thing for our family," Lorin says. "Our dad had the chance to make a difference in the industry and do some pretty interesting things."

It proved interesting for them as well.

Arno and Wanda Doerksen

In the fall of 2003 the local 4-H club decided they wanted to do something positive for the industry to raise awareness about the issue. They made a power point presentation for teenagers, then hired a communications specialist to help them prepare. They then travelled to Medicine Hat, Alberta, and presented it to Grade 7 and 8 students. The presentation talked about the care of animals, the effect of BSE on both the rural and urban economies, an outline of beef products and a bit about 4-H. The project was so well received that it was suggested they take it to Ottawa; so then the fundraising began.

They had a barbeque the following June, did some additional fundraising and by the end of September, were ready to go. They gave the presentation at an Ottawa Junior High school then got together with a 4-H group in Ottawa. The highlight was going to the parliament buildings on October 4, 2004.

Alberta Member of Parliament, Marty Solberg knew they were coming and he made sure that all the politicians attended their reception.

"It gets tiring doing the presentation for the 15th time," Barry says. "Now we know how dad feels."

Winnipeg MP, Steven Fletcher, noticed their sweatshirts and immediately knew who they were. He invited them to attend that afternoon's debate, then proceeded to race them up the hill in his wheelchair.

"He was a real nice guy, and it was so cool to be there," Lorin says. "MP Rick Casson referred to the Gem 4-H club being there and Diane Finley said some of the same things we said in our presentation during the debate."

The 4-H motto is: Learn to do by doing. Arno says the kids did more than that—they helped put Gem, Alberta, on the map at a time when producers all around were feeling pretty down. It was inspiring to see the kids so enthusiastic about promoting beef.

The boys, who both enjoy sports and music, are considering careers in agriculture. They are still too young to know for sure what they want to do with the rest of their lives, but say when they make up their minds, BSE won't be the deciding factor.

"And we're very proud of our dad. His work has made us all so much more politically aware about what's going on in the world and it's pretty awesome," Lorin says. The boys grab their lunches and backpacks, then leave for school.

There is a knock at the door as Arno's dad steps into the porch. Jake Doerksen has dropped in to say hi, to talk about how things went last night and to see what needs doing today. Although he officially retired a few years ago, Jake likes to keep active, helping out wherever he can and says he'll never really retire.

The Doerksens have a purebred and commercial cow-calf operation, small feedlot and also grow some cash crops. Their cows are mostly Hereford and Hereford-cross and they use their own Hereford bulls. Arno farms in partnership with his brother, Tim, and they have a full-time hired man.

"I never would have been able to take on the position if it hadn't been for Tim and dad," Arno says. "And, of course, Wanda is a solid anchor here at home."

Arno has always been interested in the farm, so it was no surprise to anyone when he returned home after briefly working in Whitehorse following a general course of study at University. His general course of study included theology.

"I'm here because I chose to do this," he says. There is a strength in his words that tells me he wants people to know this, that he's not here by default, that it is a good life and something that fills him, and so many others, with pride.

Wanda is originally from the town of Coaldale, just east of Lethbridge. They married in 1983. Moving to the farm was a bit of an adjustment for her, but because she was from a small town, there were no unwelcome surprises. Wanda does not work off the farm, deciding early on that with three children it would be best if she stayed home.

Arno was first asked to run as a director with the Alberta Beef Producers Association when the boys were young. Initially he resisted being drawn into the organization because the family was so busy with the boys playing hockey and involved with 4-H.

But by the mid-1990s, with Wanda's encouragement, Arno became a delegate in his area. The following year, he was elected to the board. By the late 1990s he was one of Alberta's representatives on the CCA board. He was Chairman of the Animal Health and Meat Inspection committee on May 20, 2003, and now sits as Finance and Audit Chairman for the Canada Beef Export Federation.

Arno isn't the sort of man who charges ahead without thinking things through and he likes to test his ideas before making a decision. But he definitely is not one to sit quietly on the sidelines. He says that the more contact he's had with strong leaders like Ben Thorlakson and Dave Andrews, the stronger his own ability to quickly assess a situation and follow his gut instincts.

Given the size and diversity of the Alberta industry, there have always been factions that challenge the leadership of whichever group has the ear of government. In 2002, following a strategic review, the organization restructured and changed its name from the Alberta Cattle Commission to the Alberta Beef Producers Association (ABP). Three members of the Alberta Cattle Feeders Association were added to the board. In 2003 ABP was being challenged by an association of groups calling themselves the Alberta Beef Council. Fortunately enough of the conflict was resolved and a general direction toward establishing some of the concerns was established before BSE hit.

"I think we are stronger as an industry by working together," Arno says. "It really was an effort on everyone's part and a real credit to the people involved." After the border closed, cattlemen were thrown into turmoil. Too many calls and wide-ranging opinions about what needed to be done caused Shirley McClellan to call them in for a meeting.

"Shirley called us to say that we had to pull this together, for everyone to get onto the same page," he said, adding that she made it very clear that without a united front on the industry's part, the government would be hamstrung over what to do.

Following the election, word got out that Shirley would no longer be Ag Minister. There was pressure on Arno to call the Premier and ask to keep her in place. The reasons producers wanted her to stay put were twofold.

The most pressing consideration was that she understood the issue, and there already had been so many changes at the federal level that they wanted to maintain some continuity. The second reason was that Shirley's popularity amongst producers meant one less worry for the Associations. There was no question she was doing all she could for them and the grassroots knew it.

Arno resisted the temptation because he felt that it would be wrong to presume he had that level of influence, and he didn't think it was his place to try and selfishly direct the outcome of Shirley's career.

She was promoted to Finance Minister and named Deputy Premier.

"We are all going to miss working with Shirley, but she remains a trusted friend and ally of agriculture," he says, adding that Doug Horner seems very receptive toward agriculture and the industry.

I ask him about the "If It Ain't Alberta, It Ain't Beef" slogan. Why has his province stamped its name on the perception of Canadian excellence.

He tells me that producers here make no apology for "taking the bull by the horns" and developing a brand that would help sell beef. In the late 1980s, they spiffed up the industry image, then got out in the public eye through advertising and promotion during the 1988 Olympic Games in Calgary. Their first promotion featured cowboys, and now, the female "RancHers."

"We made a huge investment in this program and it has been extremely successful," he says. "No other province has made that kind of commitment."

That's a fair answer.

Arno may be the outgoing chairman of the ABP, but he is a cattleman first. I hear it in the way he speaks, how he carries himself and his solid eye contact. I'm not going to get the politically correct answer from this man. I'm going to get the truth.

I ask Arno for the inside scoop about some of the key meetings that took place.

He tells me he was part of a delegation in 2003 that met with Paul Martin at his constituency office in Montreal before he became Prime Minister. The beef men wanted to be sure that Martin had a good grasp of the situation before taking over the Prime Minister's office. The delegation spent two hours in his office talking about the issue, stressing how important it was to improve the relationship between the Canadian and U.S. governments.

He regrets that producers were offered economic advice that fall, which, in retrospect, was wrong. He says that in this situation it was inevitable, because the pressure for answers was daily, and so intense, that anyone who offered even the slightest bit of hope was taken very seriously. This surprised everyone since ranchers are usually independent and stubborn—not easily advised or led.

Arno says that the December 23 discovery of BSE in the U.S. almost completely offset the work that had been done up to that point. By then, Canadian beef had been moving across the border in boxes for nearly three months.

"There was a real push to close the Canadian border to the U.S. and let me tell you, did we have to lobby hard then," he says. A delegation attended an intense, sweat-stained meeting, and in the end, they were able to convince Canadian officials to keep the border open to U.S. boxed beef.

Arno attended the National Cattlemen's Beef Association meeting in the summer of 2004, and said that American cattle feeders were desperately wanting Canadian cattle. He says because cow numbers in the U.S. were low, calf prices were at an all-time high. This just happened to coincide with the closed border, giving the illusion, and R-CALF basis for the argument, that the cow-calf man's prosperity was due to the shortage of Canadian cattle. The combined two factors were hurting their feeding industry. Their kill numbers were down by 3.5 million last year.

"And they've seen an increase in demand for protein, and down there even a one percent increase translates into a lot," he says.

The most recent event he attended was the State Dinner held in Ottawa on November 30. Others who attended the event besides Arno and the Ebys were Ralph Kline, Herb McLean, Neil and Marilyn Jahnke, Ben and Betty Ann Thorlakson, Dennis Laycraft, John Masswohl, and Jim Caldwell from the Ottawa CCA office.

Arno says that everyone clapped when it was mentioned that Alberta Beef was on the menu, and there was an underlying current of support toward the beef industry throughout the evening. He had the opportunity to meet with President Bush briefly.

"I shook his hand and said that I was there representing Alberta beef producers and that we appreciated him coming to Canada, and stressed how important the border issue was to Canadian producers," he says.

I asked if Bush said anything back to him.

"He said, 'That's a real beef man's handshake you've got there,'" Arno laughs.

I mentioned my earlier hopes that Bush might make a more positive announcement that night and how disappointed I had been when he didn't. I ask Arno if I was the only person who felt this way.

He said no, there were a lot of producers pinning their hopes on that visit.

"My sense leading up to that evening is there would be a cynicism that would grow if Bush didn't announce a date for the border opening when he was here," he says. "And there was."

Arno says that shortly afterward a letter was sent on behalf of the Canadian industry to the U.S. government, stating that if the border doesn't open soon, there is a very real chance that the relationships that have formed within the industry between the two countries could be irreparably damaged.

"In truth, we told them that this is no longer a beef issue, but it is becoming a Canadian issue," he says. "We wrote that we are moving ahead with "Made in Canada" solutions to this problem, and it won't necessarily be in their best interest."

A cynic would say that the whole idea is preposterous, that all the industry is doing is setting itself up for embarrassment. How often in history has the little guy risen up and held his own against a giant?

I ask him how he envisions the "Made In Canada" solution.

Arno says he would like to see Canada's dependency on the U.S. slaughter industry closer to ten percent. He wants to see slaughter capacity increase so that if the border were to ever close again, the dip in the market would be temporary until the packers are able to ramp-up production. He says the overseas markets are being pursued aggressively right now and the answer to our export woes lies across the ocean.

"When the Asian agreements are made, Canada has a good chance of meeting the requirements," he says, explaining that our solid traceback system and a willingness to give the customer what they want is what will open doors to new markets. "I believe that when those consumers taste Canadian meat, and as we get recognition and can prove value as good as what is stamped USDA, we can go head-to-head with the U.S.—and we won't lose."

I can feel myself becoming excited by Arno's enthusiasm.

"And even though the border is set to open, we need to stay behind the push to see these ideas continue until they are reality," he says. "And if we do, we'll never be in this position again."

I ask Arno about this crisis and what he has learned from it.

He hesitates for a moment, then says that it was never promised that life would be easy. This crisis is just one of life's many lessons and that every generation has its hardship. This generation won't know the full effect of what all this will mean to the beef industry until many years to come.

One thing he is most thankful for is the mostly fair and factual reporting by the media. Arno is very aware of how potentially devastating the outcome would have been if an adversarial relationship with the media had developed early on. He said the industry and government took its lumps where they were due, but the amount of misinformation that was published was very small.

"A recent CTV poll asked what the single most important issue to Canadians is right now, and 65 percent who responded said BSE," he says, explaining that it is the intangibles like clean air, mountains, blue sky, and grazing cattle that earns us our goodwill. Eighty-five percent of the population believe the word of ranchers, and that's because of the way we live our lives and the choices we make. We hold typical, Canadian values and our country has the respect and trust of the world.

We are Canadian. That is our brand. Arno is ready to sell it to the world.

CHAPTER THIRTY ONE

*"My thought is that we have to approach the necessary changes
in our industry like the pilot who first broke the sound barrier.
Pilots would go up in their jets increasing speed until they hit
that invisible wall of sound. When they did hit the wall the
planes would begin to shake terribly and the pilot would
announce to the tower, "Buffeting, buffeting!" Then the pilots
would pull back on the wheel in an effort to slow the planes
down and stop the shaking. The planes would go into a nose-
dive and crash to the ground.
Then one day a pilot went up and changed the pattern.
When his plane hit the wall and began buffeting,
he did not pull back on the wheel.
Instead, he pushed the wheel forward and immediately flew
through the wall and broke the sound barrier."*

— Agnes Jackson, past President of the B.C. Cattlemen's Association,
taken from *Beef in B.C.*, October 2003

Three days until Christmas. I've been home now for a little more than
a week. Life feels almost normal again as I settle back into a familiar daily
routine that no longer means getting in the car and driving to meet with
strangers.

All of the interviews have been transferred into a binder with dividers
separating each province visited. I feel badly that I can't travel to Quebec
and the Maritime provinces. With a looming deadline and already more
information than I need, it is time to start writing. I pour myself a cup of

Kerri Leigh, Ken and Clinton Hinsberg

coffee and sit at the desk. Opening the binder I flip through Alberta and Saskatchewan, stopping at Manitoba.

My home province. Not the place where I was born, but my adopted home. I remember the first time I came here. It was shortly after Mark and I met. The month was February and I'd never experienced such cold temperatures before. That weekend we drove north to the farm from Winnipeg where he was living. I still remember being on the highway, looking out over the seemingly endless fields, a thick layer of snow covering most everything. The land was so flat I could see for miles. The farther we drove, the thicker the bush became, the deeper the snow, the towns situated wider apart. The five-mile drive off the highway to the place where Mark grew up was tree lined and dark, leaving me completely lost.

Many years have passed since then and the memories of that weekend have faded. One thing I do remember clearly though is my first impression of the farmhouse. The warmth of wood heat and an ever so faint tinge of smoke met us when we opened the door. The floor creaked quietly as we walked across it. Everyone else was asleep. Mark turned on the light over the kitchen sink, sipped a glass of water and glanced out the window at the temperature gauge angled out from the wall.

I remember whispering what a lovely house it was. I said it twice, actually, which must have seemed overdone to him since there was nothing special about that old house. He probably thought I was just being polite, but I sincerely meant it. This place felt authentic and it was almost as if I knew deep inside that my destiny was here, that these people would become family. I was 19 and in love. To me, this was the greatest place in the whole wide world.

I'd never seen a small town arena before, so stepping into the big old barn in Ashern was a new experience. That was 22 years ago. Since then, I have, through personal frostbite trials and interviews with other hockey moms, determined that Ashern has the second coldest arena in the province. The coldest is in Riverton—a lovely community directly east of here, near the shores of Lake Winnipeg.

Being able to withstand frigid weather is a characteristic that makes Manitobans proud. Sure, other parts of the prairies experience similar temperatures, but few have cold snaps as extreme or prolonged as what we have here. That's why our provincial capital is known as "Winterpeg." Though secretly jealous, we scoff at Albertans and their chinooks. We justify our scorn by saying that a mid-winter thaw does nothing except grease up the roads and get our hopes up.

The biggest challenge raising cattle here is the long winter feeding season, which usually begins in October and continues into May. The comparatively inexpensive land prices and healthy precipitation levels work to the cattleman's advantage. The Interlake and northwest parts of the province are rock-infested and suited well to grazing. At one time, land here was nearly given away. This attracted many immigrant families with empty pockets but strong, determined backs.

Manitoba's cow herd sits around 650,000—the third largest in the country. The feeding industry here is small by comparison, but persistent. Fat cattle and culled cows were shipped mostly to the U.S. before the border closed. The majority of British-style feeder calves go to feedlots in the west, while the larger-framed exotics are favoured in the east.

Manitoba sits right in the middle of the country and we borrow a bit of culture from neighbours on either side. We don't consider ourselves easterners, even though our football team is in their conference, but our landscape doesn't have the windswept look of the prairie. The half of us who wear cowboy hats say we own a ranch, while the other half wear ball caps and prefer to say farm. Some of us use horses and dogs during roundup. The rest use ATVs. We fancy ourselves westerners, and though our time zone is central, we feel as neglected by the federal government as everyone else west of the Canadian Shield.

Although I've always wanted to be a writer, there was nothing I'd experienced that moved me to put words on paper until I moved west. There is something inspiring about this place and the people who live here.

Flipping though my notes takes me back to September. I pause, and begin reading over one of the many interviews done early on. That warm feeling I get when the words start to formulate starts to rise up; feeling inspired, I shuffle through a stack of photos at the edge of the desk. I turn on the computer.

Ken and Kerri Leigh Hinsberg.

"Be careful what you wish for, you just might get it."

We'd chuckled at the saying as we sat around the Hinsberg kitchen table in their home near Rapid City, north east of Brandon. Kerri Leigh was describing how she and Ken met nearly 15 years ago. Tired of being alone, she had placed an ad in the personals section of the *Western Producer* newspaper. She was looking for "a kindhearted, honest cattleman with a good sense of humour."

Ken Hinsberg answered the ad.

"And the rest is history," he laughed.

We chatted for a little while longer, then I asked how they were managing.

"We're doing okay," Ken shrugged.

I was prompted to call them because of a letter that Kerri Leigh wrote to the editor of the *Winnipeg Free Press*. It was a heartfelt plea for understanding, a request that Manitobans take seriously the crisis that cattle producers were facing. The letter became a front-page story about the Hinsbergs. A few weeks later, a five-part series ran in the Brandon Sun, exploring how communities have been affected by the drop in cattle revenues.

"Some people don't believe that the rancher is suffering, but if that's the case, then why have the small towns that service our industry been flung into economic crisis?" Kerri Leigh asked. She pulls out the series from the *Sun* and hands it to me. "Our industry is the only one that buys all its inputs at retail and sells at wholesale."

I asked what made her decide to write the letter, to offer themselves up like that for public scrutiny.

"We had to put a face on BSE," she said, explaining that there was very little in the news by that time about the crisis. When the border opened to boxed beef, the public started to think the problem was solved.

"Which is ironic when you think about it. People were thinking we are okay now, but meanwhile, producers are being squeezed tighter than ever."

Kerri Leigh said that they had received numerous calls from producers who said they were in a similar situation. Some said that if they didn't get the grain off that fall, they would no longer be able to afford to farm. Many people called to thank them for putting into words what they were thinking.

There is a lot of wisdom and experience behind this young woman's dark eyes. More than you might expect.

Kerri Leigh tells me she was born on a third generation cattle ranch near Williams Lake, B.C., and raised in virtual isolation. She had no siblings and was home schooled. Both her parents were university educated, extremely independent people who fostered those same qualities in Kerri. She learned responsibility at a young age—working with her father who taught her how to deliver calves, background them and how to feed animals to finish. Her dad, Bill Fredling, now owns a 10,000 head feedlot in southern B.C.

Kerri Leigh left home to obtain a college degree in Beef Cattle Management and Agri Business when she was in her teens, returning home a few years later. Reminiscent of centuries past, when Kerri Leigh came to

Manitoba she brought a dowry with her—20 cows.

Ken was a grain producer from the Rapid City area who loved cattle. He grew crops and ran a small herd of 50 cows. After he and Kerri Leigh married, their focus switched to mostly cattle. It took a number of years, but gradually they expanded the herd. They run a commercial herd of Charolais-Angus moderately framed females, and also have purebred Charolais cows and bulls.

The Hinsbergs are considered young producers. He is 40, she is 34. They have an 11-year-old son, Clinton.

Like so many other Manitoba producers, they were hit hard by the 2003 drought and had to buy feed. A few years prior to BSE, they started expanding by keeping back more heifers and buying land. They bought a new-to-them truck and had to replace the main feeding tractor once the repair bills became too costly and more than the old machine was worth. They say the debt they have is all a part of doing business—especially when young and just starting out.

I ask how many cows they have now.

Kerri Leigh tells me their herd sits at 150.

That's a tough number. The economy of scale is such that the overhead to run a 100-head operation is nearly as much as it costs to run 200 head, but the income is only half. They have too much work for an off-farm job, but barely enough to make a living and service debt.

Ken says that prior to the border closing they were doing just fine. This time of year they would ship a handful of cull cows to pay the fuel bill. Now, with the low cull prices and the escalating price of diesel, it takes closer to 15 animals to cover expenses over the same period. Ken has been putting in long days, making a bit of income by combining grain for others, but is growing tired. It is hard to keep going when everyone he talks to is so discouraged, he is beginning to feel all his efforts are in vain.

Kerri Leigh says she is quick to try and lift his spirits when he starts feeling this way, but now the pressure is even starting to get to her. She glanced at their son, Clinton, who was sitting at the end of the table listening quietly to his parents talk. Their house trailer is nice, but small. It would be near impossible to keep all of their worry from him.

"Go get your 4-H banner to show her," Kerri Leigh said.

Clinton hurried to his room at the end of the trailer and returned a few minutes later carrying a Grand Champion Yearling Heifer banner and trophy. I listened as Clinton described how happy he was to have won. He is a likable, guileless child who has an innocent kindness to him. I follow Clinton back to his room to see what else he has won. The room is tidy and there are only a few toys. The wall was covered in banners and ribbons.

Typical purebred breeders. All their money goes back into the cattle. Their sacrifice means prosperity for the rest of us.

Just weeks before I went to see them, low calf prices, loss of purebred sales, virtually no cull cow income and a feed bill sent the Hinsbergs in to see the bank manager.

Kerri Leigh explained that they owe only two years on a baler and mower loan and three years on the tractor and truck. The bank asked them to bring in a long-term proposal about how they plan to lower debt. Kerri Leigh put together an outlined proposal of how they planned to invest in Natural Valley Farms. The deal is that they would retain ownership of their cattle and begin feeding up to 1,000 head of cattle for Natural Valley. The Hinsbergs would supply the grain and labour, and be paid a daily feeding rate. Kerri Leigh did the math and it looked good. Custom feeding has helped others; she reasoned it could help them as well.

She took the proposal to the bank, but they weren't interested in looking at it.

Kerri Leigh said the only suggestion the bank did favour was consolidating all their loans and spreading the payments out over 15 years, and that the Hinsbergs provide one and a half times the dollar figure in security. Kerri Leigh objected, and having slept on the idea, hasn't changed her mind.

"What they call a long-term solution is to extend our debt over the long term," she said. "All we really need is just a little breathing room to get us over these tough few years, but all they care about is making sure they get paid."

Which is what banks do.

"We have never missed a payment," she said. "But if we do this, we will be worse off in the long run because we'll be paying more than ten additional years of interest."

That is how banks make money.

I've heard that there is tremendous pressure on the banks right now to not foreclose. Some managers are under a great deal of stress, venting and pressuring their non-agricultural customers, too. Kerri Leigh's decision to go to the media is a public relations nightmare.

But she says that's not the reason she did it. All they want is a bit of understanding. This is their life; they have put years of hard work into it and have no plans to give up now. In other words, the Hinsbergs aren't going anywhere. All they want is to get out from under the constant pressure they are feeling. They want to be optimistic about the industry again so they can fully appreciate and feel the changes they can see coming.

"Because, believe it or not, it's a rather exciting time to be in the industry," Ken smiled. "The changes that are being forced upon us will eventually be a good thing, and we want to be a part of what emerges from all of this."

"We have to," Kerri Leigh added. She reached out and laid her hand over his. "We just absolutely have to."

When it came time to leave, I took a photo of them by the cattle, then we stood out by the car and shook hands. I wanted to tell Kerri Leigh it was their story that solidified my decision to make this my next book. I wanted to explain how for more than a year, I'd been pushing aside the issue, trying not to think about it, because as a writer to feel something so strongly means it must be written down. I'd tried writing about the issue early on, but the resulting newspaper articles left me feeling self conscious and wanting. I'd hoped to foster an understanding, but the issue was too fresh, too uncertain, and much too big to explain in a thousand words.

Chores on the ranch are a never-ending cycle that begins the day you take over the farm and doesn't end until the day you leave. And while grain growers are given a reprieve between the harvesting and planting seasons, the cattleman's work is never done and even increases over the winter months.

Once the cows are home and the fields are snow covered, winter feeding begins. The longer the feeding season, the more demanding and expensive this becomes. Calves that are kept over are fed hay, grain and sometimes a feed supplement, while the cows and bulls are fed mostly hay. There are always a few animals that come in from pasture in poor condition, either from a case of footrot or some other illness. They are usually separated from the other animals and the producer needs to decide if they are worth saving. If they are young and in reasonable condition, they will receive a supplement of grain to help improve their condition before winter sets in.

A herd of 300 cows will eat at least 2,400 bales of hay a season, which explains the frantic need to put up hay the summer before. Cattle must be fed—this is one fact that does not change and there is no compromise. If a producer does not put up enough hay because of drought or flood, he must buy enough feed to last the winter. Most will agree it is too costly to buy in hay and do so only when absolutely necessary. The difficulty buying hay lies in the fact that it is only bought when there is a hay shortage, meaning everyone else needs it, too. Demand forces up the price. Generally speaking, years that producers have to buy in feed are the times they make no profit or find themselves losing money on the ranch. Hence the popularity of the saying "Make hay while the sun shines."

Straw is much easier to acquire because it is considered basically worthless to the grain producer, so it is sold for comparatively cheap prices. Good quality straw, especially from oats, can be fed to cows but must be supplemented with grain or a protein source like alfalfa hay. Straw is mostly used as bedding.

If everything goes well, chores take most of the morning and two hours in the afternoon, depending on the set-up and how many cattle must be fed. If the tractor doesn't start or a hydraulic hose breaks on the loader, a race begins to get the equipment fixed before dark. The cows will stand and wait around the feed bunk, watching and listening for the tractor. Although it sounds hard to believe, hungry cows have a way of making the cattleman feel guilty. In the same way some dog owners will swear their dog knows how to smile, cows give reproachful looks. It's a bit unnerving to look into a pen full of scowling cows.

Every producer knows how it feels to spend a whole day fixing equipment with freezing hands and then to still have hours worth of chores to do afterward. A heated machine shed and an extra pair of hands on days like these is a blessed luxury that not everyone can afford.

Everything on the ranch is made more difficult by a stormy forecast. Severe weather demands the cattleman must spend more time outside in it. Cows bawling around the watering bowl is a sure sign that it has frozen over. If caught early, a hole can be punched through to get water flowing again, but if the temperatures are particularly frigid, it is near impossible to get ahead of the ice buildup without firing a blow torch or dumping a dozen kettles of boiling water on top.

Non-producers will sometimes scoff at the farmer for buying a tractor with a cab that provides heat in the winter and air conditioning in the summer. A six-month stint of having to go out twice daily to sit on an open tractor in freezing temperatures, made worse by a relentless wind, is a quick way to change a person's mind about what is considered necessary on the ranch and what is not. Many producers who cannot afford a tractor with a cab face that extra challenge getting the work done. It is weather that ages the cattleman, and cold temperatures make for arthritic hands and knees.

University research centres and agriculture extension specialists are always looking for ways to help the rancher feed easier for a lower cost. An interesting study suggests that feeding cows late in the day will lessen the chance they will calve in the middle of the night. Producers who subscribe to the theory start pushing back the afternoon feeding by late December to get their cows into the new routine.

And while producers anticipate both the beginning and the end of calving season, most will agree that the day they look forward to above all others is the last feeding day—usually the morning before the cows and new calves are turned out to pasture.

On December 29, 2004, the news that cattlemen have been long anticipating finally comes. U.S. Secretary of Agriculture Mike Johanns announces that because Canada is deemed a minimal risk region for BSE, that young, live cattle from Canada will be allowed into the U.S., beginning March 7, 2005. The final rule also allows the importation of other ruminants such as sheep, goats, cervids and camelids.

Jubilation is cut short, however, as the following day, the Canadian Food Inspection Agency (CFIA) announces another suspected case of BSE. On January 2, the case is confirmed positive in a 10-year-old Alberta dairy cow. No meat from the animal entered the human food chain or the animal feed systems.

"The fact this animal was born before the feed ban just confirms the rigor of our systems," Dennis Laycraft tells the media. "We have all the measures in place when animals are processed to remove any risk of infected tissue, so this really is more of an animal health issue than a food safety issue." Laycraft also explains that this new case does not affect Canada's minimal risk status, which allows for two cases of BSE per million head in a 12-month period. In Canada, that rate is 12 cases a year.

By year's end it is estimated that the industry has lost more than $5 billion.

An Alberta feedlot makes headlines when nearly 200 cattle die after the feedlot is forced into receivership and a management team is brought in to oversee the operation.

General feelings were summed up in a tongue-in-cheek reply by cattlemen reading the story. Now the bank knows how cattle producers feel. It took them only a few weeks to lose $200,000. At least we can spread that figure out over a lifetime.

On January 11, more bad news is announced when another case of BSE is confirmed in Alberta. Unfortunately, this cow was born after the 1997 feed ban. Federal Agriculture Minister Andy Mitchell orders a quick review of Canada's feed controls. Political critics and producers at the grassroots question whether the CFIA has mishandled implementation of the 1997 feed ban and want to know if feed mills have been following the rules correctly. Effect on the cattle market is instantaneous. If producers were lucky enough to sell their cattle before 11 a.m., they got a good price; otherwise, most cattle that moved through the ring after that sold for five to 10 cents a pound less.

This brings the total to three home-grown cases of BSE; four, if the U.S. animal is included in the tally. Concerned consumers are quoted in the media asking whether the meat they buy in the stores is from Alberta, but there is no noticeable downturn in consumption.

U.S. agriculture officials send a team to Canada to evaluate the third case and determine if there is sufficient concern to reconsider opening the border. Later, they give Canada good marks on safety measures to combat BSE and report, much to the disappointment of R-CALF, that there is no reason to impede trade.

Nine U.S. Senators introduce a motion to keep the border closed, but in order for it to pass, it will require support from both the Senate and the House of Representatives, as well as President Bush.

Confident that the border will open on March 7 as planned, John Masswohl, former Canadian diplomat to Washington, tells delegates at the Manitoba Cattle Producers Association Annual meeting: "The border will open. The earth would have to shake, the seas would have to part in order for it to not happen."

Chapter Thirty One

"What most people don't seem to realize is that there is
just as much money to be made out of the wreckage of a
civilization as from the upbuilding of one."
— Margaret Mitchell, *Gone with the Wind*

Another flip through the notebook takes me to the town of Winkler, Manitoba. I'd travelled there in early fall and had been surprised by how much the community has grown since I was there last.

Winkler is in the south-central part of the province where the land is flat and the soil is rich. When fields here are in full bloom, nowhere on the patchwork prairies are the colours prettier. This area is known as prosperous, its people honest and hardworking.

I wonder how Paul and Garreth Spenst are doing. Looking back over my interview with them, a sentence jumps off the page.

"I don't want to work for Cargill my whole life," Paul had said.

I'd turned off the highway at the Tim Horton's, following directions to the massively green Real Canadian Superstore. The Spenst family is building a meat store and chose a lot directly across from what will likely be their biggest competitor.

The day I arrived, the building looked half finished. Piles of lumber were stacked under sheets of plastic and long cardboard boxes of siding were out of the weather, sitting against the building. A circular saw was set up on a table outside and I was impressed by how surprisingly neat it looked for a construction site.

A young man was standing on the hood of a half ton, inserting a piece

Paul and Garreth Spenst

of fascia under the eaves. He saw me, hopped into the truck box, then onto the ground. He introduced himself as Paul and then I shook hands with his brother, Garreth. They invited me out of the wind into the building—at this point a framed-in, insulated shell. The roof was on, but the windows weren't in yet. The place was large and smelled of new wood and freshly poured concrete.

I wondered out loud if the rest of the crew was on their lunch break.

The brothers smiled when they said that the family is doing most of the construction themselves.

"Every week we're learning a new job," Garreth said, adding that their father is usually there, too. "That way we keep our costs down and learn something as we go along."

The Spensts tell me that they are third-generation cattle producers who grew up on a farm near Rosengart, settled by their grandfather. The brothers are farming a 360-head cattle operation in partnership with their parents, Garry and Connie Spenst. They feed their animals to finish, and had a pen full of fat cattle when BSE was discovered. They began butchering on a small scale to get rid of the animals, and it was the prolonged closure that solidified their decision to go into the retail business in a bigger way. They are too far in to turn back now, and are excited about the possibilities.

I told them they looked a little young to take this on and was surprised by their ages. Paul is 28 and Garreth 24. They believe age works to their advantage.

"We are very fortunate the ages we are when this happened," Paul said. "We are young enough to go in a new direction, to make changes. We sat down and talked about it and decided that we don't want to rely on big companies like Cargill, the U.S. or the government to earn our living."

Their plan involves fattening steers without using growth hormones, electing instead to maximize genetics through selective breeding. The animals will be slaughtered at Plains Processing in Carman, then brought to the store for cutting and processing. The Spensts plan to also sell chicken, pork and a full line of deli meats, including sausage made in-house.

The brothers said that they believe that consumers want to know and trust their butcher. They plan to focus on quality and provide good value for the money. Then Paul said something that shocked me. I had asked him to explain it twice, to be sure I was hearing him correctly.

Paul believes that young, fat cattle are being sold to the packing plants out west and that the top cuts from those animals are being sold into the U.S. market. Because of a shortage and strong demand for meat there, the meat is being sold at a premium.

Meat from cull cows is being shipped to the Canadian grocery stores and sold for almost the same price as what young meat is worth.

It's no wonder people complain that sometimes their meat is tough.

The Spensts can't prove their suspicions, but are confident enough about this theory to speak publicly about it.

"The packing plants are taking advantage of the Canadian consumer who have wholeheartedly supported cattlemen," Paul said. "That's not right. We believe consumers deserve better than that."

The packing plant sits at the opposite end of the spectrum from the ranch. It is no wonder that cattlemen and packers do not relate well to one another.

Packing plants have been called the necessary evil, the end of the road so to speak, the place where animals are turned into meat. Words used to describe this segment of the industry are competitive, low-margin, cut-throat, profit-driven. The managers describe themselves as thick-skinned and pragmatic.

Early in this economic crisis, politicians and consumer groups began to question why producers were being paid so little for their cattle, but that meat prices in the stores did not reduce by a proportionate amount. It appeared that the aid package intended for cattlemen ended up profiting the packers instead.

Those defending the packing industry said that the conclusions drawn by critics were too simplistic, and that the business of turning animals into meat and then marketing that product is more complex than people realize. This is a fair statement, so managers and spokespeople in the slaughter industry must have become frustrated trying to make others understand their point of view.

It appears that when hearing arguments from this sector, facts are best understood when the plants themselves are divided into two categories: fat cattle plants, or the facilities that slaughter animals under 30 months of age; and cow plants.

The fat cattle plants owned by Cargill at High River, Alberta and Tyson Foods (also called Lakeside at Brooks, Alberta) were exporting around half of the meat they produce. When the border closed, they found themselves with no market for 50 percent of their product, and with a daily kill rate of thousands of animals, meat was piling up fast. They cut back on production, but their overhead costs remained the same. Spokesmen for the companies say that they honoured forward contracts made prior to May 20, so it is easy to believe they initially lost millions.

Once production levels returned to normal, packers say that they lost between $150 and $200 per animal in the reduced sale of meat products that Canadians do not eat—certain cuts and offal products like tongue, heart, liver and tripe. Cargill operates its own rendering facility and reported that they suddenly found themselves without a market for bone meal, which was traditionally used as fertilizer or pet food. Now, instead of getting paid for this product, they were having to pay between $62 and $100 a tonne to have it hauled to a landfill site. This is a low-margin, high-volume business, so both profits and losses can add up quickly.

The reason for consistently low prices for cull cows is even easier to understand. Plants like XL Foods near Calgary would have incurred near identical losses as the fat cattle plants, but also had to suddenly implement a procedure to deal with cows over 30 months of age. A nine-point protocol program was developed by the Canadian Food Inspection Agency that called for strict rules for decapitation, cutting into the spinal cord, handling of the head, the way the carcass is split and how the knives, saws and sharpeners are cleaned to ensure that any potential material from the brain and spinal cord does not come in contact with the meat. Implementation of this procedure means that while it used to take two minutes to kill the cow and split the carcass, it now takes 20 minutes, which cuts back on productivity and profit. The unpopular cuts that were normally sold into ethnic markets in the U.S. are now being ground into hamburger and selling for a lower price.

According to Canfax, there is 180,000 tonnes of cow meat produced annually in Canada. Before BSE, 72,000 tonnes were exported live into the U.S., 65,000 packed and exported, and 43,000 eaten in Canada. Suddenly, all that meat had no place to go. Packing plant spokesmen were critical of the federal government for continuing to allow offshore beef into the country on supplementary import permits, saying that it was making marketing beef in Canada more difficult for them.

Plants that slaughter both fat cattle and cull cows were faced with all the above expenses, plus the additional costs of creating a segregated kill line so that meat from animals under 30 months of age would not cross paths with cow meat. The packing industry was in as much turmoil as the feedlot sector.

Because the packing plants were overstocked with beef, they were paying feedlots prices below the cost of production. There was tremendous pressure on the federal government to create a program that would bail out the feedlots. In their haste, the government ignored warnings from the CCA that the program was flawed, and went ahead with the first fat cattle program. Just as the CCA predicted, fat cattle prices plummeted when animals flooded the market, driving down the price.

Criticism from the federal opposition prompted an investigation into packing plant profits by the federal Liberals. In October 2003, packing plant executives were called before the House of Commons Agriculture Committee to justify their pricing policies. M. Paul Steckle and other committee members accused the packers of taking unfair advantage of the industry by lowering the price they pay for cattle while continuing to charge high prices for beef. In the ensuing months, the committee was applauded by most everyone as it demanded answers and even requested to see the packer's financial information. As the investigation continued, opinions became divided over whether it is right in a democracy to expect private business to open its books for public scrutiny. The packers argued that this could give their competitors a clear look at their bottom line.

When everything shook out, it appeared the committee was justified in its indignation, but was slightly off the mark. The reason the packers were paying low prices for cattle but beef prices did not come down in stores is that even though there was an oversupply of cattle, there wasn't an oversupply of popular cuts because of a lack of slaughter capacity.

In defence of the committee, the fat cattle packing plants could have avoided all the bad publicity had they simply paid a reasonable amount for fat cattle, discounting them marginally, instead of dropping prices as low as 30 cents a pound. This created a huge discrepancy as these animals normally sell for 90 cents a pound. It appeared that the packers were taking advantage of the situation.

Matters were made worse by the fact that these packing plants have divisions or subsidiary companies that own and feed cattle. After the program was announced, they slaughtered their own cattle at around 30 cents a pound, then applied for the subsidy from the government. When questioned about this by reporters, a spokesman at Cargill explained that the company feedlot operations are a separate entity, and that the plant owned the cattle and was poised to take a hit on the devaluation of inventory. This is a fair statement given that the timing of the funding announcement was June—at least six weeks before the announcement that the border would open to boxed beef.

However, it's a difficult explanation to accept completely, given the fact it was the packing plants that devalued the cattle in the first place. In the end, Cargill received back $8.99 million from the program.

A spokesman at Tyson Foods justified their reimbursement by saying that it was Lakeside Farms that received the payment, not the packing division, and that the $32.9 million Lakeside received was rolled back into the purchase of calves that fall.

While technically these answers are correct, bouncing paper losses between companies is a clever way to ensure that, overall, a company doesn't sustain any red ink at all.

Once the situation was carefully analyzed, it was determined by both the Alberta government and a few independent analysts that the packing plants didn't do anything illegal, since it is not illegal to make a profit.

What they did do was gamble by continuing to process meat when there was little market, collect the subsidy owed anyone who could get their fat cattle slaughtered, and stockpile the meat until the border opened to boxed beef in early September. That's when their gamble paid off.

CHAPTER THIRTY TWO

"The farmer is proud, stubborn and hopeful.
He's like an aging prizefighter. He may be getting
long in the tooth, but he's still willing to get into the ring
and go his rounds with anyone.
But I think his spirit is being broken by this crisis.
And if you break the spirit of the farmer,
you break the spirit of the community as a whole."
— Jason Durish, veterinarian in Collingwood, Ontario.
Quoted by Hartley Steward, columnist for *The Sun*, 2003

Busy is the best word that best describes Robert and Betty Green. The Green family run a large herd of commercial cows near the town of Fisher Branch, Manitoba and feed their calves to finish weights. When BSE hit, Betty was President of the Manitoba Cattle Producers Association and for years prior to that she and Robert were both involved in local politics. In spite of their busy home life, the Greens always involved themselves in local politics and encouraged their five children to participate in 4-H and other community events.

I invited the Greens for supper last fall and as we relaxed in the living room afterward, they spoke candidly about what this time has been like for them. Betty said that early on, the most serious decision they had to make was whether to allow CBC cameras into their home. The media wanted a behind the scenes look at life on the ranch and Betty's profile made them a likely target. After exhausting the pros and cons of allowing themselves to be filmed, Robert and Betty decided it would be a positive thing to do for the industry.

Betty and Robert Green

The camera crew arrived at 6:00 a.m. and followed the family through its daily routine. They were filmed feeding the cows, teaching calves to suck and mixing feed rations for the steers.

"They asked us some pretty tough questions," Betty said, adding that the objective was to show the general public what life on a ranch is all about and how much is at risk. Sometimes she found her voice catching and tears sprouting in her eyes at the depth of what was asked and the finality of some answers.

"Robert and I, in our day-to-day lives, were trying really hard not to go there, not to think about all the negative things that could happen, but this forced us to say it out loud," she said.

By sundown that day, the CBC had shot plenty of footage and after the crew left, Robert and Betty had no regrets, but they were nervous. They had been truthful, believed sincerely in what they were saying, but were concerned about how the documentary would be edited and how they would appear. The program was pieced together and shown all across Canada. The Greens had no complaints about how it was put together, but still felt uneasy after it aired.

"It's difficult to explain," she said. "On one hand you feel good, like you did the right thing, but to see your life splayed out like that leaves a person feeling vulnerable, almost weak."

Which sums up how this whole issue has made cattlemen feel.

As President of the MCPA, Betty was interviewed numerous times over the next year, but almost daily early on. Pressure was mounting in Manitoba because of continuing drought and grasshopper infestation. They had 8 loads of fat cattle ready for market, and like others who finish cattle here, they needed to access the U.S. packing plants. Demand for Betty to make correct decisions and to say the right thing to the media were constant.

Betty's answers during one interview showed signs of fatigue and stress. When the interviewer asked what might happen if the situation isn't soon resolved, she paused and the audience could hear her collecting her thoughts. Her voice broke when she replied the reality of the situation was something she couldn't let herself think about. Her humanity shone through in those moments, and it said more about her and the situation than the perfectly scripted answer she was wishing for in that moment.

As difficult as this was, Betty believes that there was something about opening up that gave reassurance to others. Since then, they have received countless calls from producers.

"A fellow called and I recognized his voice," she said. "He had no hay left and only $300 in his bank account." His only choice was to buy hay or turn his cows into the wildlife management area. She said that as he spoke, his voice became increasingly quiet.

"It scared me. I phoned someone I knew from his area to go and pay him a visit, make sure he was all right," she said.

It is believed that over the past 20 months, there have been cattlemen who have quietly committed suicide. There is no way to know for sure the reasons in each individual case, but it is reasonable to expect that stress from BSE fallout could be a contributing factor.

Betty said it is not exaggerating to say the issue brought an entire industry to its knees.

"There are men I've known and respected my whole life who have called up in tears, crippled by uncertainty," she said. "Others call just looking for hope, for a reason to hang on."

She said that there have been a few cattlemen on the edge of retirement before the border closed who called, begging them to buy their cows, or at least help them find someone who will. "They said, 'I just can't do the work any more; I just want out.'"

Betty doesn't have a lot of patience for people who say that the struggling producer was destined to fail anyway, and that the closed border will rid the industry of people it doesn't need. She says that tragedy lies in the fact that we have lost some young producers and that older producers' retirement funds are now compromised.

Staff from the Rural Stress Line came to an MCPA board meeting to give directors and staff advice on how to deal with the influx of calls everyone was receiving. As it was, the Board's Executive Director, Keith Robertson, suffered a heart attack that first year.

Betty tells us her schedule is not as demanding now, but during that first year, she was on the road most days and on the phone every night. Robert said it was difficult for him to be home alone, how much he missed her input on the farm.

"We've always been partners who worked and made decisions together," he said. "Sometimes I was left not sure what to do."

He said the really difficult part for him was that the issue never left them alone. There was never a time that they could just close out the world, just be together, pretending that this wasn't happening.

Betty chuckled at the remembrance of having to finally shut off her cell phone the morning of their son's wedding. While they were in the reception line following the ceremony, at least a quarter of the people coming through to offer congratulations also leaned forward and whispered,

"So when do you think the border is going to open?"

Before Betty was elected to the MCPA Board, she was the Chairperson of the Lakeshore School Division. In the mid-1990s, the board decided to shuffle principals within the division between schools. It was a controversial decision that was met with a lot of opposition.

She remembered walking into the community hall where there was a reporter and a few hundred annoyed parents and teachers gathered. Someone from the Board pulled her aside just as she was on the sidelines, mentally preparing to address the crowd.

"He told me, 'this is the hardest meeting you'll ever chair,'" she laughed. "Looking back on what I have faced since, that was one of the easiest."

Rural communities have always been vulnerable to progress and hardship. Small businesses are the first to feel the effects of an economic downturn. Improved roads and faster vehicles mean that the small-town businessman no longer has a cornered consumer. His margins have shrunk over the past three decades, and his customers have more choice about where they shop than ever before.

Communities reliant on agriculture will suffer along with producers, because farm operations today are being run by folks whose parents taught them how to make do with what they can afford. The rancher will tighten his belt until there are no more notches, then punch another hole through the leather and tighten up some more. Businesses that don't sell the necessities won't sell much during times like these.

History has shown that when small businesses start to disappear from an area, so do the people. Community clubs, arenas and schools will close. In the early 1990s, Canada Post shut down rural post offices nationwide, dissolving the final thread that kept people in an evaporating community. Some towns now only exist in the memories of old-timers or recollections in community history books.

It is too early to say how small communities will weather the aftermath of BSE, but reports in community and agricultural newspapers say that towns that rely heavily on the cattleman's business are hurting.

Every business that expires leaves locals out of work and gives those living on the outskirts one less reason to come to town. A dying community cannot attract new businesses, sees a loss in tax dollars, has difficulty keeping professionals such as doctors, and gives little incentive for retirees to want to settle there. Once malaise settles over a town, it becomes extremely difficult to turn the situation around.

Wally Happychuk was born and raised at Sundown, Manitoba, in the southeast part of the province. He returned to nearby Vita 25 years ago as the Agricultural Representative.

I have met Wally a few times at cattle events and travelled to Vita on a few occasions. It is a quaint little town along a quiet highway—a bare-bones place with a handful of essential services including a grocery store, credit union, auto repair business and gas station. The community seems to be holding its own throughout the crisis.

Whether Wally realizes it or not, he is highly regarded by cattlemen here and is well known and respected across the province.

I give Wally a call to ask him what the last twenty months have been like for him.

"Those of us who work closely with the farming community, well, we have been feeling the stress," Wally says. "These are people we know personally, and it's pretty hard watching them struggle."

He says that his department provides extension services, and from that standpoint, there is only so much he can do to help. In a small town like this, everybody knows everybody and what is happening with the neighbours. When a producer starts selling off equipment or takes an off-farm job, it is usually out of necessity.

I ask Wally if there are any statistics available that show how many farms have been lost because of BSE.

He says he hasn't seen anything yet, adding that even if something is put together, he isn't sure how accurate it would be. He says that approximately 10 percent of the producers in his area are no longer in the cattle business. Some were forced to sell out by the banks, some elected to quit, others retired. The loss of equity will be very difficult to measure, so he thinks that factor, combined with the fact most producers are too proud to admit that they weren't able to weather the crisis, means the exact numbers will never be known for sure.

"This is cattle country here," he says, estimating that 70 percent of his workload involves the cattle industry. "These are very proud people."

Wally says the most difficult adjustment producers had to face was the overnight drop in the industry, which went from a position of buoyancy to one of pessimism instantly.

"If the downturn had come slower, guys would have weathered it better," he says, "but prices were really good and there was expansion happening, and the guys who were starting to background and finish were hit particularly hard."

Wally stressed that the combination of missing out on those peak years of the cycle and having increased debt due to expansion hurt a lot of operations.

"They will never make up those losses and it will take a lot before that same level of optimism returns to the industry," he says. "For some, it never will."

Dr. John FitzGibbon is a professor at the University of Guelph. He and Suzanne Young and Cassie Barker prepared a paper that addresses the Social and Institutional Responses to the BSE crisis. They write that while the economic factors are well publicized, little has been done to address the social and emotional hardships facing ranch families.

They explain that the financial strain is taking a toll on family relationships, self-esteem, and farmers' sense of control. Farmers are often exposed to uncontrollable and unpredictable operational constraints and strains because their financial well-being is at the mercy of domestic government policies, international markets, and the forces of nature. The threat of economic disaster is present in the lives of producers more often than any other occupation.[24]

Farmers have different ways of coping with stress. Most seek help and support from the local farming community, however some feel alienated because family and friends don't like to talk about issues, especially those involving finances. Farmers have been taught to be stoic, to hide feelings of perceived inadequacy. The BSE crisis has put an incredible amount of strain on farm women who recognize changes in their spouse, and children who sense their parents are struggling.

In Manitoba, the rural stress line saw a call increase of 40 percent after the border closed. Janet Smith, Manager of the Farm and Rural Stress Line says that calls started to trickle in shortly after May 2003 and as the realization struck how serious the situation was, calls came more frequently. The stress line staff are all professionally trained and most have a farming background. Those answering calls were well versed on the details of the financial programs available. A lot of questions were asked about how to find financial help.

"Usually it is a compounding of issues in their lives that causes a person to call," Janet says. "Some are looking for program information, others are worried about the border, and in 2003, the drought. There was a lot of uncertainty and fear."

Janet says that most of the male callers begin by asking a financial question, then when prompted, will admit that they are also looking for someone to talk to. Most don't want to burden their wives with their worries. Many aren't willing to see a counsellor, saying, "I'm not crazy, I just can't pay my bills." Janet says that initially it was mostly men who called, but then as time went by, calls from women concerned about their husbands started coming in. The women say their husbands aren't sleeping well and some show signs of depression. Sometimes the women are overwhelmed themselves, especially if they have taken an off-farm job to help support the family.

Kim Moffat is one of the stress line counsellors. She and her husband are producers who live near Strathclair, Manitoba. Kim tells me that they both had good paying jobs, but elected to give up city life and returned to the family farm. Kim was raised on a farm near Hamiota, and she remembers one day a number of years ago, sitting with her father, talking about the warm feeling it gives farmers to know they are feeding people. She says that as they spoke, her father turned quite serious. He said that farming is about more than the fuzzy feelings; that there is a greater responsibility attached to food production that a lot of people don't understand. It deepened Kim's appreciation for her upbringing and the life she and her husband now lead. It also helped her understand the depth of emotion ranchers are feeling when they call the stress line.

I asked Kim if she found it hard living with BSE and talking about it with struggling producers.

"It actually helps to talk with other people who have similar feelings," she says, adding that she has a background in psychiatric nursing. "And it really feels good to share information with people and to help alleviate some of their anxiety."

Kim says that when a situation starts to build up and producers feel they have lost control, they sometimes start to lose perspective. Her job is to offer a non-judgmental ear and talk them through the current circumstance, recommending a place for them to seek professional services if necessary.

The work is very rewarding and she has met a lot of wonderful people over the phone. She can tell that most are hardworking victims of global circumstance. Days and even weeks after talking to someone, she'll sometimes wonder how that person is doing.

"And even when the border opens some of the problems will still be there for these people," she says, adding that she expects to see a different type of stress from people once the industry returns to a perceived normal. "It will take some time to recoup the financial losses that have been the result of the border closure."

Like everyone else tied to the industry, Kim sometimes becomes frustrated with talk about the border and occasionally she too, will have a bad day but it is made easier by the folks she works with. The stress line staff are a great group of people who are very understanding toward one another. She has learned that sometimes it is best to avoid a social situation if she thinks the talk might get too depressing and the speculation too frightening.

"I have to practise what I preach," she says. "Get enough sleep, eat well, fit in some exercise and most importantly, do something each day that brings a little joy into your life."

Chapter Thirty Four

Our poets have told us again and again,
The blessings that beasts have conferred upon men.
How sheep give us wool, and goats give us milk,
How hens give us eggs and worms give us silk.
But no one has ever acknowledged in full,
Our debt to the natural urge of the bull.

— Anonymous

"Come see what's in the barn."

"Guess what I found when I went out to feed this afternoon?"

"I thought that cow looked like she was getting close. I guess I'll have to start checking from now on."

Regardless of how a producer elects to announce the first calf of the season, it sends a ripple of excitement through the house. Everyone will pull on their boots and head out for a look.

The sight of a wet, wobbly newborn standing on a bed of straw warms a cattle producer's heart. The cow will lick his head and butt, sometimes looking behind herself as if to say, "Where did this come from?"

The announcement of the first calf signals the beginning to the busiest time on the ranch. Unfortunately, it does not always mean the first calve is alive and healthy, but often it is a premature weakling that will die. Early calves sometimes surprise you though, and thrive in spite of the odds against them.

The only certain thing about ranching is that the calves will eventually come and even if things go well, it isn't going to be easy.

One of Mark's favourite sayings is that "every calf has a story." Few animals on the ranch move through completely anonymous. There is something about each cow and most calves that cause the rancher to remember them. Sometimes it is quite insignificant, like a white, diamond-shaped forehead marking or the fact this might be Laurie's first 4-H heifer. Maybe she is a fence crawler (a cow that can't be kept in and teaches others the same habit) or the calf that had to be rescued from under a pile of hay dumped in the bale feeder where he'd been sleeping. He might be the first-born bull calf, or the heifer born in the storm, or the last one born on pasture in July. This cow is the orphan named Baby, who was bottle-fed until she learned to steal sucks from the quiet cows.

For us, the first calf came last night, while friends Art and Jackie Jonasson were visiting. Mark and Art have always been good friends and we've been seeing more of them since they became neighbours. Art is a former school teacher who grew up with cattle, quitting teaching when the cow herd grew too big. Jackie has always been on the farm and is one of the most competent farm women I've ever met.

I'd asked them the same question that Roberta Rampton, a reporter with *Reuters*, asked me.

What is it about cows?

Art and Jackie looked at one another and confessed they had to think for a minute. The first thing that came to mind was how much they enjoy calving season. They said that despite of the work involved, they actually look forward to time spent outdoors calving cows.

"It's so rewarding," Jackie said.

Art admitted that he likes the lifestyle and enjoys working together as a family. He looks forward to each day being outside in nature and especially likes haying season and making feed.

Jackie said she likes to watch cows eat and finds that being around them is quite relaxing. We all looked at one another and laughed.

"It sounds kinda crazy, doesn't it?" he asked.

"It sure does," she added. "But that's just what we do."

Our son, Laurie, came in right at that point and announced we had our first calf. Mark smiled, saying that our calving record so far is 100 percent.

"Don't say that," Art warned, and we all laughed, knowing exactly what he meant. Bragging will almost guarantee the next calf will be born dead.

Every rancher knows this theory well. If you say you didn't have one caesarean last year, you'll have three within the next two days. If you boast your bull throws small, easy-to-deliver calves, the next one will weigh 130 pounds and die the following day. Saying your tractor never gives you any trouble will almost guarantee a $5,000 repair bill within a month.

"When things are going , it's best to keep your mouth shut," Art said.

Another calf was born today, and Mark and Laurie are out in the barn right now helping a heifer deliver a set of twins. These aren't our heifers, but we will share in the profit of the calf crop since we agreed to feed and calve out 70 young females for a friend. He'd bought heifers and bred them with plans to sell them in the fall, but the market was soft, so he elected to keep them and have us winter them instead.

The decision to do this will add a full month to the beginning of our calving season, which usually starts in early March. We've been assured that the heifers have been bred to an easy-calving bull and by the sound of the voices coming from the kitchen now, it appears that we have four live calves from three heifers. So far, so good—but we won't actually say this out loud.

In places where the weather is mild and the feeding season short, many cows give birth on pasture. The first contact a cattleman might have with the calf is during round-up in the spring. The cows and calves will all be brought home, the male calves castrated and everything branded before they are turned out to the summer pasture. Producers who calve this way report about a two percent death loss—either cows come in without a calf or sometimes a few cows don't come back at all. Calving season for these producers does not mean the same level of intensity as what producers in the colder regions face.

In Manitoba and parts of the prairies, a newborn calf will freeze to death if left outside for too long. This fact motivates cattlemen in the colder climes to watch their herd closely, or move back their calving dates to avoid the cold weather. It is becoming increasingly popular to calve cows during the months of April and May in Manitoba. Those who do, swear it cuts back on the workload. Producers who stick with the traditional winter months of February and March, say that while it may be easier in some ways, it's harder on the calves to endure a wet spring. Either way, calving season has its challenges that amount to a lot of work.

During the night and especially once the temperature dips below minus 20 degrees Celsius, many cattlemen check the cows every two hours once calving season begins. This becomes quite an onerous task, so producers aim for a calving season that lasts no more than six weeks. Of course, there are always cows that calve later than that, but once spring arrives, there is less chance that a calf will freeze its ears, feet or tail if not noticed right away.

Calving time means the producer spends more of the day outside in the barn and with the cattle than anywhere else. This is by far the most difficult time of year. There is no time to anything but care for the cattle. The demands will wear out even the toughest, fittest man. Most producers will admit to falling asleep on the tractor or taking a nap on a pile of hay in the corner of the barn because he was too exhausted to get to the house.

The cattle producer's day usually begins with checking the cows in the morning, followed by feeding and then chores. One chore that most producers do daily is tag the newborns and castrate the bull calves. By tagging early the producer can be confident which calf belongs to which cow (sometimes cows try to steal another cow's calf) and confusion will reign otherwise. If the cattle are purebred, they must be weighed soon after birth as this is vital information needed if the animal will be sold as breeding stock.

Walking through the pen to get a look at the day-old calves, tells the producer whether or not the calves are being well-mothered and adjusting to life outside the womb. It is vitally important that a calf gets up and begins sucking soon after it is born. The mother's first milk contains colostrum, and this provides the calf with necessary nutrients and antibodies that will give it a healthy start. If the calf doesn't get this, it will weaken and possibly die within a few days.

Genetics seems to play a factor in how quickly a calf starts sucking. Generally speaking, exotic calves tend to be born bigger and are not as aggressive as the smaller, livelier, British breeds. Few Charolais calves will get up and suck as quickly as an Angus calf, but because the Charolais will come in heavier from pasture in the fall, the cattleman will spend the extra time needed to get the calf started. This is why breeding programs are important and why crossbreeding dams and sires with desirable traits is popular.

Genetics aside, there are countless reasons why the producer must intervene to help a calf get started. If the cow had a difficult time giving birth, she might lose her desire to mother and will ignore the calf or become confused over which one is hers. Sometimes a cow's udder will become swollen so the pull from a sucking calf hurts and she will kick it away. If a cow has twins, she may not have enough milk for two, so the less aggressive calf will suffer. Often times, the producer will adopt a calf to a cow whose calf has died, or to one that he knows from past experience has plenty of milk and doesn't mind raising two calves.

Overly large calves are often sluggish. If the calf is weak, gets too cold after birth, is premature, or born with bad foot joints and has difficulty standing, the producer must help it get started. Sometimes a conscientious producer will supplement a slow calf's diet with bottle feeding. Feeding calves this way is a nuisance, but it gets needed nutrition into their bodies and helps stimulate the desire to suck. This also teaches a timid calf to be more aggressive with the udder.

Even after a calf is sucking successfully there is no guarantee that it won't become sick. Every producer has at least one bad experience with a diarrhea called calf scours. The diarrhea can infect other calves and it is made worse by wet, confined areas. If not caught early and calves are left untreated, they will die. Scours and other infections such as pneumonia can wipe out a third of the calf crop if a producer isn't diligent—and sometimes even if he is. Vaccinating cows and sometimes the newborn calves helps, but cold wet conditions cause a great deal of stress. All producers will agree the biggest challenge they face is keeping the calves healthy until they are put out to pasture.

Helping a cow deliver its calf usually means moving the animal into the barn where she can be restrained in a head gate. This makes dealing with her easier and lessens the chance that the cattleman will be injured. This is done if she is showing signs she is ready to calve but the birth is not progressing. Knowing if and when to interfere is a skill acquired over years of tutelage, usually under the instruction of an experienced cow handler. Some people have an enviable knack with cows and immediately recognize the signs of trouble and follow the necessary course of action.

Twins, unusual presentation or a large calf are birthing problems that require the producer to intervene. This is the reason cattlemen wear T-shirts under their long sleeved work shirts—so that outer layers can be stripped off when it comes time to reach inside a cow and investigate what might be wrong. Pushing the calf back, extending its legs or turning the calf around usually solves the problem and it is born easily after that. If the calf is large, or the mother doesn't have the strength to push it out on her own, the producer will attach straps to the calf's legs and pull in rhythm with the cow's contractions.

Often times the calf will be born alert and breath right away. Other times, the producer will have to clean out the calf's mouth, turn it upside down to drain fluid from its lungs or give it mouth-to-mouth resuscitation. These are tense moments and the cattleman feels a desperation to do whatever he can to save the calf.

Calving season out the maternal instincts in both men and women, and a producer will tell you the satisfaction of saving a calf is the most grat-ifying experience of ranching.

Every year, even the most experienced cattleman will be faced with a difficult birth. This means being able to hold up under the physical and emotional pressure of helping a cow deliver her calf without injuring either. Sometimes the producer is faced with the knowledge that he can only save one and not the other. Calves are sometimes born deformed or crippled and these are sad cases that will bring a tear to even the hardened cattleman's eye, especially if the calf must be put down. Knowing when to call the vet-erinarian is something a producer learns over time, but even that decision does not guarantee a live calf and cow. The unfortunate thing is that no matter how diligent the producers, sometimes calves or cows die.

It is important to show the cow her calf immediately after it is born so that her natural instincts take over and she begins mothering. This is some-times difficult with an assisted birth or if there is something wrong with the calf. A cow, once free of the head gate, is near impossible to stop. Most react quietly, but every ranch has a few ornery females. The trouble is you don't necessarily know who they are until the first time they chase you around the barn.

The real killer, the cow that should be shipped directly to the packing plant, is the one that can't be brought into the barn in the first place. She will snort and charge and not let anyone near her calf. Cows like these pres-ent a host of problems. And while the image of an irate cow chasing the farmer around the barn is a humorous one, the reality exists that there are cattle producers injured or killed each year by overly protective cows.

It is 4:45 a.m.

I vaguely recall Mark climbing into bed a while ago, but I didn't allow myself to wake up enough to check the time. His breathing is noisy and his muscles are twitching. After more than 20 years of marriage, I recognize these subtleties as a sign that he spent most of the night working. When he finally came to bed, overtired and in quest of sleep, his muscles couldn't set-tle down. Now, the natural rhythm that usually begins waking him daily around 6:30 a.m. is battling against exhaustion.

I pull back the covers and quietly get up. A pair of sweat pants, sweat-shirt and thick socks sit in a pile at the edge of the dresser. I pull all of this on, find my glasses and leave the door open a crack as I make my way to the kitchen sink. I glance out the window at the thermometer. Minus 25 degrees Celsius. I flip on the light over the sink and start a pot of coffee brewing, but the thought there might be a wet, newborn calf lying on the frozen ground pushes me quickly toward the porch. I pull on a pair of thickly quilted, canvas coveralls and a pair of snowmobile boots. I tuck my hair under a woollen toque and cover my hands with thin, tight gloves. The giant rechargeable flashlight Mark received for Christmas is sitting on the floor beside his crumpled coveralls.

I flip on the farm bathroom light and plug the flashlight into the charger on the counter, lifting last year's model off its base. I glance through the pocket-sized calving record book that lies open on the counter, checking the times to see that a calf was born around 2:30 a.m., 11:00 p.m. and 8:10 last night. The colour and sex of each is in one column, and next to that the cow's tag number. Mark will use this information when it comes time to age verify the calves. Being able to give an approximate birth date should help open markets to Canadian beef.

Pulling a pair of thick leather mitts over my gloves, I reach for the door knob. A stickie note above it reads: Watch out for #58 in the barnyard.

Pulling open the inside door I notice the storm door is lined with frost. This old door has been opened thousands of times over the years, so it no longer sits right on the frame. The cold air grabs me the minute I step into it, so I pull up my hood. The countless trips we've made from the house to the calving pens have stamped the snow into a hard-packed trail. The sky is clear this morning, but still black and lit with stars. The yard light illuminates the gate and farther in the distance, are four lights: two high on poles in the main calving pen, one above the barn doorway and another on a pole at the edge of the barnyard.

My boots crunch in the snow, filling the silent air. The sound of coyotes howling cause me to flip back the hood to listen. They are far in the distance, and even if they were nearby I wouldn't be overly concerned. The big outdoor dog chases away anything that comes too close.

The sound I'm really listening for is not as obvious as yipping coyotes. It is the quiet, unique sound that a mother cow makes shortly after her calf is born. It is a combination of guttural licking and humming, almost as if she is singing a song with a melody of both surprise and pride.

The ambiance in the pen changes slightly when there is a new calf. The cows seem more attentive, less relaxed. I am careful not to clang the gate too loudly because the sound will alert the cows that I am coming. My job is made much easier if I catch them by surprise, since my objective is to see if there are any cows that look like they might calve in the next few hours. It is a maternal reflex that causes a cow to quickly stand up and hide signs that she is close to calving. I stop by the wide gate and flip on the flashlight, watching for movement. All is still. A few cows cough, others look in my direction. Soft grunts rise up as they lie chewing their cud. I laugh to myself at the sound made by one young cow who grunts so loud she sounds as if she's carrying a piano up a flight of stairs. Odd, considering some cows make no noise at all.

Steam from their bodies has dried into frost across their backs. People wonder how cows are able to survive over the winter. If always kept outdoors, they grow thick coats of hair, and when healthy and well fed, generate enough heat to keep themselves and the cows around them warm. Many cattlemen believe their cows do better in a steady cold, especially if out of the wind, than in a barn where it can become damp. Our cows are only moved indoors if they need help calving or to avoid separating them from their cold, newborn calf.

Only a few cows are standing this morning and a handful are over by the watering bowl. Opening the gate, I shine the flashlight ahead as I walk quickly through the pen but see nothing that requires my attention. I open another gate and make my way to the other side of the barn. A quick look through tells me everything is quiet. I check the barnyard last. A cow is standing in front of the closed barn door. She lowers her head and bawls. I circle around her and shine the light on her tag—she is #58. She shakes her head a bit and bawls again. I scan the ground for a calf but see nothing close. I feel safe with an oak fence between us, so I shoo her away from the door by pushing the gate inward, forcing her away so I can slide open the barn door.

The ceiling light is on so the large room is cast in a golden glow. It feels a good ten degrees warmer in here. Two calves are sleeping peacefully in a pile of straw under a low-hanging heater. One calf is tagged #58, born yesterday, so I deduce that Mark brought these newborns in from the cold. Cow #58 is not too pleased to be separated from him, but it is not necessary that the cow sleep in here, too; as she will only make a mess.

There is a cow and calf in the back pen. She stands up awkwardly as I approach, so I slow down, not wanting to disturb her. Calves sometimes get stepped on by a nervous cow, but not as frequently as you'd expect considering how much time they spend on the ground surrounded by heavy feet.

I can hear the hum of the heaters that warm the two enclosed maternity pens built along the back of the barn, and can see light shining between the frame and the plywood doors. I turn the latch on the first door and pull it open enough to peek through. Both sides have a cow and a calf. Everything looks fine here, so I slip back out of the barn and once again circle around #58 who follows me until she realizes I don't have her calf. She goes back to guard the barn door and bawls again.

Only one more spot to check. Shining the flashlight along the far side of the barn, I see heifers and week-old calves sleeping nestled in the warmth of one another. In the far corner, something doesn't look right, so I let the light shine there a bit longer. A heifer is lying awkwardly on her side, close to the fence. I watch her heave and push through a contraction. I move a few steps closer and shine the light on her back end. Two small dark hooves are floating inside the placenta and about six inches is showing. Backing up, I hurry out of sight, through the gate, then back over the fence and quickly back toward the house. Now I must make a decision—when to wake up Mark.

Lots of women I know can handle this sort of situation themselves, but I am too inexperienced and timid to move a cow into the barn by myself. I step into the warm house and pull off my work clothes, making note of the time. I will go back to check in about 20 minutes. I pour myself a cup of coffee and turn on the computer.

It isn't long before I'm back outside. Endless trips between the house and barnyard are the reason that producers building new barns will include a small, heated room in one corner so that they can read or play solitaire while waiting for a cow to calve. Our barnyard is close enough to the house that we don't need this, but an outdoor camera on a rotor with a monitor in the kitchen would be really nice.

It is noticeably lighter now, but I still carry the flashlight. As I open the first gate, I look toward the fence where the heifer was lying. Blinking hard I try to focus on something on the ground, and shine the light in that direction. A small dark lump is lying this side of the fence. I start running over the frozen, lumpy ground. As I get closer I can see the heifer has just stood up and is looking at her calf, which was born too close to the edge of the fence and has slipped under the bottom rail. Shining the light on the calf's face, I see the amniotic sac is still covering it. I toss the flashlight to the ground and land hard on my knees beside the calf. Whipping off my mitts, I try to get a grip on the thick, slippery membrane which is tough but transparent enough that I can see the calf's wide, staring eye through it. His mouth is partially open and he isn't breathing. My hands are shaking and the only sound I hear is my heart pounding.

Reaching into a coverall pocket, I dig to the bottom and pull out a three inch spike. I carry it for this very reason but up until now have never needed to use it. I jab it through the thick membrane and force my fingers through, peeling back the sack, opening his airway. I begin rubbing his chest with one hand and stick my other fingers in his mouth. His legs are limp and there is no resistance from him as I press down, rocking him back

and forth. Using all my strength, I grab ahold of his hind legs, and standing up, lift him up bear-hug style, as high as I can. He is heavy and slippery
and I don't think I can hold him very long.

I chastise myself for not being brave enough to sneak up behind the
cow to break the water bag when I first noticed the calf coming; I wish I'd
woken Mark up to help me; I regret that I am not stronger.

Suddenly, I feel slight resistance from the calf. I shake him until I can't
hold him any longer and then let him slide to the ground. His eye moves
and he starts gasping for breath. I glance up at his mother who has been
watching me with interest from the other side of the fence. I rub the calf
some more, in long strokes using the arm of my coveralls, imitating a cow's
tongue. I stop when he begins lifting and shaking his wet head.

I have just saved a little life. There are no words to describe how I feel
right now. I jump up and want to high-five someone, but nobody is here
except the cows.

By now, his mother is craning her neck over the top of the fence, calling quietly to the calf. My arms and legs are wobbly from the adrenaline
rush and it takes the rest of my strength to push him under the fence. As
soon as he is on her side, the heifer begins sniffing and licking, and then the
singing begins.

In some Celtic myths the cattle belong to a woman, symbolizing
mother earth. When cows are stolen, it symbolizes the end of life. When
they are recovered, rebirth occurs. Other scholars have compared cattle
raiding to bride stealing; both are equated with fertility and both women
and cattle are highly valued in such societies. In the Irish tales, the goddess
is identified with the earth and plays the role of mother, lover and warrior.
She is the giver of all life and is identified with cattle and the earth.[25]

My calf "save" today is nothing compared to what some women do
every day. Shortly after moving here, I was surprised to learn that Ashern
had a female veterinarian. Then I met Helen Metner, and a few years later,
I interviewed her about her lifestyle.

Helen was originally from Moosehorn, a town seven miles north of
Ashern. She moved away to obtain her degree, met and married Ross
Jermey, then the couple returned to the area in the 1980s.

I had asked Helen what it was like being a female in what appears to
be a male dominated industry.

She smiled. Not much over five feet tall, Helen is strong, capable and
knowledgeable. She said that at first some of the men weren't sure if she'd
be strong enough to assist with a difficult calving or perform a caesarean.

Helen said there was a certain amount of satisfaction gained in proving them wrong. She confessed that while strength is a factor, technique is equally important.

Cattlemen aren't as chauvinistic as people might assume. Many men grew up on farms where the women worked alongside the men. They also rely heavily on their wives and some will even admit that there are some jobs on the ranch that women are instinctively better at doing. Calm, maternal, non-threatening mannerisms suit cows well.

I never forgot the things Helen said and learned to view a woman's role on the ranch differently since she opened my eyes to it.

Helen and Ross decided to give up the practice around the time their third child was born. For a while, producers here were concerned that the vet board would be unable to find a suitable, permanent replacement.

Then in 2000, Keri Hudson and Tanya Marshall came to town. Fresh graduates from the Western College of Veterinary Medicine in Saskatoon, Keri and Tanya were friends looking for a rural practice to share. They seemed a little inexperienced to tackle the responsibilities of a clinic that was 80 percent large animal, but seemed up to the challenge. They jumped in and got to work.

They discovered that unfortunately, there wasn't really enough business to support two full-time veterinarians here, so in 2001, Tanya left. Keri liked the area and was in the early stages of a relationship with local cattle producer Calvin Reykdal. They bought a home together situated between the Ashern practice and the Reykdal ranch, then in the fall of 2003 they married. Calvin normally provides that extra pair of hands and bit of muscle needed during calving season, but for the last two years, his wife hasn't needed the extra help.

I am sitting in the clinic lunchroom waiting for Keri as she finishes spaying a cat. I can hear customers coming and going and the murmur as some ask questions or buy a few supplies. The clinic is quite well stocked with agricultural and pet supplies, medications and vaccines.

The door pushes open and Keri steps inside. She gives me a "sorry I'm late look," and I wave it off as okay. The patients come first. I know, because we have dogs that are very important to us.

I stay at the small table where I am already sitting and it is easy to write, while Keri takes a seat on the couch across from me. She is a serious, quiet woman who has a strong presence. She gives you the impression that she has the guts, stamina and brains to have become whatever she wanted. A doctor. Firefighter. Police officer. Professional athlete. Fortunately for us, she decided to become a vet.

I ask how the closed border has affected her business.

She says that when BSE hit, many producers immediately cut back on their veterinary bill. Records at the Ashern clinic show that prior to BSE, the vet would do an average of 150 to 160 caesareans a year. In 2004, that number dropped to only 60. Before, she would assist with at least 200 calvings, but this year, helped producers only 80 times. Workload during what is traditionally the busiest time of year has dropped by 50 percent.

"Producers are taking more chances," she says, explaining that before, producers would bring in a cow for a caesarean, but now he'll try to get the calf himself to save on the vet bill.

"Most people don't like to shoot their cows," she says, but knows for a fact that some producers have resorted to this when things have gone wrong. Not as many are willing to try and nurse a sick animal back to health. She is seeing less animals being brought in to the clinic. Before, there were a lot more producers who would tell her to do whatever it takes to save an animal. Now they aren't as likely to go to these lengths, simply because they can't afford to.

"It is easy to see how an economic downturn can hurt small rural communities," she says, adding that billings from the winter season carry her through most the year. "I had two calving seasons that I got a lot of sleep, and enough spare time to take up jogging."

Keri and I speculate for awhile on the "what ifs."

She says that if she wasn't committed to staying here, or if she was trying to support a family, or was a type A professional who needs to be busy all the time, she might be motivated to leave.

Anticipating that the 2005 season would be slow, the clinic invested in a tipping table and Keri began doing hoof trimming. She has also put effort into building up the small animal clinic, something there wasn't time for during the winter months prior to BSE.

When the BSE sampling program began, Keri jumped on board and began picking up samples from animals that fit the category, shipping them in for testing. The program paid $175 a sample—$100 for her and $75 to the rancher. Her clinic is one of the smaller ones in the province, but she sent in enough samples to rank as one of the top three participants across Manitoba.

"It's certainly not how I thought I'd spend my winter," she says, adding that the extra income helped pay a few bills. She thinks one huge benefit to the program was that it got vets out to the farms so that they didn't lose touch with producers. She says the most difficult thing to hear from them is an uncertainty and lack of optimism.

I ask if it has been difficult to collect her accounts. I have often thought how hard it must be for her to send a bill for a caesarean when the calf is born dead, or if the cow dies, too.

Keri says that economics dictates that she must send a bill and that her clients understand this. Producers know when they bring an animal in that the outcome is uncertain, that they are taking a financial risk—some times are more riskier than others. She tries to not let herself think about how difficult it may be for her customer to pay, but admits that over the years there

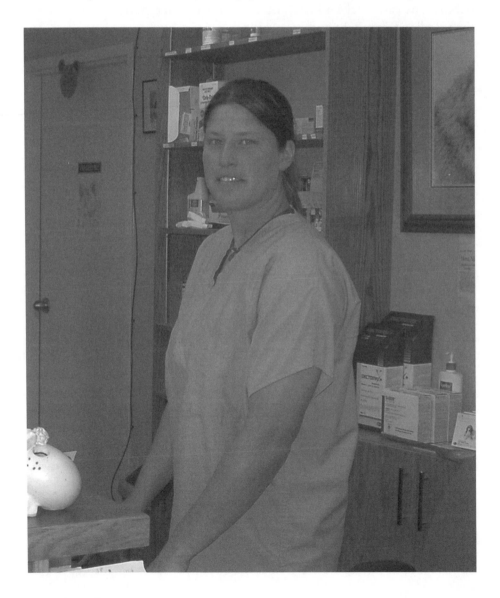

Keri Hudson Reykdal

have been times she hasn't billed when things haven't gone well.

"Sometimes I just write if off as a learning experience," she says.

There is ongoing concern in most rural practices that chain stores in the neighbouring towns can buy veterinary supplies in bulk and charge customers less than what the clinic charges. This cuts into a vet clinic's profitability, making it harder for it to survive. Some producers will support both while others will choose one over the other. Not all producers go where the price is the cheapest. Some will say that if the vet leaves town because she can't make a living, the store owner isn't going to come out in the middle of the night and do a caesarean.

Keri appreciates that support and says while using her services keeps her in business, it is for the benefit of the cattleman in the long run, too. She is glad to see that producers are continuing to vaccinate, but worries that more aren't checking for pregnancy—a service she'd built up but has watched dwindle since the border closed.

"It's just not practical to keep cows around to feed if they aren't going to give you a calf," Keri says, adding that the fall before BSE she'd done 7,000 preg checks, but that dropped to less than 1,500 last year. "This is one aspect of the business that I hope comes back this fall, because I hate to see producers feeding open cows."

As for what the future holds, like everyone else connected to the industry, Keri can't be sure. She believes that even if the border does open soon, it will be a while until she sees her business return to pre-BSE levels. Producers have lost money and are now out of the habit of calling her for help.

Keri isn't likely to give up, though. She's in the business of treating livestock, and like her customers, is in it for the long haul.

Most calves are born unassisted

CHAPTER THIRTY FIVE

"By not opening the border, the U.S. has helped to
create a formidable market competitor. We are now set to
become the second-largest beef exporter in the world
and set to become a significant competitor to the U.S.
in all the markets on the globe."
— Ted Haney, President of the Canada Beef Export Federation.

Tax season. The least favourite time of the year.

Like the veterinarian, our accountant makes house calls.

Harold Reid is sitting at the end of the kitchen table. His laptop is plugged into the wall and he is keying figures into our tax return. Mark has a stack of bills summarized and he answers Harold's questions while I make supper.

Take your time, I say. Only bad things happen when you rush the dentist, hairdresser or whoever is doing your taxes. I pour myself a glass of "whine," adding that it also isn't a good idea to let your accountant drink— at least not until after the taxes are done.

Harold is one of the partners in the Sensus Partnership of Chartered Accountants, formerly Bellas and Reid of Birtle, Manitoba. The firm's head office is in Russell, with satellite locations in Brandon, Shoal Lake and Langenberg.

Harold grew up on a farm near the small town of Isabella, where he played hockey for the now-defunct Isabella Canucks. He obtained his Bachelor of Commerce Honours Degree from the University of Manitoba and has been practising since 1979.

Harold and his wife, Carmella, also run a 300-head cow herd and have

Jackie Jonasson

started feeding their calves to finish weights.

I ask how he manages to get all the work done, especially with tax time clashing so badly with calving season.

"I don't do all the work, I just say I do," he chuckles. Actually, it is Carmella who runs the farm and he helps out on evenings and weekends.

Mark and I like the idea that our accountant has a practical understanding of the cattle business. It makes the trip to the accountant more interesting and tax season less painful.

Once the computer is cleared away and supper is served, I pour Harold a glass of wine, then ask his opinion about CAIS—the Chartered Accountant Income Security Program.

He catches the joke immediately, so I can tell he has heard this before. The program is really called the Canadian Agricultural Income Stabilization program, and it was designed and funded by the federal government to provide agriculture producers with financial help during difficult times. It replaces the Net Income Stabilization Account (NISA) and the Agricultural Income Disaster Assistance (AIDA) programs.

"Accountants really like working with CAIS, but we don't like the pressure it puts on our staff," he says, adding that not everyone who applies is going to get a payout and clients find that frustrating.

Harold explains that the first thing producers must do is fill in all the paperwork, which means going through the last five years worth of farm income, expenses and inventory. Producers not able to do this themselves can hire an accountant to do it for them, but are forewarned this can be a lengthy, expensive process. However, once the initial paperwork is done, annual updates are easily managed.

I have heard conflicting opinions about CAIS, and there is a lot of confusion surrounding who will get a payout and who won't.

Harold explains that the program does make sense and it does work, but there is a lot of misunderstanding around what it is designed to do. He says CAIS has faults that have to be corrected, but that basically it is a good program. He believes it will compensate producers fairly during disaster years. Because it is based on each individual operation, it is very difficult to generalize who will receive payments through the program and who will not.

I ask Harold to give me an overview of how the program has worked for his clients.

"In general, what I have seen is that the producers who have received payouts are the ones who have seen a drastic difference in their margin over the three-year average," he says, explaining that a producer's annual margin is gross qualifying income minus qualifying expenses. The margin used to calculate a CAIS payout is the average of the last five years, not including the highest and lowest year. The current year is then compared to the average year, and a payout is triggered on the difference.

Basically, Harold says that if producers don't get a CAIS payout, they should count themselves lucky. It means they didn't lose that much money. He explains the reason why a lot of ranchers haven't received payouts, even though their income is less, is that traditionally, cattlemen will lower their costs in lean years to stay viable and to match their income.

"To my way of thinking, CAIS is an insurance program," he says. "I hate to see guys pay to set it up and then quit if they don't get a payout." He says the only way the program will work during a disaster year is if producers keep providing the data to use for comparison. He is trying to encourage farmers and ranchers to do more of the paperwork themselves once it is set up if they can't afford the $500 to $1,000 annual bill. "It's a fairly inexpensive form of insurance, considering what it will get you if disaster does strike."

Harold says that CAIS is a complex program designed for the new generation agricultural producer who is very business oriented and thinks in terms of production costs. He says the days are gone when a man can just climb on his horse and bring the cows home. The need to understand and manage finances is becoming increasingly important.

Unfortunately, this means that in order for producers to thrive instead of just survive, they will have to find the time to sharpen their pencils and start crunching numbers. Harold says he hates seeing producers working hard and spinning their wheels while worrying themselves to death.

One of the most unfortunate circumstances surrounding CAIS is that there may soon be a government fee attached to each annual CAIS review. He believes this could have been avoided if producers and farm lobby groups had not spoken out so quickly against the idea that producers would have to deposit money into private CAIS accounts.

But producers don't have any money, I argue.

Harold explains it is that knee-jerk reaction that has caused the problem. He says that they didn't need to have the cash.

"The banks and credit unions all want everybody in CAIS," he says. "That way if there is a disaster, they still get paid." He explained that the financial institutions were in the process of agreeing to loan producers the money for a CAIS contribution, charge them four percent interest, and then pay the same amount back in interest as if the money was sitting in a savings account. It would have been nothing but a paper transaction that cost the producer nothing. It also would have had no effect on debt/equity ratios.

"It has gone from something that wouldn't cost producers a nickel, to something that will carry a government charge," he says.

March 2, 2005

The sound of the side door banging closed tells me that Mark is home. I am in my office, sifting though producer comments about CAIS.

One young fellow said that it appears older producers who are winding down and generating less income are receiving CAIS payouts.

Another said that he diversified and that the money he made in crops helped offset the cattle losses. He invested more money and time, but ended up with less return.

An older producer lost money, but didn't receive a payout since neither his expenses associated with the custom work he did, nor the cost to rent land, are allowable CAIS expenses.

It's easy to see why producers are frustrated with the program.

Footsteps toward my office cause me to pause and look over my shoulder just as Mark pushes open the door and leans in.

"Have you heard the news?" he asks.

News? What news? I don't even try to guess anymore what might happen next.

He waits, teasing me a bit. It's a game we play when he knows something I don't.

Then he tells me that R-CALF was successful in its bid to have their case heard in a Montana courtroom. Today, the judge ordered a temporary injunction to stop the USDA from re-opening the border.

Mark says that speculation is swirling that R-CALF may also apply to have the movement of boxed beef shut down.

Most cattlemen are now long past the point of making their decisions based on the border opening. Only those who desperately need access to the U.S. market are hanging on to hope. For many, this announcement is just another bump in a roller coaster ride that has become our life. We no longer run to the radio and flip on the television to hear every detail of the latest round of bad news, and we aren't crippled by it. Disaster is expected. We have learned to hunker down to wait things out.

Mark tells me the announcement came halfway through today's cattle sale at the Ashern Auction Mart.

A feeling of dread starts to creep in when he says that the phones started ringing immediately after the announcement as feedlot owners called buyers to cancel orders. The price immediately dropped by 10 cents a pound.

Buyers wanting cattle for themselves were left wondering what to do. Do they trust the report and buy cattle anyway, speculating the setback will only be temporary? Will prices in the next few weeks be higher or lower? And when it comes to sell these calves, will there be a market?

The sellers were also in a quandary. With calves ready to come through the ring, do they pass and take them home? How long will R-CALF be successful? There has been little good news in this crisis to date, so producers are tired of being optimistic, then having their hopes dashed. Only five minutes to decide how much of a financial hit he's willing to take on a whole year's worth of work. Will the banker agree with the decision once it's made?

Mark tells me that our neighbours, the Halldorsons, had calves at today's sale.

I don't even want to ask.

Before BSE, it was the nightmare of every cattleman to have his calves at a sale and suddenly, inexplicably, have the market collapse. Until 2003, this was a baseless fear that never materialized in the modern-day industry. Now it is a possibility every day.

"Their calves came through the ring just a few minutes before the announcement," Mark says. "They got a good price."

He says that the auction mart staff had to quickly decide whether to continue with the sale. They decided to keep going, which gave those producers who were selling a choice. Some decided to pass their calves and arranged for trucks to take them home. Others just shook their heads and let them sell.

The sale order in Ashern depends on what time the first load of cattle arrives at the yards the day prior to the sale. Had the Halldorsons been ten minutes later leaving their farm that morning, their story would have ended differently. As it is, other friends and neighbours took the hit this time.

A few days later, I stack up the news releases and read through them.

In late February, Prime Minister Paul Martin announced in a news conference that Canada won't take part in the controversial U.S. Missile Defense plan. Martin is quoted on CTV news: "Ballistic missile defence is not where we will concentrate our efforts. Instead, we will act both alone and with our neighbours on defence priorities outlined in the budget."

Days later, U.S. Secretary of State, Condoleeza Rice, postpones a planned visit to Ottawa. A senior U.S. State Department official, who was on board a flight with Rice on their way to London, England, confirms that the cancellation was a direct consequence of Martin's decision.

Chris Sands works for the Centre for Strategic and International Studies in the U.S. He says that Martin sent signals in the past that he was in favour of the program.

"The one thing you don't do with Bush is double-talk him," Sands said. "Bush is very frustrated with the way Canadians are making decisions about everything from Iraq to missile defense." He added that the consequences of Martin's decision could impact trade areas such as softwood lumber.[26]

It was two days later on March 2 that U.S. District Court Judge Richard Cebull blocked the USDA's decision to re-open the border. The next day, American Senators voted 52-46 in favour of squashing the USDA's plans as well.

On March 5, President Bush called Prime Minister Martin to discuss Canada's decision not to take part in the anti-ballistic missile defence program. For 30 minutes the leaders talked about defence, BSE and a number of other world issues. Martin said that he won't support the weaponization of space because critics of the program believe its deployment could lead to an international arms race.

Reading all these news releases in order makes one understand how a conspiracy theory can develop and take off. I don't want to believe that President Bush would deliberately make us sweat this out. And, it is preposterous to believe that the American government would allow irreparable damage to its own cattle and packing industries in a school yard fight with Canada.

Frustration and anger rippled across Canada in the weeks following R-CALF's court win. Canadian officials and especially Agriculture Minister Andy Mitchell looked shellshocked as they met with media shortly after the announcement. It was the 27-page explanation from the court that accepted every R-CALF argument and rejected every USDA argument that surprised everyone.

Cebull said in his report that dropping the ban on Canadian cattle would attach a stigma to all meat unless consumers can distinguish between products from the two countries. "Once the Canadian beef is allowed to intermingle with U.S. meats, it will open a flood of speculation," Cebull wrote. "Neither the contaminated meat nor the stigma associated with contaminated meat could be removed from the U.S. cattle industry and the substantial, irreparable injury will have occurred."[27] Legal experts now say it could be 12 to 18 months before this matter is resolved in the court.

The USDA appeals the decision and that case will be heard in Seattle, Washington July 13. On July 27, R-CALF's petition to keep the border closed indefinitely will be heard in Montana.

Meanwhile, industry leaders in Canada emerge from meetings resolute in their plans to forge ahead with a Canadian solution to the problem.

CCA president Stan Eby says, "Canadian cattle producers are determined to regain control of their destiny. We are positioning the industry to deal with whatever circumstances arrive."[28]

Paul Steckle, Chairman of the House of Commons Agriculture Committee, goes one step further and accuses the Americans of covering up their own BSE problem.

"I submit that from a purely scientific perspective, it is difficult, if not impossible to accept that the U.S. is free of BSE," he said. "The United States with its millions of cattle could not possibly be 100 percent free of BSE. It is not realistic in any sense of the word."[29]

Over the last few months, word has trickled through the mainstream media, and growing stronger every day, that the closed border means cutbacks at the American plants. Cargill says it will scale back production at seven of its plants and Swift & Co. announced it would cut back by 20 percent. A number of smaller packers who relied on Canadian fat cattle were put out of business altogether, and the producer-owned Iowa Quality Beef Supply Cooperative just couldn't survive any longer in market competing so heavily for fat cattle.

U.S. beef organizations including the American Farm Bureau, National Cattlemen's Beef Association (NCBA) and American Meat Institute are now beginning to vocally oppose R-CALF's actions.

And while Canadian producers are glad for the support, they are not foolish enough to believe that these organizations are taking a stance against R-CALF because it is the neighbourly, trade-friendly thing to do. These U.S. groups are motivated by the fact their industry is hurting.

Jay Truitt, a cattleman with the NCBA, scolded R-CALF in the Association's newsletter. Truitt reflected the growing concern in the U.S. that the growth of Canada's slaughter plants might permanently take business away from the U.S. packers.

"We end up restructuring this industry out of the United States and into Canada," Truitt said, noting that processing capacity north of the border has increased from 55,000 a week to 83,000. "Shame on R-CALF and

KAREN EMILSON

the groups that have done that."

U.S. analysts speculate that if the trend continues much longer, a downsizing in their beef industry could be permanent. They believe that export competitors will increase market share, competitiveness and leverage, and that Canada will continue to increase its kill and process capacity and will ramp up exports of boxed beef. Meat will still make its way into the U.S., but at the expense of American value-added industries.

They worry that if R-CALF is successful in banning boxed beef, then Canada will adopt 100 percent testing for BSE. Initially the Canadian industry objected to the idea, saying it will only test for science-based health reasons, but it is a trump card the industry holds and can use to gain access to the Asian market. This will give the compact, Canadian industry an advantage over the unwielding numbers in the U.S.

Reports out of Japan are that R-CALF's actions could delay the reopening of the Japanese border to American beef because they view the U.S. and Canada as an integrated market. Fear-mongering by R-CALF that Canada's meat is not safe casts doubt on their own product. Japanese officials also say that political pressure from the U.S., including the recent talks between President Bush and the Japanese Prime Minister, has only delayed decision making.[30]

On April 14, 2005, a former U.S. health inspector currently in Canada, claims that the USDA covered up cases of BSE in the U.S. in the late 1990s.

Lester Friedlander told the Canadian Press and testified in Parliament that USDA veterinarians sent samples of brain tissue of cattle suspected of being stricken with BSE to private labs where the illness was confirmed. The USDA elected to run their own tests on the same samples and reported the results as negative. Friedlander was employed as a chief inspector at a packing plant in Philadelphia, but was fired in 1995 after he criticized what he believed were unsafe practices. Friedlander has offered to take a lie detector test to prove that what he says is true.

No one on the Canadian side of the border was surprised to hear that the USDA denied the allegations.

Walk softly and carry a big stick.

It's a well-known quote and piece of advice that Canada's beef industry needs to think about long and hard. That's the feeling I have after getting off the phone with Ted Haney, President of the Canada Beef Export Federation (CBEF). Ted is preparing for the organization's Annual General

Meeting in mid September so his thoughts are on what he plans to say during his address to the membership. He sounds pressed for time, a bit frustrated, and following our lengthy conversation, I understand why.

CBEF is one of the few good news stories throughout the whole BSE crisis but surprisingly it is seldom mentioned in the news, overshadowed by the pressing desire to get the U.S. border re-opened.

CBEF is the vehicle designed to deliver the "Made In Canada" solution that Arno Doerksen talked about and it has respected industry leader and former CCA president, Ben Thorlakson, at the helm. This export federation has the potential to be the Canadian beef industry's stick, but there are factions nationwide who aren't yet prepared to swing it. I'm not talking about Haney, Doerksen or Thorlakson—but a collective national mindset that fears offending the United States.

The only way the Canadian beef industry can be assured that it never suffers again as it has these past two years, is to decrease its dependency on one market. While most industry leaders support the concept of expanding overseas markets, there are factions so focused on resuming live cattle trade with the U.S. that they are undermining the independence the industry has achieved to date. If we alow the industry return to the integrated North American market that it was built upon, export dependence on the U.S. will return to pre-BSE levels—100% live cattle and 90 percent meat. If that happens, the grassroots will once again be as vulnerable as it was in May 2003.

When I worked for the Manitoba Association, there were directors nationwide who thought CBEF was a waste of time and resources. The belief existed that Canada only needs the U.S., and that cultivating overseas markets was nothing but an expensive hobby. It is true that Manitoba does need the U.S. because it has no processing capacity. But nationally, most producers agree that the Canadian industry cannot allow its dependency on the U.S. to return to pre-BSE levels.

Ted Haney says that possibility still exists as long as the Canadian industry refuses to make changes that will give the overseas customer what it wants and that may mean implementing stricter regulatory standards than what the North Americans are accustomed to meeting (i.e. BSE testing).

As long as the U.S. border is open to boxed beef, existing processors can't be bothered to make changes to satisfy foreign markets, and Canadian industry and government leaders worry that if Canada sets its standards too high, the U.S. won't be able to keep up. That might offend our neighbours to the south throw a monkey wrench into plans to re-establish the north american trade model and trade retaliation might follow.

Ted believes we don't need the U.S. as much as some might think. With fewer live cattle being sent south, and Canada's processing capacity on the rise, Canada will soon be positioned to increase overseas trade. Right now, Japan, South Korea, Taiwan and Mainland China remain closed to North American beef and are 600,000 tonnes short of the beef they need. Ted says this is an incredible opportunity for Canada to skip ahead of the U.S.—but instead, we are allowing American negotiators to take the lead and speak for us in trade talks.

It appears that Japan holds the key to accessing the Asian markets and they want to be taken seriously—not bullied—over their consumer concerns about BSE. The recent announcement that they have changed their domestic regulations that BSE testing is no longer required on cattle under 20 months of age is good news for Canada. It means that once the 2006 calf crop is on the ground and can be age verified, Canada should have no trouble selling as much meat as it can produce into Japan. But the worry is that if the border opens soon, live cattle trade with the U.S. will resume, expansion of Canada's packing industry will cease and the ability to supply overseas markets could stall.

"We must position our industry to out-perform all competitors in these and other international beef markets," Ted says. "We have no way of knowing how long until another animal health or economic issue is exploited by protectionists in the U.S. cutting off our market again."

CBEF is an independent, non-profit organization developed in 1989 by industry visionaries wanting to expand markets beyond the U.S. The head office is located in Calgary and there are satellite offices in Mexico, Japan, South Korea and Hong Kong. The organization's budget sits at $3.5 million.

In the year prior to BSE, Canada's exports to Asia and Mexico totalled 132,665 tonnes totalling $499.7 million. Enough overseas markets have reopened to boxed beef that pre-BSE levels are within reach by the end of 2005. Ted says the goal is to increase these exports to 700,000 to 800,000 tonnes by the year 2015 which would reduce Canada's dependency on the U.S. to 50 percent.

Members of the Gem, Alberta 4-H Club in Ottawa, Ontario

CHAPTER THIRTY SIX

"Old cowboys will tell you, in tough times
hang on to her tail and she'll pull you through.
Hang on and hang in."
— Bill Creech, Lloydminster, SK/AB, talking about the cow

What I enjoy most about spring is the return of songbirds to the bushes in the backyard. Our bedroom window opens to the east. As the days lengthen, we are awakened early to the sound of singing and the morning light as it filters through the oak and poplar bush that nearly surrounds our home.

This morning, a woodpecker is hammering on something metal, while a squirrel chirps for its mate. The air smells of dew-damp grass and a faint breeze tells me that it is warm outside already. A ten-day stretch of unseasonably cool weather has finally broken.

I suddenly realize why I'm feeling so melancholy.

Today is May 20.

Of course I remember where I was two years ago today. I'd been in Winnipeg running errands and getting a haircut. The day ended at a Chapters bookstore, signing books as part of a fundraiser for the Winnipeg Public Library. The subjects of my first book, twins David and Dennis Pischke, were also there. As it turns out, this was the last book signing we would do together. David died a year later after suffering a massive heart attack.

I was oblivious to the BSE announcement until I got in the car to drive home. There were at least five missed calls on the cell phone display, so I knew immediately that something was wrong. One of the calls was

Miles Anderson

from Claire De'Athe. Assuming I'd heard the news, she left a message. I quickly switched on the radio, and as they say, the rest is history.

Today I will tackle the cattleman's growing concern over input costs. Who can I ask to go through their financial records and itemize the last ten years for comparison? Not an easy thing to ask someone to do.

In the meantime, there is a news story to investigate.

Imagine letting a year and a half pass without getting a haircut? Thinking of Miles Anderson and Jay Fitzpatrick makes me chuckle. The two are acquaintances who haven't cut their hair since the winter of 2004 and say they won't until it re-opens. I decide to call Miles at his ranch near Fir Mountain, Saskatchewan. His wife Sheri answers the phone. We chat for a bit, then she tells me he has just walked in the door.

Once I have Miles on the phone, I ask what prompted him to let his hair grow long.

He tells me that this all started by accident in the spring of 2004. He'd been busy all through calving season and hadn't had the chance to get a haircut. Someone teased him about how shaggy he was looking, that his hair was starting to curl up under his hat. Miles made an off-the-cuff remark that he wasn't going to cut it until the border opened.

"I didn't think much of it at the time, expecting like everyone else that the border was set to open that spring," he says. "Then everyone started razzing me, so of course, I had to stick it out then."

Miles says he didn't think the media would catch hold of the story and certainly was not expecting it to make national news. When the story did break, it happened during a lull—nothing had been reported on the border situation for weeks. He was glad that his hair protest brought the issue back into the spotlight, in a positive, humorous way.

Here it is, more than a year later. I ask how he wore his hair before now.

"Short," he says, adding that he has never had long hair, not even in the 1970s when it was fashionable.

"My hair is a bit curly so it tends to bush out as it grows," he laughs adding that it has grown past his shoulders now. "I can't hardly wear a cap anymore." He tells me long hair is a nuisance and it's hot so he has to keep it tied up off his neck when he's working.

I ask if he's prepared to go another summer with his hair like this. What if the border doesn't open until sometime in 2006?

He tells me he'll stick it out until cattle cross the line, and doesn't think he'll have to wait too much longer.

"At least I sure hope not," he says. "I've got some fat cattle that are nearly ready to go."

I flip on the switch in the basement storage room and make my way to the shelf at the far end. Up high are a stack of shoeboxes that have a year written on the end of each in black marker. Standing on a small stool, I pull down the box marked 1995. Taking it up stairs, I grab a cup of coffee, then sit at my desk. Opening the box, I pull out the stacks of receipts all paper-clipped together. A sheet of manually calculated totals is folded around the envelopes from the bank holding cancelled cheques. I've promised Mark that someday soon I will computerize the farm bookkeeping for him.

Taking a blank sheet of paper, I draw a line down the middle, printing 1995 on one side, 2004 on the other.

In 1995 we bought a new diesel pick-up truck at a cost of $37,395.

In 2004, a new gas pick-up with similar bells and whistles cost $53,565.

Farm diesel fuel cost 34 cents a litre in 1995 and we burned 22,000 litres of it at a cost of $7,490. In 2004, it cost 62 cents a litre for 26,800 litres totalling $16,624. It is predicted that the price will continue to escalate to over $1 a litre by the end of this year.

It 1995, the same accountant charged us $69.00 to file our tax return. Last year, it cost $752 to get five years worth of CAIS forms filled in, plus a $627 fee for our annual return.

In 1997, Mark bought a new 95 horse power, Case IH tractor with an Allied loader at the retail price of $89,674. This is a necessary machine that he uses everyday—feeding the cattle in the winter and making hay in the summer. I make a quick phone call to the dealership and the salesman tells me that a comparable tractor now retails for $126,000.

As I go through the list and add everything up, I am finding an increase of up to 30 percent on most everything including vet supplies, fencing materials and the cost of hydro. The only areas that have not gone up by a wild amount is the insurance bill and property taxes—and what we get for the product we produce.

Revenue from the calves in 1996-1997 is about the same as it is now. Cow revenue is considerably less. In 1997, Mark culled 35 cows and received a total of $29,104. If he culled that many at today's prices, it will only bring him $11,233. If in 1997, he used that cull revenue to pay the fuel bill, he would still have $21,614 left over. Today, he has to find an additional $5,391 from someplace else.

Even if calf prices to return to pre-BSE levels, it won't be enough to offset costs if they continue to rise at this rate. What is the solution? That is the question on every producer's mind.

While I am not shocked by the figures I've written on this page, I am surprised by the sensation of opening this box and going through all these receipts. It is best described by going back to your elementary school and walking the halls. I am surprised by the memories triggered by opening this box. It feels like spreading all your hopes and dreams out on the table.

The money we have spent these past twenty years is in direct proportion to the amount of work we've done. Reflected on these slips of paper are many things forgotten, and mistakes made. I can still feel the excitement over buying a new piece of equipment, like our first four wheeler and, best of all, Mark's first truck.

For years we drove a car because he was working out and I was making regular trips to town. Once we took over the farm, everything changed. Not having a truck and trailer was impractical—how do you take a cow to the vet without one? Mark was proud of that truck and drove it for nine years until it finally gave out. We almost traded it off last fall, but thought best to wait until after the border opened. That decision cost us $10,000 when the truck suddenly died and became virtually worthless as a trade-in. Another unfortunate decision made because of BSE. We've all made them.

In these boxes is the deal to buy our half of the farm and then his father's half when he retired, as well as our decision to expand, which came about slowly, as we thought we could afford it.

I gather everything up and pack it back in the box. I close the lid and take it back downstairs. As I slip the box back onto the shelf, in between years 1994 and 1996, the realization strikes that all our neighbours and friends have a row of boxes just like this. Ten years from now, when we go back and open up 2003 to 2005, what memories will come flooding back?

What is it about cows that keeps us here doing what we do?

It is a simple question, but the answer is complex. I chuckle at the thought that I have travelled all across Western Canada interviewing people, while one of the best cow men we know, lives just a half mile away.

I call Paul Johnson to ask his opinion of cows and the business of raising them. Paul is retired now, but says what he enjoyed most about raising cattle was time spent developing a breeding program.

"A person can make quite a study of it," he says, adding that he liked the years they spent raising purebred Charolais cattle. He always looked forward to calving season even if it is the most difficult time of year and still enjoys the feeling of a new start that each calf crop brings. Time spent with the cattle taught him how to handle them and what to expect.

"Cows are much like people you know," he says. "They have different personalities." We talk a bit longer and conclude that while a cow might kick you, she's never going to stab you in the back.

Paul and wife Bev raised four children here. Their three daughters, Debbie, Lorraine and Marlene, are university educated professionals. Their son, Greg, and his wife, Teresa, have taken over the farm. They have five children.

The Johnsons are glad that Greg was interested in ranching because it would have been very difficult to sell out and drive away from a whole lifetime worth of work. This way, Paul is able to keep a hand in things and contribute. He still has the option of helping out, and he usually does everyday, but now he has the freedom to choose. What he enjoys the best is that he no longer has to make the decisions. He leaves that to Greg, who inherited a love of the lifestyle from his parents.

I ring him and ask, what is it about cows that makes him want to keep doing this?

Greg's immediate reaction is that he was born into it. For him, getting up in the morning and going outside to check the cows is a natural thing. He is good with the cattle because he has spent his whole life working with them.

Greg says he enjoys the work because each day presents a new challenge brought on by circumstances like the weather and change of season. The responsibility of caring for animals has helped shape his sense of priorities, which are caring for his family, his cattle and the land.

I have only one more call to make today.

I have been thinking about Ed and Glori Dalke all afternoon. It's been eight months since I interviewed them and wonder how they fared this winter. I am curious to know if the calves bought in Maple Creek are ready for market yet.

Ed answers the phone. He tells me that they are doing fine but preoccupied right now with plans to open a retail outlet for beef in Morden. They hope to sell frozen, wrapped meat direct to the consumer in whatever quantities the customer needs. They will sell a side of beef, a quarter, hamburger or steaks.

Knowing how busy they are, I'm a bit surprised by his news. I asked what made them decide to do this now.

Ed says that they had considered opening a meat shop prior to the border closing. Their livelihood has taken a beating and they are tired of

352

KAREN EMILSON

waiting for others to decide their future. This seems like a good way to market fat cattle.

He tells me they have made arrangements with a provincially inspected abbatoir in McCreary, Manitoba, to do the processing.

I ask him to explain the difference between provincially and federally inspected plants.

He says that a provincially inspected plant has requirements that allow meat to be sold in retail outlets or restaurants within the province. If the Dalkes had planned to ship out of Manitoba or across the border, the meat would have to be processed at a federal plant, which has stricter guidelines to meet international protocols.

"We're getting a real education in beef cuts, too," Ed laughs. "But that's good. It's important we learn the other side of the business."

He projects they will need to butcher around 300 head of cattle the first year to stock the store. Demand will dictate numbers after that.

I tell him this is a good fit. They live only eight miles from town and have access to all the fat cattle they need. This is a no-frills way for consumers to buy meat from producers who've been meeting the quality standards of big packers for more than two decades.

But a quick calculation of the number of animals turned over in their feedlot annually tells me that the Beef Shop is not the answer to their problems.

Ed quickly agrees.

"This is just a way to add a little value," he says. "Don't get me wrong, I'm still in favour of getting that border open."

I ask Ed when the Maple Creek calves will be ready to go to market.

He sighs, telling me that he has cattle ready to go now, but that prices aren't good, because everyone along the industry chain is waiting for results from the July hearings. He says that if he sells at today's price, he'll lose money.

"We need for the border to open this summer," Ed says, explaining that if he suffers another loss, he won't have enough equity to buy calves this fall. A feedlot operator who can't buy calves is out of business real fast.

A month later, on June 24, 2005, the U.S. announces its first homegrown case of BSE.

Cattle in Dalke's feedlot

CHAPTER THIRTY SEVEN

*"It is not fair to ask of others what you
are not willing to do yourself."*
— Eleanor Roosevelt

The BSE discovery in the U.S. happened at a most opportune time. The announcement comes just weeks before the Montana court case that will determine whether or not the USDA is placing the American consumer at risk by allowing live cattle in from Canada. The discovery of BSE punched a whole mess of holes in R-CALF's argument. From the Canadian perspective, the timing was perfect.

The report that the animal was traced back to a Texas herd was even better news. What was strikingly odd about the discovery, however, is that it was made on a cow that was slaughtered last fall. According to the USDA, they suspected last November that the cow was infected with BSE because initial screening had indicated the presence of the disease. They submitted a sample to a more thorough test, but it came back negative, so officials announced the animal was free of the disease.

Since then, the conflicting test result caused concern within the USDA. The department's internal inspector ordered new tests. This time, they returned positive, and the internationally recognized lab in Weybridge, England, confirmed the cow had BSE.

There is much speculation surrounding why the discovery was made now. Is it just one more coincidence causing producers to shake their heads? Is it finally the break negotiators on side with Canada need?

Conspiracy theorists suspect that the USDA was prompted to release a positive test result to quieten accusations coming from Canada and their former employee, Lester Friedlander, that BSE is being covered up by the USDA.

Others believe that the government agency is sending R-CALF a message. If they continue hell bent on scaring the public away from supposed BSE infected meat, they will have a hard time backtracking when they have multiple cases of their own.

Maybe the USDA is tired of defending their policies against accusations from producers in their own country and it is time they took their lumps.

Producers in Canada are not pleased to hear another case had been found in the U.S., but are relieved that the animal was born there and not here. The immediate reaction is hope that the discovery will weaken R-CALF's case.

If the closed border taught the Canadian industry anything it is to treat others how you'd like to be treated. Response from industry officials was magnanimous. They immediately came to the American industry's defence, saying that it was consistent with risk assessments that a few additional cases of BSE could be diagnosed in North America and that there is no cause for alarm. They say that food safety precautions are in place in both countries, and the discovery shows that testing protocols are working. As in Canada, meat from this animal did not make its way into the food chain. They say there is no reason for Canada or any other country that imports cattle or beef from the United States to impose any new trade restrictions. The Canadian border will remain open to American beef.

July 14, 2003

In a courtroom in Seattle, Washington, yesterday, a panel of three judges heard the USDA's appeal against the March 2 decision to keep the border closed. There is much speculation over what a positive ruling will mean, but nothing has been reported yet.

The phone rings. I glance at the clock to see it is 5:30 p.m. I pick up to hear Claire De'Athe.

"It's over," she says, voice soft with relief. I haven't heard her this happy in a long time. My immediate reaction is annoyance. I don't want her and everyone else to get their hopes up only to see them struck down again. I cautiously tell her that there's nothing yet on the news.

"I know," she says. "But I just got off the phone with Jim Quintaine. He says that the ruling is in our favour and that the border will likely open within days."

This is one of those times in a person's life where you say something was too good to be true. I tell her that word from the politicians and industry officials is still uncertain.

"They don't have the same contacts as Jim," she says wryly. "I just thought you and Mark might like to know."

I hang up in disbelief. Maybe Claire is right. I glance at my manuscript, all 600 pages of it, sitting on my desk, nearly ready to go to the printer. This means the end will need to be redone. I laugh out loud at the irony of this. There is no better, more satisfying reason to begin rewriting.

The official announcement is made on the 11:00 p.m. news, long after I am in bed. The next morning we wake to hear that the border is now open to Canadian cattle and that it is expected the first loads will cross the line within a few days. Mark turns up the radio good and loud, and we listen to it over and over again. All day, and throughout the next, I half expect bad news to follow. I feel like Chicken Little, expecting the sky to fall.

I've been wanting to interview James Bezan for months.

He is our MP and a cattle producer. Knowing he was in the Seattle courtroom on Wednesday prompts me to call to see if he is back in Ottawa or at home in Teulon. I leave a message on the answering machine.

"Oh sure, now you want to talk to me," James teases when he calls back. We chat for a few minutes, then he calls out to his wife, Kelly, to help decide what night will work best for them. I am told to bring Mark and our niece, Emma. Kelly will make supper.

We've never been to the Bezan ranch before. I've left the directions at home, so we go by memory, turning off Highway #7 just north of Teulon. We follow a winding driveway that takes us to a tidy yard and small, stucco house surrounded by trees.

The air is still and smells of freshly mown grass. Cheerful voices echo in the yard, the only sound on this clear, warm evening.

James lifts the lid on the barbeque and backs up a bit as a plume of smoke rises up. Using tongs, he flips the steaks and rearranges them. Kelly tells us to hurry in, to get away from the mosquitoes that are rising up from the cool grass.

"How do you guys like your steak?" he calls out as we make our way toward the gazebo. James taught me how to properly grill a steak about 10 years ago, and I haven't yet thanked him for it. I mention this as we shake hands and hug in greeting. It's been nearly a year since we saw them last. Their daughters Cortney and Taylor look a little older. They tell us their youngest daughter, Cassidy, is away at summer camp.

Kelly offers us a drink as we sit on lawn chairs around the table. The girls take Emma into the house to listen to music. I overhear them tell her that later on they will show her their horses.

Though we've been acquainted with the Bezans for years, I have to ask James to tell me his history. He says that he grew up in Inglis on a cattle ranch, an upbringing that makes him proud. James can trace his family's connection to cattle back seven generations, to the Ukraine, where his great-great-grandfather was a bull buyer for the Czar.

"Maybe that sort of explains why five of dad's seven kids are ranchers," he says, adding that the love for cattle is born into a person and is something that is difficult to explain.

He and Kelly bought this place in 2002. James worked as a foreman at the Red River Feedlot after graduating from Olds College in Alberta. A job as manager of the Gunton Bull Test Station brought him to the Teulon area. During the late 1980s he was hired as General Manager for the Manitoba Cattle Producers Association and stayed in the position for seven years. When the border closed, it put an end to the export business he started around the time he left the MCPA. James was 38 and considered a young rancher.

Experience gained while with the MCPA and as an exporter gave James immediate insight into what the closed border could mean for the industry. He called a Winnipeg talk radio program and spoke at length on air. James predicted long-term, devastating effects that if this situation is not taken seriously, ranchers could see economic hardships as devastating as the Great Depression of the 1930s.

Speculation was already mounting over the effect depressed cattle prices would have on the Interlake Region. With little industry and sparse tourism, the towns occupying the land between the lakes rely heavily on agriculture, especially cattle.

A rumbling started that James should put some of his knowledge to use. With his export business at a standstill and having a ranch too small to occupy all his time, he began seriously considering the suggestion to run for Member of Parliament. He'd always been interested in politics, but thought that it was something he'd do when he was older, after the girls were grown. But the more he thought about it, the more it made sense to consider the possibility now—while at loose ends and feeling motivated by worry over the future of rural Manitoba.

I remember James phoned a few months after the border closed to ask our opinion about whether or not he should consider seeking the nomination for the Canadian Alliance Party. Locally, the party would be looking for a new candidate since current Member of Parliament Howard Hilstrom announced he would not be seeking re-election. Howard is also a cattle rancher and had done a very good job representing the area.

My immediate thoughts were yes. Cattlemen needed to support every candidate with a thorough understanding of the industry. James' background in this respect is excellent and I couldn't think of a better person to represent our interests.

He started campaigning in July, but lost at the nomination meeting in September, disappointing a strong contingent of supporters. But when the Progressive Conservatives and Alliance merged to form the Conservative Party of Canada in November 2003, another round of nomination meetings began. Conservative members wanted a say in who their candidate would be.

Mark and I once again attended the meeting. It was immediately apparent that James' earlier loss had seasoned him. He seemed even more focused and determined this time around. There was an excellent slate of candidates and while the rigors of campaigning seemed to have tired some of them out, James was energized by it.

Mark laughed at this, saying it was typical James. After a long day of MCPA meetings, the directors would be ready to go home, but James was always ready to continue debating an issue long into the night.

Although we were biased, we thought he spoke the strongest that night. He had a thorough understanding of the issues affecting Interlakers and gave insight into the closed border that dug deeper than the superficial comments politicians were making up to that point. Two days later, after the final meeting was held and the votes tallied, Kelly phoned to tell us the good news.

A federal election was called in May 2004 and was held June 28. James won the Selkirk-Interlake riding, becoming our MP.

Since then, life for the Bezans has become a whirl of activity.

One of their first considerations was what to do with the cows. The herd stayed on pasture at home until late last fall, then they were moved to a brother's farm for the winter feeding and calving season. They are back home now on pasture.

Kelly, who works as a nurse, cut back her hours so that she would be at home more with their girls. James flies regularly between Winnipeg and Ottawa and spends most of his free time doing constituency work. He takes Kelly and the children along whenever he can. So far, the family is enjoying all the excitement.

Lately, though, James' schedule has been gruelling. He says this is a difficult time in the House of Commons with a lot of important bills coming forward. He was named the Associate Ag Critic for the Conservatives, so he has been putting in extra time on the closed border issue and other agricultural concerns. Locally, controversy over Devil's Lake and the doctor shortage in Ashern is occupying a lot of time, as well as expansion of the Red River Floodway and the health of the two lakes.

James tells us he was invited to St. Paul, Minnesota, on June 9, to attend a BSE forum hosted by the USDA. This was a roundtable discussion called "The Safety of North American Beef and the Economic Effects of BSE on the U.S. Beef Industry." James was one of a handful of Canadians asked to observe as American producers debated the issue among themselves. He says that he was both pleased and a bit surprised that afternoon by the reaction toward Canadians from American producers.

"They were pretty good to us," he says, explaining that as Canadians we tend to hear and focus mostly on comments from the vocal R-CALF supporters, but that most U.S. producers are just like us.

"About 80 percent of the guys who stood up from the floor and spoke were in support of re-opening the border," he says. "And that was before they found BSE there." One cattleman said that the prolonged closure means that they have lost ground and a share of their international market to Canada. He said that as a cattle feeder in the U.S. who raises and sells a grain-fed product, being able to buy high-quality cattle from Canada worked to his advantage. Keeping the border closed means that those cattle and producers who were once his allies are now his biggest threat.

James says that market access to quality beef is something that North Americans take for granted. Because it is top quality and consistently available, our product is envied by cattlemen worldwide.

James tells us that on July 12, he and colleague, Larry Miller, MP for Bruce-Grey-Owen Sound, made the trip to Seattle, Washington to witness the USDA's appeal proceedings.

"The courtroom only holds about 60 people so I wanted to make sure we were there early, otherwise we wouldn't get in," James says, explaining that he expected there would be at least that many R-CALF supporters present. He managed to get up the elevator and in line just moments before a big line of cowboy hats came marching in.

I ask how R-CALF won the injunction back in early March.

James says that he wasn't all that surprised R-CALF was successful in that round, in fact, he was predicting it. He knew that Judge Cebull was sympathetic to R-CALF's cause, and that the USDA might have under estimated the lobby group's determination.

This time, however, they were better prepared. James says that only the American Meat Institute, R-CALF and the USDA were allowed to argue the case before the panel of three judges.

"The USDA got off to a slow start, and after about five minutes of stuttering and stammering that didn't amount to a whole lot, I was sitting beside John Masswohl from the CCA and leaned over to him and said, 'We're toast.' The judges started getting impatient, too, and accused the USDA of wasting their time."

James says that the comment helped focus the lawyer's attention and what he said after that turned into a brilliant argument. It was apparent immediately that the judges were well versed in the issue and had thoroughly reviewed Judge Cebull's earlier decision. James says that it was obvious Cebull erred when he took into consideration R-CALF's position, while ignoring the USDA.

"The USDA shot down every single R-CALF argument, making it almost impossible to appeal to the Supreme Court," he says. "My thoughts are that in order for Cebull to save judicial face, he should not even hear the upcoming case on the 27th."

By the time James left the courtroom, he was sure we had won. Later that afternoon, it was announced that the court overturned Cebull's March 2nd ruling. In any event, James says that the Conservative MPs have hired a lawyer and prepared a brief, and plan to attend the hearing in Montana. They will only be allowed to observe, but hope to balance off some of the R-CALF media statements with the Canadian perspective. He hopes that the CCA and Alberta Beef Producers will be granted intervener status.

I ask what will happen if Cebull does decide to go ahead and rules in favour of R-CALF again.

James says that if that were to happen, the USDA would file an immediate appeal, and if they lost that, it will likely take another four to six months for the case to make its way to a higher court. He says that producers need to prepare for the worst, that they might have to go through another uncertain fall run. He also says we need to be prepared that the border could shut down to boxed beef.

We begin discussing the chances of this, but are distracted by the sound of bawling cattle. At first the calls were low and sporadic, but over the last few minutes, the sound has become a distraction. James stands up and looks out in that direction, telling us that he and the girls moved the cattle to a different pasture today. First thoughts are that the cattle have found an open gate. James hurries down the steps and across the grass to a spot where he can see past the bush. Everything looks fine, so he returns a few minutes later. Cattle do that sometimes, get all riled up over nothing. It's the time you don't check that they take off down the road.

This visit turns into a marathon. We talk about the future, craving a celebration to the end of BSE, but cautiously aware that we could still be tripped by the July 27 hurdle. James is very concerned about cattlemen in his constituency, worrying how some might react to another negative piece of news.

"If the climate isn't more optimistic by this fall, we are going to see guys starting to walk away," he says quietly.

I ask how many producers have quit or gone bankrupt.

He says it is hard to say for sure. As long as the border stays closed and times remain uncertain, financial institutions are vulnerable, too. It is not in their best interest right now to call in loans. Any land, cattle and equipment that is confiscated would need to be re-sold so the bank could recoup its costs. As long as the market is depressed, these items have little re-sale value and that may be protecting some cattlemen.

James says there is tremendous worry at the grassroots that when the industry shows signs of recovery, the banks will start pressuring the more vulnerable producers. The Conservatives have met with the Canadian Bankers Association and Farm Credit Corporation and these organizations both seem understanding and supportive toward the industry.

"Only time will tell," he says.

On July 18, the first loads of Canadian cattle cross the Ontario border near Niagara Falls into Lewiston, New York. The cattle were owned by Ken Schaus of Schaus Land and Cattle Company in Elmwood, Ontario.

Two days later, U.S. Judge Richard Cebull announces the July 27 hearing would be delayed to give him the opportunity to read the review from the federal appeals court. He says that once this is done, he will decide whether further hearings are necessary.

R-CALF chief executive officer Bill Bullard says they are prepared to return to court and will to do so as soon as possible.

Six days later the report is released, saying that Cebull erred on all counts when he sided with R-CALF. The court's 56-page opinion attacked and refuted, one by one, all the reasons R-CALF had for keeping the border closed.

The high court said that Cebull should have respected the judgement and expertise of the USDA about safety risks instead of blithely accepting the word of R-CALF. In response to this, Judge Cebull postpones the hearing indefinitely.

This time, it finally is over.

July 27, 2005

One last interview to do.

I leave home at 5:30 a.m. with my niece Emma sleeping on the seat beside me. Three hours later we pull into the feedlot. Two cattle liners are sitting a few feet away from the corrals as I wind my way down the long driveway, turning away from the house toward the processing shed. A man is standing on the cattle truck, up high, with one foot through the vented panel, the other resting on the truck driver's shoulder. Glori Dalke is watching them.

My eyes sting at the sight. I really didn't think the border would open this summer.

Seeing us get out of the car, Glori hurries over. She is holding a stack of papers in one hand, a pen in the other. We wrap our arms around one another in a giant hug. We have become friends throughout this nightmare.

I tell her she looks wonderful.

She tells me that's exactly how she feels. The worry is gone from her face and took with it the hardness from her pretty eyes. She is content, relaxed and exhilarated.

The Dalkes sold 18 loads of cattle and shipped the first four loads across at the Emerson crossing into Minnesota two days ago. The animals were sold to Tyson Foods at Dakota City, Nebraska, and Swift & Co. at Grand Island. Four more loads went yesterday and two will go today. By next week, the pens will be almost completely empty.

Ed and Eric appear from the sorting pen, faces wide with smiles, as they introduce me to their veterinarian, Rick Wiens. Rick is a certified vet with the Canadian Food Inspection Agency who is trained in the rigors of what must be done to get animals across the border post-BSE—at a time of increased U.S. biosecurity protection demands.

Rick came out to the feedlot yesterday to check the teeth of all the cattle scheduled to leave today to be sure that all are under thirty months of age. Then he typed all the national identification numbers into his laptop, sorting it numerically. The numbers were then transferred by hand to the official paperwork, which must be stamped by the CFIA vet in Morden. The cost of $25 a load, plus $1.50 a head is charged back to the Dalkes by the CFIA. They also pay $5 a head for the vet to age verify the cattle.

Rick has just finished sealing the trucks. The seal is a metal tag that will certify that the container hasn't been tampered with—that no animals have been taken from or added to the load after it leaves the feedlot.

It's all hogwash as far as we're concerned, but those are the requirements. A quick calculation on Ed's part shows that he is still better off to pay the costs associated with the paperwork than ship 750 miles to Calgary. Mileage is just one factor.

"Because of the slaughter method they use in Dakota City, the animals yield four percent more, so on an 800-pound carcass, that amounts to 30 pounds," he explains. "That adds up."

We watch as the trucks slowly pull away, turn out of the driveway, then disappear down the road. With them gone, we decide it is time to move into the house.

As we sit at the dining room table, Ed tells me he had the chance to sell the cattle prior to the USDA's appeal on July 13, and talked it over with the family. At the price they were offered they would barely break even. They decided to gamble that the negotiators on Canada's side might be successful this time. The decision turned out to be the right one, and once word started filtering through the industry that this time the border would open, prices went up. The Dalkes sold at a high point two days after the border opened, and got a very good price. They will be able to pay their bills, make up some of last year's losses and have enough to finance calves again this fall.

I ask about the paperwork. Is it really the nightmare that everyone predicted?

The Dalkes say it is detailed, and a nuisance, but for them still worth tackling since their feedlot is small enough that they only ship a few times a year. They explain there are many steps to it, that once the vet has everything verified, the paperwork must be couriered to a customs agent. From there, the package is sent by courier to the border where it waits for the trucks to arrive. The most difficult aspect is timing it all correctly. Truckers have been warned not to arrive before the paperwork. The customs officials need three hours prior notice to process everything, and are backing up these demands with threats of a $5,000 fine for the first offending truck, and an additional $15,000 for each truck following in a convoy.

The house is busy today. The kids are back and forth and Glori is up and down out of her seat, answering the phone and helping their youngest son, Austin, print something off the computer. He has written a BSE story and wants me to read it. There are a few tense moments when Glori returns to the dining room after taking a phone call. The worried look has returned to her eyes.

"They are sending the trucks back," she announces. "Apparently the seal was done incorrectly."

Ed glances at the clock. The trucks have to make the 600-mile drive to Nebraska and arrive before the plant inspector leaves for the night. The pressure is on to get this sorted out.

I sit and wait as the Dalkes make a few phone calls. No, the trucks don't have to come all the way back to the feedlot. Yes, the vet can go out, meet the trucks and properly seal the load. Ed returns awhile later, shaking his head. Apparently the seal is a fussy thing that requires looping through one specific link but not another. It's an understandable mistake.

"Nobody said this was going to be easy," he says. Apparently, Rick has been running non-stop since the border opened.

Once the issue with the trucks is sorted out, we talk a bit about how exaggerated the whole BSE issue became.

Ed stresses that this never was a food safety crisis, but an economic one. He feels strongly that while it is important to have strict food safety standards, they can't be ridiculously impossible to follow, otherwise producers become hamstrung.

We talk about the expansion of the Canadian packing industry and Ed agrees this was a positive move on the part of the industry. He wishes he could support it, but says it makes better economic sense for him to go south. What keeps everything moving along the chain is the competition factor.

"It is so critical in Manitoba that we have access to the U.S. market," Ed says, adding that with increasing fuel costs, distance is going to become an even heavier factor. "Even if only some of us ship south, everyone will benefit from having an open border."

We all pile into the car and drive to Morden to see the Beef Shop. It is scheduled to open within a week. The store has a kitchen-like atmosphere with plenty of display and freezer space. A few finishing touches are being done before the large walk-in freezer is stocked. Large windows let in plenty of light. The walls are bare, but over the next few months they plan to add photos of the ranches where they buy cattle. They already have a refrigerated truck stocked full with meat to sell.

Ed gives me a few packages of meat to try. I ask if he knows where these animals came from.

"Maple Creek," he says. "You'll have to let us all know if you like it."

We leave the meat store and finish our visit in customary fashion, at a large table in the middle of Rocks Restaurant in Morden. We are surrounded by townsfolk and workers on their lunch break. People have heard the Dalkes are shipping this week and offer congratulations.

Austin, LeAnne and Emma are at one end of the table; Shane and Eric join us soon after we sit down. The mood is busy and celebratory as we order lunch. The kids talk about what they might have for dessert. Ed, Glori and I smile back and forth at one another, the way parents do when enjoying time spent with the kids.

As the plates are placed in front of us, Glori gently holds back Austin's hand, signalling him to wait. She asks LeAnne to say grace. We bow our heads and listen as LeAnne gives thanks for the food we are about to eat and the blessing they have just received.

Nobody cares that afternoon when the USDA announces it may have another case of BSE. Cattlemen are not surprised a few days later when the test results turn up negative. The first case may have got us what we needed. It no longer matters anymore. Producers in Canada are in celebration mode. They have an open border, lots of cattle to sell into a strong market, and a promise of better times ahead to take to the bank this fall.

Emma's older sister, Lace Ann, is also staying with us for the summer. Lace got her driver's licence this week, so I offer to make a meal in her honour. Our son, Laurie, and his girlfriend, Alison, will be here, too. I ask Lace what she wants for supper.

"Steak!" she exclaims. We have been eating a lot of hamburger and chicken lately and she noticed that the Dalkes were kind enough to send home steaks.

We plan the menu and cut open the cryovac packages, laying six tenderloins to thaw on a plate. I tell the girls this is the best cut of meat you can buy. They understand that even cattlemen save steak, especially the tenderloin, for special occasions. A few hours later, they watch as I sprinkle Hys® seasoning salt on both sides.

Later, when everything else is nearly cooked and ready to serve, I light the barbeque and close the lid. It sits like this until the temperature is hot. I lift the lid and one by one, place the steaks on the grill. I let them sit over the heat for about three minutes, then using tongs, turn them over. Dark grill marks show me the meat is seared on one side. I wait, then flip them again when the second side is seared. This locks in the juices. Then I turn the heat down a bit, hurry to the kitchen to fetch a clean plate and the bottle of our favourite barbeque sauce. I flip the steaks again and add a thick drop of Cattle Boyz® to each steak, spreading it with a spoon. The big dog's tail pounds rhythmically on the deck as the meat sizzles on the grill. The cat rubs against my leg. They, too, will eat well tonight.

Experience tells me the back, right-hand side of the barbeque is the hottest, so that's where I put the steak I plan to serve Mark. The left front is the coolest, so Laurie's is placed there. All are flipped, without puncturing, almost continually over steady heat. I resist the temptation to cut the meat to check for doneness, because doing so lets out juices. I've learned by trial, and a lot of error, that it takes eight to ten minutes to achieve medium rare on this barbeque. I leave Mark's on 30 seconds longer. Tonight we celebrate as a family with good food, homemade wine and a rich dessert.

I've heard of steak that is so tender it can almost be cut with a fork.

Now, I've actually eaten one.

CHAPTER THIRTY EIGHT

"Since the dawn of time men organized themselves
by intelligence and aptitude.
I'm sure my ancestors were herders.
I don't completely understand why I love cattle and our ranch,
but I do.
I'm not just someone on this land—I am a part of it."
— Claire De'Athe, Carberry, Manitoba.

Like the cows that they care for, it is difficult to put a finger on exactly what it is that sets cattle men and women apart. Cattle people are a unique sector of society who view the world differently than do other people, and it's almost as if spending so much time with the cows makes a person more like them. It is understood that the kids come first. You have to hang out with your friends. Material things, although essential in today's world, are secondary to survival. All we really need is good food, clean water, family and a warm place to lie down at night. Lead and we'll follow, but push too hard and we'll run right over you.

Early in my journey across the prairies, I visited Doug and Claire De'Athe at their ranch near Carberry, Manitoba. It was a sunny, warm, September afternoon. Dogs greeted me when I got out of the car, tomatoes were ripening on the front porch. Claire hollered to come on in, don't mind the mess, and to pull up a chair. I came at a busy time—halfway through harvest.

I became acquainted with the De'Athes in the early 1990s and came to know Doug and Claire better when we worked together on the MCPA

Doug De'Athe and grandson Brydon Biehn

board. Doug was the director for their district when I was hired; Claire was the director when I left.

The De'Athes are cow people to the bone.

They are practical, insightful, humorous and filled with plenty of good old-fashioned cowboy wisdom. They don't like regulations and are quick to bring forward the grassroots perspective. They are especially critical of policies that will affect the average cattleman's everyday life and are never afraid to make their feelings known.

The day I visited them, we toured the ranch, and then that evening when the work for the day was done, we sat at the kitchen table to discuss their thoughts on BSE. By then, they'd worked through the emotional cycle that everyone has experienced, and had their focus set on the future.

"The best thing about middle age is knowing that like everything else, the affects of BSE will soon pass," Claire said. "We are very optimistic about what will come of this."

Doug nodded in agreement. "If I had the money, I'd buy 200 cows right now."

Both Claire and Doug were raised on cattle farms near Carberry. Like the lifestyle they've chosen, the De'Athes have known each other their whole lives. They married and began ranching with Doug's parents, Brydon and Pearl on the home place. Doug drove a truck off and on and Claire worked as a nurse. While those choices were an economic necessity, the years spent commuting now feel like a waste, because the career that makes them feel most complete is right here.

Like everyone else, the De'Athes were bombarded by uncertainty when the border closed. They realized early on how much the stress was getting to them when one day they found themselves standing in the barn-yard all hollering at one another. They saw right then the power the situation had to make or break a family.

"Later we laughed about it," Claire said. "But at the time we knew we had to talk through it. We decided that we couldn't let this affect our relationships. The realization hit us that we may not always have control over our circumstances, but we can choose how we react." Talking about it lifted some of the burden, made them more patient with one another, and like so many others, they began finding enjoyment in life's simple blessings.

"We've learned to take even more pleasure in our land and the quality of our cattle," she said. The De'Athes run a herd of mostly horned Herefords and Angus-cross cows.

Claire said that one time she had a quiet 16-year-old cow that was a great mother and one of her favourites. When the day came that the cow had to be shipped, she taped a note to one of the cow's horns that read, "This is one great old cow. Treat her with respect."

Doug and Claire said one of the things about this crisis that bothered them most was selling their old cows and bulls. Buyers were sending culls to a slaughter facility in Quebec. There were times the De'Athes chose to put some of the physically challenged animals down on the farm, rather than putting them through the stress of such a long trip.

I asked if they applied for any of the government programs. The De'Athes have been long opposed to any financial help that might be deemed countervailable by the U.S. Like so many in the cattle industry, they say that subsidies make for unfair trading practices that result in tariffs and disgruntled trading partners. But the De'Athes agreed that the circumstances surrounding BSE were urgent, unprecedented and required extraordinary measures.

This was the first time in their lives the De'Athes had ever received government help. They thought about it long and hard before applying to CAIS, which in the end, helped make up some of their losses. They also enrolled their calves in the set-aside program and while thankful for the help, orderly marketing makes them uneasy.

Claire predicts that these past two years will leave those producers who survive hard-bitten, that it will be more difficult to walk over them again. The changes to the industry, including the expansion of slaughter capacity in Canada, was hard won and necessary, but was achieved at the expense of so many at the grassroots level. Claire anticipates and worries about the future.

Both their families have been on the land for generations and the thought that the family's time here might end pains her. She says their biggest fear is that their children or grandchildren might want this lifestyle, but circumstances might prevent them from ranching, and the time-worn traditions so important to them won't carry on.

The De'Athe's son, Sam, helps out a bit, but they say that ranching "isn't his bag." Daughter, Sharon, and son-in-law, Lavern, live in the house across the yard. Sharon is an accountant and Lavern is a nurse. They both work in Brandon, and while not interested in owning the ranch, choose to live here for the lifestyle. They want to raise their two small children here, in the country, close to grandparents.

Daughter, Signy, on the other hand, has what it takes to run a cattle operation—experience and desire. Signy was always interested in the ranch from the time she was a little girl. She is a graduate from Olds Agricultural College in Alberta and worked for a few years at the Lakeside Feedlot in

Brooks, Alberta. She came home to ranch with her parents in 2002.

"And there are two other little people we need to consider," Claire said, getting up and searching the kitchen for a package of photos. She sits down and hands me a stack of snapshots of Sharon and Lavern's children, Brydon and Marie.

"We can see the desire in them," Claire said proudly, explaining that some children like to play with toys and others want to do chores. "Cow" was one of Brydon's first words. "Some people have a love of livestock and others don't. If you don't have it, then just forget it, because you'll never make it. Either a person is suited to this lifestyle or they're not. If they are, it shines through at a young age," Claire says.

The De'Athes are a conversational bunch and there is never a bland moment while with them. They each have at least a hundred good cattle stories to tell, but it's the one-liners that start people laughing. Their words have just the right amount of truthfulness to make a person stop to think.

The De'Athes have a code they live by that is part cowboy, part just plain old them. They don't consider themselves lucky, but persistent and that understanding gets them through the rough spots. They believe that a person should always look after the bad jobs themselves.

When the De'Athes say someone is "old as dirt" they mean it as a compliment. They believe that being called a cow is better than being called a sheep. Doug's dad always said, "A good bull is half the herd, a poor bull is all of it."

The De'Athes strongest belief is in the land and its ability to provide. They are keenly aware of the environment and the role cattle producers play in managing it properly to keep it healthy.

"Cattlemen are the best land stewards there are," she said. "Give them the information and they'll make the right decisions."

While on the MCPA board, Claire especially enjoyed working on the environment committee. She says it is crucial that producers have a say in future government regulations. The worry is that the government will regulate unnecessarily to the point of impracticality.

"They just ball things up," Doug added.

We finish the visit talking about the uniqueness of where they live. They told me that many farmers over the years have tried to make a living in these sandy Carberry hills, but failed to grow enough crops to sustain themselves. The story changed when people here expanded into cattle and turned the land back to it natural state, then put the cows out to graze. The De'Athes believe strongly that it is wrong to try and change a place and the most successful are those who opt to enhance the land's natural state.

"You don't choose the land," Doug smiles. "The land chooses you."

With the U.S. border open now for just over a month, it is still too early to know the lasting effects the BSE crisis will have on cattle families. The closed border cost the industry $7 billion and affected every cattle producer in the country.

And while most of the focus has been on the financial hardships, little was mentioned about the emotional toll on individuals left to cope in a state of uncertainty for two years. This was a fearful time for cattle producers and their families who have relied for generations on the security of the ranch to provide, always able to follow up their handshake and pay their debts on time. The stoic cattleman endured this crisis, set aside future worries, and kept producing food as they always have.

Grieving changes to the industry took nearly two years. And like the death of a close friend, a person moving on afterward realizes that life will never be the same again.

In the early stages of this crisis there was much denial as Canadian producers refused to believe that they somehow allowed BSE into the national herd. Producers could not accept that their livelihoods might be at risk and hoped that the Americans would treat Canada better than they treated other countries with BSE in the past. When half a year passed with no results, the bargaining began. What do we need to do to get our export borders open? Tell us and we'll do it.

In spite of great effort, circumstances kept the border closed and that fuelled an anger that resulted in finger pointing, lawsuits and digging for blame. Finally, producers began to realize that the answer wasn't going to come from outside the industry and they would have to take control of their own destiny. Once producers accepted the new normal, they were able to stop grieving what the industry once was and start looking toward what it must become. Some producers worked through this process very quickly and began pushing early for change, while others needed the full two years to come to the realization. No doubt there are some who want the old way of doing business to resume, and others still who believe not enough changes have yet been made.

During any crisis, those involved can only look back for so long before they must start moving forward. The past decision to feed cattle parts back to cattle was wrong and unnatural, but it was done nonetheless. As an industry we cannot dwell on this mistake, but work to ensure it never happens again.

Like so often in war and catastrophe, it is the little guy who stands to lose the most—his life, all he's worked for, or in the case of BSE, a livelihood.

As much as this crisis affected the cattleman's life in many ways, aspects of his everyday routine didn't change much at all. The weather was as difficult as ever, and the seasonal cycles came and went. The calves were born as intended, grew, and were cycled in and out of the feedlots. Life for the cattleman continued on.

The question that lingers beneath the surface is one that folks aren't ready to discuss, and it is: How much integrity has the industry lost? How many producers were pushed to do things for economic reasons that they normally would never have done?

One of the most difficult lessons cattlemen learned through all of this is that they are not immune to disaster. They have always believed that dealing honestly and living a wholesome life would offer an assurance they would be treated fairly in return. The most disconcerting realization living through the aftermath of BSE, is knowing that tomorrow they could wake up and be faced with a similar crisis.

A new study explores a theory on the origins of BSE that is being taken seriously by experts on the disease. The study suggests that BSE may have developed in cattle that were unknowingly fed human remains from the Indian subcontinent that were inadvertently mixed with cattle feed in Britain during the 1960s and 1970s. Hundreds of thousands of tonnes of mammalian remains—whole and crushed bones and carcass parts—were imported to Britain for use in fertilizer and animal feed. Nearly 50 percent came from the countries of the Indian subcontinent.[31]

In India and Pakistan, gathering large bones and carcasses from the land and rivers has long been an important local trade for peasants. Hindu doctrine instructs that bodies should be cremated and the remains deposited in a river, preferably the legendary Ganges. But because of the cost of cremation, many corpses are only partially burned. In 2004 a group of volunteers working to reduce pollution in the Ganges retrieved 60 human corpses from its waters in two days over a 10-kilometre stretch of the river[32] proving this type of contamination does exist.

The hypothesis is that the remains of humans from that region, some of whom were infected with classic Creutzfeld-Jakob disease (CJD) were fed to cattle that became ill with a bovine strain of the human disease. The remains of those cattle would have been rendered and mixed into new batches of feed in keeping with the practice then. Eventually a new version of the disease passed back into humans and was dubbed vCJD. This theory is long from proven and there may be no way of ever knowing for certain the origins of BSE.

Maybe cattle didn't give us CJD after all. Maybe we gave it to them.

Anyone who has felt the intensity of a mid-summer heat wave understands how it feels, after ten days of blistering hot afternoons and sweat-soaked nights, to welcome the sight of the skies clouding over. The air becomes so still you can smell the rain coming.

Out here on the prairies, we open our windows wide to let in the breeze. It comes in gusts, rippling our arms in gooseflesh, knocking vases from the window sills and blowing newspapers wide open. Black skies give way to the roll of thunder, then the rain comes, at first in slow, fat drops.

A tractor can be heard coming in high gear down the road, followed by the sound of another. The rain is bringing everyone home from the hayfield. One by one the tractors gear down then come to a stop not too far from the yard. The drivers jump onto the grass and are heard coming toward the house, but not too quickly, because they learned long ago that rain isn't something to run from, but a gift to savour and enjoy. It soaks the crops and gives life to the trees and pasture. Rain cools the cattle who move freely through it, pleasantly unburdened by biting insects and annoying flies.

Nothing compares to the laughter in a farmhouse when a rain is just right. It means a break for the farmhands, usually teenagers, who would rather be listening to music or getting ready to go out since it is Saturday night. Rain means company for grandma who has seen enough of life to know that these years go by too quickly, and relief for dad whose barley field hasn't seen much moisture since it was planted.

Black skies give mom incentive to bake a batch of cookies. Surely the neighbours will arrive soon, hoping for a cup of coffee and a visit. The house will be cool tonight, so there will be roast beef and new potatoes for supper. If mom gets help with the dishes, there might be time to make buns. No one is let go hungry.

Heaven on the ranch can best be described as sitting in a screened-in porch on a comfortable chair, listening to the pattering rain on the roof, watching as the cattle come close. Just like the rancher, cows are most content when close to home. The sound of voices will bring them near, and you can hear them munching the wet grass as they eat their way up to the fence.

Most of the calves are months old by now, doing well on their mother's milk and grass. One cow is limping and should be treated in the morning after the rake teeth are sharpened and the baler is greased. Tomorrow, while waiting for the hay to dry, the cows will be moved to another pasture.

There is much to do this time of year.

Anyone who has ever been part of a haying crew remembers their favourite field to work. It will be the spread of open land that goes off far in the distance, with few rocks to watch for and nothing that needs navigating around. When raking this particular piece, it is easy to drive fast enough to keep a good distance ahead of the baler. The teasing will come during coffee break to whoever can't keep up.

The field best remembered is the one with a strip of bush with trees along the edge, so that when lunch and coffee are brought out, workers can get out of the sun for awhile. There is a spot nearby where grandpa disappears carrying two ice-cream pails. Whoever follows him will find that the Saskatoon berries are thick and it doesn't take long until the pails are full.

Mom's favourite hayfield is the one with the gate that is easily opened and a path not too rough. Sitting on the front seat of the pickup truck is a hat forgotten by the new raker—a teenaged niece from the city who is visiting for the summer. She is on the open tractor and will be in bed with heatstroke if she forgets it again.

There's a spot under the giant oak where a light breeze will keep the mosquitoes away. Lunch might be sandwiches or it could be leftover supper from last night, brought to the field in a handled box or picnic cooler. Mom has worked outside, too, so she knows the importance of a break and a hearty meal. Once the truck stops, the passenger door opens and two pails of Saskatoons are set on the floor.

Down goes the tailgate and everyone climbs in the truck box. They will sit on lawn chairs or baler twine packages that look like a number eight. Plates will be balanced on knees as food is passed around. Drink your juice quickly before bits of hay dust blow on top. It is harder to see this in grandpa's tea, but for some reason, he doesn't seems to mind. There is butterscotch confetti cake, nanaimo bar, and the cake with the yellow icing—everyone has a favourite. Which did grandma send today?

Across the way you can see the neighbours haying fast and hard, too. There is a competition going on, a race to beat the sky that is growing dark in the west. The neighbours got into the hayfield a half hour earlier this morning. Everyone is wondering who will finish first.

For some of the crew, time spent in the hayfield is not a chore but a break from city life. Years away opened your eyes to what was left behind at home and now the necktie feels too tight and the stress is piling up.

You've taken two weeks holidays away from your job to rake wild hay with dad and it feels like therapy. It is soothing to know that tonight you will sleep in the attic bedroom of the old house, under the softness of grandma's summer quilt. You'll be close enough to the window to hear the buzz of mosquitoes and croaking frogs and the air smells so familiar and clean, that you cannot get enough of it. Tomorrow afternoon you will go back to the city, to wait out the years until the time is right to make this your living.

But for now, a Saskatoon pie has just come out of the oven. The dog is barking because the neighbours have arrived. The leaf is put in the table and stacking stools are spread around it.

Today we will just sit. Play a game of cards while visiting together and enjoy the blessing of rain.

July 22, 2005

The scissors came out and in true Saskatchewan style, the cutting of Miles Anderson's hair turned into a community event. The local MLA, President of the Saskatchewan Stock Growers Association and television cameras were all there.

Tickets and hamburgers were sold and in the end, approximately $4,000 was raised toward the building of a new curling rink at Glentworth. Stacy Poirier cut the pony tail, Jan Linthicum clipped off a bit more and then professional stylist, Pam Mielke, brought in the clippers.

"It feels real good," Miles said, adding that he shipped a load of fat cattle a few days later. When asked if they went south, he said no.

The price in Alberta was better

ACKNOWLEDGEMENTS

When setting out to write this book I had no idea what I was getting myself into. What seemed like an exciting idea turned into a challenging, emotionally draining project. One year was not enough time to do this, but thankfully no one brought it to my attention. I did it, because I didn't know that it couldn't be done.

Thank you to all the people featured in this book who welcomed me into your homes. If it wasn't for all of you, *Just a Matter of Time*, would not exist. Thank you for patiently explaining the things I didn't understand, opening your life to me, and posing (sometimes more than once) for the camera. The food was great and the beds were comfortable. If you thought I was forgetful, incompetent, a bad driver or just plain crazy—thank you very much for keeping those observations to yourself.

Thanks to Wayne and Jan Johnson for your hospitality during my stay in Lethbridge. I Hope the sight of my mud-caked, dented car parked in the driveway for weeks at a time didn't lower the property values. I appreciate all your help, and someday hope to repay you in kind.

To the Sutherlands—thank you for putting up with me when I was in Kamloops. I really had a wonderful time and appreciated your hospitality. Thanks to Margaret for loaning me your car. Sorry it was so muddy when I returned it . . .

To my sister Darlene for giving me a place to stay while in Ontario, Mom and Paul for driving me to the airport, Dad for the great lunch, and my brother, Mark, for the loan of his car. I would have washed it except it was raining when it came time to return it, so it seemed like a rather pointless exercise. Special thanks to the Ebys who were extra helpful when I stayed with them in Kincardine.

To the Eastend Arts Council for allowing me to stay in the Wallace Stegner house while working on the manuscript. I got an incredible amount of work done while there. Your town is delightful and the people friendly. I hope to return soon.

Thank you to Mike and Diane Price for the support, encouragement and for teaching me to make homemade wine. There were times over this frantic year that a glass of it was the only thing that could quieten my mind at night.

To Louise Coté who for welcoming me into your home when I needed a place to stay in Winnipeg. I was able to finish the book in a relaxing, homey atmosphere, instead of some cheesy motel—which is all I can afford right about now. Thank you, Louise, for your kindness

Thank you to Andrea Dyck for being such a fabulous friend and for sending food to my poor starving husband.

To Claire De'Athe, Ken Malenko and Riane Lee Cook who had to listen to me whine about how hard this book was to write. Your insights helped make it a better book. Your friendship over the years has made me a better person.

Special thanks to my sister Nance for loaning me her daughters for the summer. Thanks to Lace Ann for picking up the slack around the house for me while I was cloistered in my office getting this done. To Emma for taking my place and diligently preparing and driving coffee breaks and lunches to the hayfield. Knowing the men were well taken care of eased my mind and let me concentrate on the task at hand. I love you both as if you were my own.

To Jenny Gates. A wonderful editor who put in long hours and great effort to get this done.

To Dave Friesen and the folks at Hignell Printing in Winnipeg and the designers at Tetro Design. I knew I could count on you to package this up right.

To Laurie and Alison for not being offended over all the times I ignored you this past year.

And finally, the biggest thanks and my love goes to Mark and the cattle. Without you this book *really* wouldn't exist. You are my inspiration and financial backing. Not necessarily in that order.

NOTES

1. Tara Brautigam, "Scientist closes in on mad cow medicine," *Winnipeg Free Press*, June 2, 2003, Section, News.

2. Helen Branswell, "Canadian diet produces 'infinitesimal' risk," *Winnipeg Free Press*, May 21, 2003, Section, News.

3. William H. Dresher, Ph.D., and others, "Role of Copper Deficiency in Mad Cow Disease," *Innovations Online Magazine*, www.copper.org/innovations/2001/12/mad-cow.html (December 2001).

4. Laurie Winn Carlson, *Cattle: An Informal Social History*, (Chicago, Ill.: Ivan R. Dee, 2001) 220-221.

5. Edited by E.T. Russell, *What's in a Name? Travelling through Saskatchewan with the story behind 1600 place-names* (Saskatoon: Western Producer Book Service, 1973) 132, 105.

6. Ibid, 197.

7. Ibid, 8.

8. Wallace Stegner, *Wolf Willow* (New York: Viking Press, 1962) 8.

9. Shannon Montgomery, "Demand sizzles for our own beef," *Winnipeg Free Press*, July 20, 2003, Front page.

10. Barry Wilson, "BSE aid compensation details outlined," *The Western Producer*, June 19, 2003.

11. Measures to Assist Industry in Response to BSE, *Agriculture and Agri-Food Canada Website*, 2003.

12. CBC News Online Staff, "Goodale blasts trading partners on beef ban," *CBC News Website*, July 30, 2003.

13. Barry Wilson, "Vanclief unlikely to stay as Ag Minister," *The Western Producer*, November 2003.

14. Peter Schroedter, "Culture ties farmers to the land, not economic rewards," *Winnipeg Free Press*, December 2004.

15. Paul Samyn, "Bush Thanks Canada," *Winnipeg Free Press*, December 1, 2004, front page.

16. CBC News, Halifax, www.cbc.ca, December 1, 2004.

17. Ian Bell, *The Western Producer* September 8, 2003.

18. Sean Pratt, "BSE forcing ranchers to plan," *Western Producer,* July 18, 2003.

19. Ibid.

20. R-CALF United Stockgrowers of America website, www.r-cal-fusa.com

21. R-CALF USA Press Release, "USDA Unnecessarily Traumatizes U.S. Cattle Markets 3rd Time in Five Months; Agency Also Weakens United States' BSE defenses.

22. Ibid.

23. Howard F. Lyman, *"Mad Cowboy: Plain truth from a cattle rancher who won't eat meat,"* Simon & Schuster, 1998.

24. Dr. John FitzGibbon, Suzanne Young and Cassie Barker, " *The Social and Institutional Responses to BSE Crisis"* University of Guelph School of Environmental Design and Rural Development, June 30, 2004.

25. Laurie Winn Carlson, *Cattle: An Informal Social History* (Chicago: Ivan R. Dee, 2001) 51.

26. CTV.ca News, "Rice delays trip to Ottawa over missile snub," March 1, 2005.

27. Calgary.cbc.ca, "Goodale hints at more aid to beef farmers," March 3, 2005.

28. *Canadian Cattlemen's Association,* Daily update, March 28, 2005.

29. Barry Wilson, "MP questions U.S. BSE free status," *The Western Producer,* March 23, 2005.

30. Jim Wiesemeyer, *Inside Washington Today,* March 15, 2005.

31. *Canadian Press* "Feeding human remains to cows may have triggered BSE outbreak, scientists say" September 1, 2005.

32. Ibid.

Selected Bibliography

Lovenheim, Peter, *Portrait of a Burger as a Young Calf* (New York, New York: Harmony Books, 2002)

Rifkin, Jeremy, *Beyond Beef: The Rise and Fall of the Cattle Culture* (New York, New York: Penguin Books, 1992)

Adams, Michael, *Fire and Ice: The United States, Canada an the Myth of Converging Values* (Toronto: Penguin Group, 2003)

Rampton, Sheldon and Stauber, John, *Mad Cow U.S.A.: Could the Nightmare Happen Here?* (Monroe, Maine: Common Courage Press, 1997)

Carlson, Laurie Winn, *Cattle: An Informal Social History* (Ivan R. Dee: Chicago, 2001)

Elofson, Warren M., *Cowboys, Gentlemen & Cattle Thieves* (McGill-Queen's University Press, Montreal & Kingson, Ontario 2000)

MacLachlan, Ian, *Kill and Chill: Restructuring Canada's Beef Commodity Chain* (University of Toronto Press, 2001)

Blacklaws, Rick & French, Diana, *Ranchland: British Columbia's Cattle Country* (Harbour Publishing, Madeira Park, B.C, 2001)

Boyens, Ingeborg, *Another Season's Promise: Hope and Despair in Canada's Farm Country* (Viking, Toronto, Ontario 2001)

OTHER BOOKS BY KAREN EMILSON

Set in rural Manitoba during the 1950s and early 1960s, *Where Children Run* is the true story of twins David and Dennis Pischke who survived more than 12 years of abuse at the hands of a mentally unstable stepfather.

In 1995 the twins came to Karen and asked her to write their story in the newspaper. The story was picked up by local news media and when she was asked to write the book she agreed. Karen interviewed the twins, other family members, neighbours and friends. The result is an account that reads like a novel.

Where Children Run is a fast paced story that takes the reader alongside the children, as they ran into many a cold winter night into the bush to sleep around a campfire to avoid a beating. You'll meet the neighbours who tried to help and feel the desperation of children with nowhere else to turn.

In the end, you'll ask yourself, "how did they survive?"

David and Dennis Pischke grew to become hardworking, upstanding citizens. This is their story. A most worthwhile read.

Where Children Run became an immediate Canadian Bestseller after its release and is required reading in some Manitoba schools, including the Red River Community College.

Dimensions: 416 Pages
5.5 x 8.5 x 0.5 in
ISBN: 0968124208

$24.95

Reader Review from Chapters Indigo Website:

"If one thing should be said of the book "Where Children Run", it would have to be: Where Emotions Run. Anger, sadness, pity, sympathy, anxiety, hope, despair, frustration, and even laughter are the main courses in this buffet of the heart strings.

Depicted with graphic imagery while maintaining empathy for the victims of this tragic tale, this book sometimes leaves many questions unanswered. Sometimes questions that are "best left alone" are answered with a stark and striking honesty. Questions about a brutality belonging only in fiction, find answers in abuse, neglect, savagery and the darkest side of humanity. Questions that were never asked enough about the welfare of the young helpless ones are the questions you will ask yourself. Questions about how they could have survived to help shape this story of triumph and edurance, while trying to find their guidance, strength and nurturing in the twisted hands of fate and a mentally unstable stepfather.

For the first half of this book you will put it down continuously as you read through it—for the last half you will not be able to put it down until you are finished.."

Ask for it at your local bookstore, order online or direct
1-877-491-3283